THE
CHRONOLOGICAL
HISTORY
OF THE
PETROLEUM
AND
NATURAL GAS
INDUSTRIES

BY JAMES A. CLARK

CLARK BOOK CO., HOUSTON, TEXAS, USA

To Estelle

I dedicate this book because it is the most important work and she is the most important person in my life.

Edited by

CHARLES A. WARNER

Research directed by

HARRY E. WALTON

INTRODUCTION

This book has been written to answer the day to day questions about the petroleum and natural gas industries which plague the researcher, the writer, the attorney, the lawmaker, the scholar, the executive and the average person in the industries.

One of its intentions is to inspire accuracy and eliminate error in the recitation of important dates and events in the history of the industries which provide the United States with 73.7 per cent and the world with almost 50 per cent of their respective energy requirements.

Every possible fact has been recorded where the information has been available in a reliable form and where the event was considered to be of sufficient importance to warrant inclusion. Qualified experts have collected, collated and then presented the information in chronological form without editorial comment.

To qualify, an entry had first to be important to the development of the industries, either before or since the industries became commercial.

The starting point, the use of bitumen asphalt to coat the inside and the outside of the Ark by Noah, is taken from the late Max Ball's intriguing book, "This Fascinating Oil Business." Ball gave as his source of information a certain Babylonian tale inscribed on a tablet about 4000 years ago. Of course, this simply indicates that oil or asphalt or gas existed long before recorded history.

But the collaborators of this book considered the Ark incident important if for no other reason than the fact that it is the very first recorded mention of the use of oil or an oil product in the written history of the world.

In developing the chronological history of petroleum and natural gas, it has also been necessary to develop the history, although briefly, of other industries, businesses or professions such as shipping, railroads, automobiles, airplanes, petrochemicals, geophysics, geology, engineering and even the manufacture of ink, among others, that have been promoted by or have themselves promoted the development of the energy industries of oil and gas.

This book does not simply cover the petroleum and natural gas industries in the United States. It includes the world.

Entries are under the dates when certain events occurred or when certain organizations were formed. In as many cases as possible, the exact dates have been given. Where such information has not been available the event is listed in alphabetical order (behind the list of exact dates) in the year concerned. It is our hope that later editions will contain more exact dates and even more entries of significance which have been left out here because of an absence of reliable information. It is our opinion that it is better to ignore an event than to present it wrong.

Certain qualifications have been established for entries.

For instance, in the case of oil discoveries they have been limited to (1) those fields which had produced up to 100 million or more barrels of oil by Jan. 1, 1961, or (2) produced more than 10 million barrels in 1960, or (3) opened a new trend, was the site of significant legislation, or in some way earned historical significance.

Gas fields have been included (1) if they had produced a trillion or more cubic feet by Jan. 1, 1961, or (2) produced 100 million cubic feet per day in 1960, or (3) qualified on some basis similar to category 3 in the oil qualifications.

Companies and associations were included if they were active at this time, submitted necessary supporting information upon our request, or, if no longer in existence, played a significant role in the industry about which information was available.

Oil, gas, or products pipelines qualified if they were important in the domestic or foreign fields and if such information were available.

Of high value to the average researcher will be the dates of events in the history of petroleum legislation, regulation, and taxation. This will include, of course, the numerous landmark decisions by state and federal courts.

HOW TO USE THE BOOK

This book has been arranged so that its use will be very simple.

There is no table of contents.

The Chronological History simply starts on page 1.

An alphabetical listing of the chronological entries starts on page 275.

There is a sort of bibliography, which we chose to call an Index of Sources, which starts on page 313.

In order to find a specific event, the reader should consult the alphabetical listing. The reference number following the alphabetical entry is that of the year *(not a page)* and this will be quite easy to find in the chronological listing, since each item in the alphabetical listing is included in **blackface** type in the chronological listing.

To determine the source, the reader will find a number in parenthesis after each chronological entry. This number corresponds with a number in the *Index of Sources* giving the exact source from which we obtained the information.

It is the sincere desire of the author and his collaborators that this book will bridge a gap in the understanding of the petroleum and natural gas industries and the human family these industries serve.

It is even hoped that this work might enable most people to recognize petroleum and natural gas as the most vital and essential commodities in the progress of man through the machine age, the industrial age, the age of mobility, and the coming age of petroleum chemicals.

The Chronological History of the Petroleum and Natural Gas Industries

Note: Numbers in parentheses at end of each listing refer to sources of information (listed beginning on page 313).

6000 B. C.

Noah smears Ark with two coats of **bitumen** on outside and one coat inside before the Great Flood in the Tigris-Euphrates Valley. (20)

4000 B. C.

Paintings on walls of tombs portray **Egyptians** preparing meals. (51)

Builders of the **Tower of Babel** "had bricks for stone and slime they had for mortar." (20)

3000 B. C.

Holes are bored in earth by **rotary method** by **Egyptians** as shown by holes in rocks in stone quarries at the construction of the pyramids. Bore holes as deep as 20 feet have been found in hard rock and two drill cores are in the Egyptian collection of the Metropolitan Museum of Art in New York. (1)

The **Sumerians** use **asphalt** as a base for cement for inlaying mosaics. (24)

2000 B. C.

Pure **bitumen** sells for the equivalent of $30 per ton in **Ur of Chaldees.** (20)

1450 B. C.

First **artificial lighting** by "fire-pans" or "censers." (51)

900 B. C.

Natural gas utilized by the **Chinese.** (51)

1

600 B. C.

Confucius writes of wells a few hundred feet deep near the border of Tibet. (1)

450 B. C.

Herodotus describes the so-called "pitch spring" of **Zante,** an oil seepage which even now exists. (24)

400 B. C.

Streets in **Jerusalem** and **Antioch** lighted at night. (51)

320 B. C.

Greeks first find **lodestone,** or magnetite, near the ancient city of Magnesia. They apply the name Magnes to the strange rock. (7)

206 B. C.

An oil spring found at Yenchang in the northern part of Shensi Province, **China.** (45)

121 B. C.

A Chinese dictionary of this year refers to the magnetic property of a **lodestone.** (7)

102-44 B. C.

Before and during the time of Julius Caesar, a famous **"fontaine ardente,"** or burning fountain, is located near Grenoble, **France.** (46)

38 B. C.

Natural gas found in salt wells in Szechuan Province, **China.** (45)

66 A. D.

Plutarch mentions petroleum found near what is now the Kirkuk field. (1)

100

Coptic alchemists report distillation method in which vapor is delivered to a thin-necked vessel cooled with air or sponges. (4)

Pliny observes that **"Sicilian Oil,"** secured near Agrigentum on Island of Sicily, is burned in lamps of the Temple of Jupiter. Earliest mention of oil used as an **illuminant.** (43)

221-263

Ancient Chinese manuscripts describe wells drilled as early as the **Shu Han dynasty,** to tap underground strata for salt and brine. (39)

600

Wells dug by hand in **Japan** 600 to 900 feet in depth for the purpose of producing oil. (1)

615

Gas wells are known in **Japan.** (38)

2

670

Romans use oil to destroy a fleet of **Saracens.** (1)

750

"**Greek Fire,**" a preparation of distilled naphtha, employed in military operations by Arab and Mongol armies in grenades and flame throwers. (4)

800-840

Kobo Daish, a noted Buddhist, performs seven miracles in the province of Echigo, **Japan.** One of these is that of an everlasting fire, coming from the center of the earth. (46)

900

The Chinese report piping gas through bamboo tubes and using it for lighting. (**First Pipeline**) (38)

967

Massudi reports that on the oil-rich Apsheron Peninsula at Surakhany near **Baku** in the Caspian Sea, fire columns that were visible for many miles sprang from a naphtha deposit. (The Baku region then belonged to Persia [Iran]). It is said that these awe-inspiring miracles of nature, whose natural origin was unknown in those times, inspired **Zoroaster** to his cult of fire-worshiping, and a temple devoted to this religion was built at Surakhany. The gases responsible for these fires were mostly from Miocene sandstones. (46)

1021-23

Ibn Sina (**Avicenna**) makes observations about minerals in the earth. (30)

1077

Cairo burns as 1200 barrels of **naphtha** (crude oil) add fury to the conflagration. (4)

1100

Many centuries before the first well was drilled in the western world, depths as great as 3500 feet are reached in **China** with surprisingly primitive equipment. (39)

1181

Alexander Neckham first mentions the compass in a treatise. The **first compass** was of the pivoted type. (7)

1250

Vincent d'Beauvais first writes of a **compass** made by a magnetized needle floating on a straw in a bowl of water. (7)

1269

Petrus Peregrinus writes the **first geophysical paper**—a treatise on the compass. The paper contains the first description of an azimuth and graduated circle of 360 degrees. (7)

1272

Marco Polo reports witnessing streams of people going to seepages in **Baku** to collect oil. (4)

1327-77

Somewhere in this period, an early use of the word **petroleum** is found in the Wardrobe Account of the English king, **Edward III**. The entry: "Delivered to the King in his chamber at Calais: 8 lbs. of petroleum." (37)

1415

First regular street lighting in **London**. (51)

1436

Oil from a spring near Tegernsee, in Bavaria, attains such medicinal fame that it is known as "**St. Quirinus's oil.**" (20)

1480

Pamphlets at fairs and markets in Europe describe **medicinal** value of crude oil produced from the seepages at Wietze (Hanover, Germany), Pechelbronn (Alsace), Beziers (Southern France), Agrigentum (Sicily), the Modena region in the Po Valley (Italy), Tegernsee (Southern Bavaria), Galicia, Rumania and Baku. (76)

1498

The **Pechelbronn** field in northern Alsace discovered. The residents obtain oil from seeps and shallow pits for almost 2½ centuries. (10)

1500

Chinese develop art of drilling wells to possibly 2000 feet. (1)

Leonardo da Vinci, about this time, devises an earth-boring machine incorporating a four-legged derrick and drill stem. It is first such machine of which there is a sketch and description. (1)

1510

Columbus ships samples of asphalt from **Trinidad** to Spain. (1)

1521

Magellan carries 35 compasses with him when he circumnavigates the world. (7)

1535

Asphalt discovered in **Cuba.** (24)

1543

July 27—Survivors of the **De Soto expedition,** seeking to reach Mexico, use asphalt, which they found on the Texas coast between Sabine Pass and High Island, to repair the bottom of their boats. (44)

Juan Rodriguez Cabrillo, Portuguese navigator in service of Spain, waterproofs two ships from pitch deposits at Carpinteria, **California,** after seeing Indians waterproof their dugout canoes. (API—The Burning Rivers)

1549

First application of **geophysics.** During siege of Exeter, pans of water used to detect soldiers digging tunnels under ground. The pans of water were seismoscopes. (7)

1566

Gonzalo Oviedo reports deposits of asphalt near Havana, **Cuba.** (4)

1576

Robert Norman discovers the **magnetic dip,** and concludes that the controlling influence was within the earth. (7)

1580

William Gilbert first establishes the observation that the earth itself is a gigantic magnet. (7)

1589

Galileo discovers the laws of free fall and pendular motion. The geophysical unit of gravity measurement is the "Gal," after Galileo. (7)

1596

Sir Walter Raleigh discovers pitch lake of **Trinidad.** (4)

1609

The Western word, "Gas," is the invention of the Belgian chemist **Van Helmont.** (46)

1613

In the province of Echigo, across the island of Honshu from Tokyo, **Japan,** a man named Magara obtains oil and attempts to refine it to obtain **illuminating oil.** (20)

1627

July 18—A French missionary reports a "fontaine de bitume," or oil spring, near **Cuba, New York.** It is recorded by a Franciscan, Father Joseph de la Roche d'Allion. (36)

1628

Henry Gellibrand discovers the secular magnetic variation. (7)

1640

A well is dug twelve miles from Modena, **Italy,** and oil skimmed off the water that collects in it. (20)

1642

Jesuit missionaries find "thick, oily, stagnant water which would burn like brandy" in the territory of the ancient Eries, in **New York.** (43)

1650

Oil shafts dug by hand are producing in the Bacau district of Moldavia (**Rumania**). (20)

1657

Christian Huyghens first uses the **pendulum,** a geophysical instrument, in clocks. (7)

1659

Natural gas in **England** is first discovered by Thomas Shirley in Lancashire. (46)

1669

Nicolaus Steno writes a great volume pertaining to **fossils.** (30)

1670

First record of **coal gas** mentioned in writings of the Reverend John Clayton, a Yorkshire minister, who experimented with distilling coal. (38)

A map made by the missionaries Dollier and Galinee has marked on it, "Fontaine de bitume," near where the town of **Cuba, New York,** is located. It is probably the first mention of petroleum made on a map of this country. (37)

1672

Richer first reports variations in **gravity** over the surface of the earth, from observations of pendulum clock rate variations. (7)

1681

Becher and Searle take out a patent for making **pitch** and tar from pit coal. (37)

1691

Robert Boyle reports in England that a combustible gas is produced when coal is heated. (38)

1694

Eele, Hancock and Portlock make "**pitch,** tar and oyle out of a kind of stone from Shropshire, England." (37)

1697

First street **lighting ordinance** passed in New York City. (51)

1700

The Earl of Bellomon, governor of New York, sends the Royal chief engineer in America, Col. Wolfgang W. Romer, to view a spring which it is suspected holds petroleum. This is in **New York.** (36)

1705

Thomas Newcomen invents the **Atmospheric Engine** for pumping wells, which is so arranged that the engine piston connects to a pump rod to give a straight-line motion to each. (1)

1723

Peter the Great grants concessions in the Baku area to private individuals who dig wells by hand and produce some oil. (1)

In Russia, **Peter the Great** conquers the Khanate of Baku and sends a master of refining to take possession of the oil supply and see to its transportation up the Volga River. (20)

1735

Pierre Bouguer first uses the pendulum to make **gravity observations** in a French expedition in Peru, chief object of which is to measure arc. Makes the first relative gravity measurements, and first uses the invariable pendulum idea. For the next 150 years, most **gravity observations** were made by the absolute method. (7)

Johaan Leache, a traveler in the Caucasus, states that crude **Caucasian oil,** "when distilled," yields a bright yellow oil resembling a spirit, which readily ignited. (35)

Tunnels are sunk into the hillsides of the **Pechelbronn** field. (In 1745, shafts were sunk—some of them 250 feet deep.) (10)

1739

Clayton makes the first investigation of the spirit produced by the **distillation of coal.** (37)

1740

Probably the earliest attempt to evaluate the density of the earth made by **Pierre Bouguer,** a French geodesist. He attempts to measure the deviations of a plumb line produced by the gravitational attraction of a high mountain in **Peru.** (33)

Earth temperature observations are made in mines in Alsace, by **Gesanne.** (1)

1742

British Oil patented by **Michael and Thomas Betton** as a medicine. (4)

1745

James' Medicinal Dictionary lists the dark green or black petroleum of Barbados, "**Barbados Tar,**" as being widely used in medicine. (37)

The **Pechelbronn** area in France starts producing bituminous asphalt. (45)

1748

North America is visited by **Peter Kalm,** a Swedish naturalist, who publishes an account of his travels, together with a map on which the oil springs of **Oil Creek, Pa.,** are indicated. (37)

1755

A **map** is made in London, with the word **"petroleum"** written across the territory in Pennsylvania in which the oil springs occurred. (36)

1757

Benjamin Franklin attempts use of (whale) **oil to smooth waters** for mariners. (4)

1761

Oils are distilled from black bituminous shales for **medicinal** purposes, and it is found that they can be used instead of both oil of turpentine and "oil of petre." (37)

1764

A Frenchman, **Pierre Joseph Macquer, defines bitumen** as a mineral substance yielding, on distillation, "A great deal of oil very like petroleum." (35)

1765

The oil fields of **Burma** are visited by **Major Michael Symes** of the British Army; he reports that some 500 wells have been dug by hand into the oil sands and the production is being used in Burma and parts of India. (1)

James Watt, Scottish mechanical engineer, invents modern condensing **steam engine.** Patented 1769. With **Matthew Boulton,** manufactures steam engines at Soho Works, Birmingham, England, 1775-1880. Originates term **horsepower** (with Boulton). The **Watt unit** of power named in his honor. Son, James, fitted the **Caledonia,** first steamship to leave an English port (1817). (65)

1767

At an Indian conference at Niagara, New York, **Sir William Johnson** records that an Indian had brought in "a quantity of Curious Oyl, taken from the top of the water from some very small Leake." (36)

1768

Antoine Baume devises two scales—one for measuring the **specific gravity of liquids** heavier than water and the other of liquids lighter than water. To establish the scale for the latter, which was used for oil, an ordinary hydrometer was sunk in a 10 per cent solution of salt. The point to which the hydrometer sank in the salt-water solution was designated as zero, while the point to which it sank in pure water was marked as 10. After dividing that first measurement into ten equal parts, or degrees, the scale was extended. (8A)

David Leisberger, a Moravian missionary, traveling through western New York, notes that there are "oil wells, with the products of which the **Seneca Indians** carry on trade with Niagara." (36)

1769

Nicolas Joseph Cugnot builds the first **self-propelled vehicle**—a three-wheel carriage driven by steam. (38)

T. Healde publishes a work in London on the "Use of **Oleum Asphalti** in Ulcers of the Intestines, Lungs, and Viscera." (37)

1774

Nevil Maskelyne and **Charles Hutton** first devise experiments to find the mean **density** of the **earth.** (7)

1775

General **George Washington** describes a "burning spring" on the Kanawha River in West Virginia adjacent to a tract of 123 acres granted to him and General Andrew Lewis. (38)

1781

The French chemist, **Antoine Laurent Lavoisier,** invents the **gasometer,** which later develops into the gasholder. He later invents the **first portable light** by filling bags of leather, bladders and vessels with gas, lighting them and carrying them from place to place. (38)

The Earl of Dundonald obtains oil from coal by **destructive distillation,** and he later procures a patent for manufacturing various products from coal. (37)

1782

Aime Argand, chemist and physician of Geneva, Switzerland, devises a **circular burner** with a round wick. He uses camphene—a mixture of turpentine and alcohol—and finally coal oil, as fuel. (35)

1783

General Benjamin Lincoln and his troops march through western Pennsylvania, halting at **Oil Creek,** and his troops collect oil and bathe their joints with it. (36)

1784

Henry Cavendish discovers the composition of water; this is to play an important part in the manufacture of **water gas** in later years. (38)

James Rumsey, an American engineer, makes experiments with a model **steamboat** which are viewed by George Washington at Richmond, Va. (35)

1785

August 17—**General William Irvine** reports "Oil Creek, Pa. has taken its name from an oil or bituminous matter floating on its surface." (43)

1786

John Fitch builds the first American **steamboat.** (35)

Charles Augustine de Coulomb invents the **first torsion balance;** the Coulomb balance is used in physical laboratories for investigating the laws of gravitational attraction. (7)

1787

August 8—John Fitch launches **first steamboat.**

Abraham Werner publishes a **quarto on geology.** (30)

1788

B. Haquet suggests that petroleum comes directly from organic matter such as mussels. (**Organic theory.**) (22)

1788

John Fitch makes a 20-mile trip on the Delaware River from Philadelphia to Burlington by **steamboat.** (35)

1789

George Henry Loskiel reports "one of the favorite medicines used by the Indians is **fossil oil** exuding from the earth, usually with water" along the Ohio River. (43)

1790

Nathaniel Carey skims crude oil from springs near **Titusville, Pa.,** filling two small kegs; carries them by horseback to make deliveries directly to customers. (1)

Travelers along **Spanish Trail** use oil from springs for medicine for men and horses and to lubricate axles of wagons and carts. (API—The Burning Rivers) (76)

1791

Barber first tries to produce power from **inflammable gas.** (35)

A map of **Pennsylvania** made, on which the stream **"Oyl Creek,"** is named for the first time. (36)

1792

William Murdock, a Scot, lights his house with coal gas, igniting the fuel from a crude burner which is attached to a gas-filled pipe. (35)

1794

Street patents what might be called the **first gas engine.** (35)

1795

Dr. James Hutton publishes his *Theory of the Earth,* in Scotland. (30)

Joseph Scott, of Philadelphia, the first gazeteer of the United States, reports on **Oil Creek** and a bitumen resembling **Barbados Tar** known as **Seneca Oil.** (43)

1795-1800—Crude oil quoted at $16.00 per gallon. (40)

1796

August—The **first recorded demonstration of gas** in the U. S. The gas is manufactured by M. Ambroise and Company, Italian fireworkers and artists. (52)

Benjamin Rumford suggests warming rooms by means of chimneys—from which idea the **radiator** developed. (51)

1797

Henry Cavendish makes the first laboratory measurement of the **density of the earth** which determined the gravitational content. The value of this fundamental constant is now accepted as 200/3.10-9 cgs unit. The density of the earth is established as nearly 5.5g/cc-3. (7)

Carl Loscher describes laboratory experiments of first use of compressed air to lift fluid. (**Air lift**) (1)

1798

William Murdock equips the Soho Foundry with gas lighting, and studies the washing and purification of gas. (38)

Richard Trevithick makes a **direct-acting steam pump** (the famous "Cornish" pump) by connecting the engine piston rod directly to that of the pump. (1)

1798-1801—**Dr. Samuel Mitchell** publishes a "Sketch of the Mineralogical History of New York." (30)

1799

September—**Philippe Le Bon,** of Paris, obtains the first patent for making of gas. It is called a **"Thermolamp."** (38)

A Frenchman, Philippe Le Bon introduces the idea that an air-gas mixture might be compressed before ignition. His engine worked on the principle of a cannon. He exploded street-lighting gas in the cylinder behind the piston, and used an electric spark to ignite the gas in his engine. (**Internal Combustion Engine**) (35)

William Murdock invents **"D" slide valve** (used in gas meters and steam engines). (51)

1801

Philippe Le Bon (in France) obtains first **patent for gas power.** (51)

1802

March 10—First public demonstration of gas light in **Baltimore, Maryland,** by **Benjamin Henfrey.** (51)

Public display of **gas lighting** given at Soho Works. (38)

1803

Main Street in **Richmond, Virginia** lighted by a huge gas lamp on 40-foot tower by **Benjamin Henfrey.** (51)

1804

February 24—**First locomotive**—An Englishman, Richard Trevithick, operates the first steam engine on rails. On the Merthyr Tidfil Railway at the Penydarran Ironworks in South Wales, he tests his "steam wagon," but heavy financial losses make him turn to other fields. (35)

May—**Frederick Albert Winsor,** a German, obtains the first English patent for the manufacture of gas, and lectures publicly to overcome public prejudice. (38)

Alexander Humboldt advances the theory that oil is distilled by volcanic action from strata at immense depths. (**Inorganic Theory**) (35)

1805

First recorded suggestion of the use of **gas for cooking.** (38)

1806

December—**First gas mains** ever laid in a public street when Winsor has pipes laid from Haymarket to St. James Street in London. Pipes are made of sheet lead. (38)

Oil is found when salt brine is sought near the **Kanawha River** in western Virginia. **David and Joseph Ruffner** put down a well near Buffalo Lick on Campbell Creek, which they abandon because it produces petroleum instead of salt water. (15)

David Melville of **Newport, Rhode Island,** lights his house with coal gas. (51)

David and Joseph Ruffner drill **first (salt) well with a springpole** 5 miles southeast of Charleston, W. Va., on the Great Kanawha River. It is also the first well in which **drive pipe** is used, the **first to case off the surface sand** and gravel, and the **first to use tubing** and a **packer.** (79)

1807

January 28—**Frederick A. Winsor** lights Pall Mall in **London** with coal gas, the first successful demonstration of **street lighting.** (38)

August 17—**Robert Fulton's Steamboat** Clermont makes initial run on Hudson river.

Mr. **F. Cuming,** in his "Sketches of a Tour of the Western Country," describes collection of oil from creeks, wells and walled or dammed areas by **blanket dipping.** "By this method 20 or 30 gallons of pure oil can be obtained in two or three days by one man." He says a flannel or woolen cloth is spread over the oil surface, pressed down, drawn up and run through the hands to squeeze into a vessel. (43)

Oil, from a spring located in the middle of **Oil Creek** on the **Hamilton McClintock** farm, sells for one to two dollars a gallon. (36)

1808

A "bag of wrapping" constituting in effect an open-hole **packer** is used by the Ruffner brothers to shut off upper undesirable fluids in a 40-foot brine well. (1)

1809

Samuel Clegg invents the **"Argand" burner,** which uses two concentric tubes with gas in the space between the two rings. (38)

John Dalton studies the action of electric sparks on **hydrocarbon gases.** (26)

William McClure publishes a booklet on **"Observations on the Geology of the United States."** (30)

1810

Joseph Hecker introduces method of producing **kerosene from crude,** but his secret, lost when his business failed, had to be rediscovered by Lukasiewicz in 1850. (76)

1812

April 30—The British Parliament grants a charter to **The London and Westminster Gas Light & Coke Company** and the **first gas company** in the world comes into being. (51)

It is known that an oil resembling turpentine can be made from coal-tar by **destructive distillation,** as well as red and black varnishes. (37)

David Melville, of Newport, R. I., successfully makes gas in his home and lights his house and the street in front of it. He is granted a patent in March, 1813, for his **gas-making machinery.** (38)

1813

David Melville introduces gas lights at a cotton mill at Watertown, Mass., and at a mill near Providence. (38)

The entire length of **Westminster Bridge,** in London, is lit by gas—with no accidents reported. (35)

1814

DeWitt Clinton, president of the Literary and Philosophical Society of New York, suggests that oil from the famous spring near Cuba, New York, might be used for lighting the cities of the United States. (36)

George Stephenson builds the "Blucher," credited with being the first successful **locomotive.** (35)

A salt well dug to a depth of 475 feet on **Duck Creek**—30 miles north of Marietta, **Ohio**—discharges "periodically, at intervals of from two to four days and from three to six hours' duration, 30 to 60 gallons of petroleum at each inception." (15)

1815

December 9—**Samuel Clegg** constructs his **first gas meter**—a "wet" type. It is not, however, a commercial success and is not adopted for many years. (38)

December 28—**Gas lighting** first proposed for Philadelphia, Pennsylvania, by **James McMurtie.** (51)

Accum publishes the first treatise on **gas lighting.** (38)

The first **gas mains** laid by **Samuel Clegg;** are 2 inches in diameter but soon found to be too small and are replaced by 4- and 6-inch mains. They are cast iron pipe in 4½-foot, 6-foot and 9-foot lengths. Service and house pipes are formed of old musket barrels with the muzzle of one screwed into the breach of the next. (38)

William Smith publishes the first **stratigraphic map** in England. He is recognized as the father of stratigraphy and geological maps. (30)

A works near Sunderland, England, belonging to Messrs. Featherstone, produces "petroleum" and ammonia from coal. (37)

A gas well discovered at Charleston, **West Virginia.** (46)

1816

April 23—**Rembrandt Peale,** artist and naturalist, lights his painting salon and museum in Baltimore with natural gas. (35)

June 17—The **first United States gas franchise** is issued to the Baltimore Gas & Electric Company, permitting **Rembrandt Peale** and others to manufacture gas, lay pipes in streets, and to contract with the city of **Baltimore** for street lighting. Baltimore is the first United States city to light its streets with gas. (51)

The first interior commercial use of gas is in the New Theater, in **Philadelphia,** where gas lights are installed. (52)

1817

February 5—**Gas Light Company of Baltimore, first gas company in America,** incorporated. (51)

February 7—The city of **Baltimore** gas-lights one of its streets. (35)

John Malam invents an improved type of "wet" **gas meter** that results in the construction of meters universally employed in the early days of the gas industry. (38)

David Melville uses gas for lighting a lighthouse in the United States. (38)

Wu Lin-Fang discovers petroleum oil in the vicinity of Chu-huang-keng, an oilfield in northern **Taiwan.** (45)

1818

Amos Eaton publishes his "Index to the Geology of the Northern States." (30)

Oil fire ignites most of South Fork of Cumberland River, Wayne County, **Kentucky.** Oil was escaping from salt well. Blaze extended down Muskingum to the Ohio River and thence to the Little Kanawha River in **West Virginia.** (API—The Burning Rivers)

1819

The first gas company in **France** formed to light the city of Paris. (38)

Martin Beatty drills a salt well on the Big South Fork of the Cumberland River, 28 miles southeast of Monticello, **Kentucky.** It spouts petroleum in such quantities that it is abandoned. (36)

1820

A pitch-like substance, known as **Albertite,** is discovered in Albert County, New Brunswick, Canada. This deposit was rediscovered by **Abraham Gesner** in 1839; and in 1852, Gesner claimed the deposit by right of discovery. (63)

John Malam invents a "dry" type **gas meter,** but it is not greatly successful. (38)

The process of manufacturing **"oil gas"** patented by Taylor and Martineau, who secure an Act of Parliament (May, 1821) authorizing the erection of an oil-gas works in England. (38)

Natural gas discovered near **Pittsburgh,** Pa., by a salt works drilling for salt water. Gas ignites accidentally and burns down the plant. (38)

Retorts of fire clay construction make their appearance. (38)

1821

Natural gas discovered at **Fredonia,** New York, in the form of a "burning spring." Residents drill a 27-foot deep well and "log-pipe" gas to nearby houses for lighting. (38)

At Oakland Plantation, owned since 1787 by heirs of Jean Pier Manuel, **rotary** principle **drilling** tools used with percussion methods by **P. Prudhomme** to drill for water in Natchitoches Parish, **Louisiana.** (1)

1822

The **Boston Gas Light Company** chartered by special act to serve the city of Boston. On January 1, 1829, the first public lamps are lighted in Dock Square. (38)

1823

In London, **Samuel Brown** successfully operates the gas vacuum (**internal combustion**) **engine.** (38)

March—The **New York Gas Light Company** granted a charter, and organized on May 12, to serve the city of New York (population 145,000). Gas sells for $10.00 per Mcf, and by September, 1825, over 1700 burners are installed. (38)

John Malam patents dry line **purifiers.** (38)

The Dubinin brothers erect stills in the village of Mosdock, in the Caucasus. (35)

1824

In England, the **Imperial gallon** adopted as a statutory measure. Its capacity is equal to 277.42 cubic inches. (63)

Principle of **cathodic protection** is described by **Sir Humphry Davy.** The first wide-scale use on distribution systems of cathodic protection was to come 105 years later in New Orleans, La. (38)

Broadmeadow invents the first **gas exhauster**—a blower. (38)

1825

March 24—Patent issued to **L. Disbrow** on 4-legged **derrick.** Another issued on November 1, 1830. (1)

June 4—At **Fredonia,** New York, during a visit to the United States, General Lafayette arrives by stagecoach at the old Taylor House at 2 a.m. to find the city and the inn brilliantly illuminated in his honor by natural gas. (38)

Brooklyn Gas Light Company organized. (38)

Michael Faraday discovers **benzene** and recognizes **unsaturated gases.** (26)

The first patent for a **gas regulator** granted in England to **Samuel Crossley.**

First record of the **"gas stove."** It is described as a piece of gas apparatus for cooking by enclosing the circle of a gas flame with its reflecting cone in a cylinder of tin. (38)

Swedes first use a "mining compass" in magnetic prospecting for ores. This marks the first application of **geophysical exploration** to a search for minerals. (7)

John Stevens, of Hoboken, N. J., constructs a **locomotive** in his shops and runs it on a circular track in his backyard. (35)

Oil recovered from 12-foot sand pits in Wirt County, **West Virginia,** and used as a liniment for burns and horses. (4)

1826

Drummond, an Englishman, discovers and patents the oxy-hydrogen (**lime-light**) lamp. (38)

1827

Berlin is the first city in **Germany** to be lighted with gas. (38)

1828

First gas works in **Boston,** Massachusetts, built on Hull Street. (51)

John Brunton, chief engineer of West Bromwich, England, Gas Works, develops a **vertical retort charging** method. This method, however, did not come into use until nearly 50 years later. (38)

New York City's **"Great White Way"**—Broadway between Grand Street and Battery—lighted by gas lamps. (38)

The **"Stourbridge Lion,"** a **locomotive** imported from England, is the first to run on a public railroad in the Western Hemisphere. (35)

1829

January 1—First gas lamps in **Boston,** Massachusetts lighted in Dock Square. (51)

A salt driller strikes oil at 175 feet on the banks of Rennox Creek, **Kentucky,** a small tributary of the Cumberland River. The oil catches fire on the river and burns for several weeks. The gusher becomes known as the **"Great American Well."** (10)

1830

September 15—The gala trip of George Stephenson's "Rocket" and seven sister **locomotives** on the Liverpool and Manchester RR really ushers in steam rail transportation. (35)

November 1—**L. Disbrow** receives patent on earliest mechanical **drilling machine.** (1)

A considerable amount of oil received annually in New York City and sold to **apothecaries.** (36)

First **base-burning stove** in United States. (51)

R. W. Fox first discovers that **electrical** currents and **potentials** are associated with certain ore deposits in Cornwall. The electrodes Fox uses are polarized and not practical. (7)

James Sharp, of Northampton, England, demonstrates the use of **gas for cooking** in his own home. (38)

Geological surveys established in Massachusetts, Tennessee, Maryland and in several other states. (30)

Peter Cooper, in the United States, secures a patent on the steam **locomotive.** (38)

Charles Lyell publishes the first of his volumes on "The Principles of Geology." (30)

The **Manhattan Gas Light Company** organized in New York City. (38)

Samuel F. B. Morse patents the magnetic **telegraph** in the United States. (38)

Auguste Laurent obtains **paraffin** by the distillation of bituminous shale. (37)

Karl von Reichenbach isolates **paraffin wax** from wood tar. (24)

Marcus Samuel starts business in London as a small Oriental importer. (Shell Oil Company)

1830-40

Golden age of **whaling** of US East Coast. By 1850 sperm brings $2.00 to $2.50 per gallon, some as high as $5.00. Pine forests at that time produced sylvic or rosin oil from heavy end of turpentine. Best of this is camphene which produces a bright flame and costs 50 and 65 cents per gallon. (76)

1831

The **first internally fired coal gas generator** invented by George Lowe, of London. (38)

1832

A charter for a gas light company in **New Orleans** granted to James Caldwell. The system is not completed until 1835 when the city was first lighted with gas lights. (38)

The **first gas meter** made in U. S. at Baltimore by Samuel Hill. (38)

Richard Barnes secures a patent for the **heating of buildings** by combustion of gas or oil. (38)

Bartlett-Hayward Company established. (38)

1833

S. P. Hildreth writes as follows regarding the early use of petroleum: "From its being found in limited quantities, and its great and extensive demand, a small vial of it would sell for 40 or 50 cents." (37)

Prof. **Benjamin Silliman, Sr.** distinguished Yale chemist, visits the oil springs at Cuba, New York, and records his findings. (36) The same year he experimentally distills crude petroleum. (35)

First **telescopic gas holder** erected at London. Hutchison, the engineer of the company, lays claim to (and patents) the invention on October 12, and from that period on, because of the extended applications of gas lighting, and the limited sites of the works, telescopic holders are used. (38)

1834

Inorganic theory of origin of petroleum advanced by **Virlet d'Aoust and Rozet.** (24)

The city of Philadelphia decides to build its own gas works, and begins erection of a plant at 22nd and Market Streets. This is the **first municipal gas system in the U. S.** (38)

First pipe foundry, established at Millville, N. J., produces the first U. S.-made cast iron pipe used in gas distribution systems. (38)

1835

A gas light company organized in **Pittsburgh,** Pa. (38)

1836

February 8—**Philadelphia** puts its gas works into operation with 19 private lamps on its lines and gas selling at $3.50 per Mcf. (38)

The United States Congress establishes the Queen Anne wine **gallon** of 231 cubic inches as the **U. S.** standard **measure** of capacity. (63)

New York organizes a **geologic survey** with a staff of four geologists and the same number of assistants. (30)

The English Parliament passes stringent laws subjecting all **horseless vehicles** to enormous tolls. (35)

1837

February 4—**Laclede Gas Company** predecessor chartered as one of five early predecessor companies. The first was St. Louis Gaslight Company. Laclede Gaslight Company and Carondelet Gas Light Company both chartered in March 1857 and merged with St. Louis Light and Fuel Company in 1889 under the retained name of Laclede Gaslight Company. In 1947, the assets of the St. Louis County Gas Company were acquired and present corporate name was adopted. (50)

A charter granted to organize a gas-light company in **Cincinnati,** Ohio; operations finally got underway in 1841. (38)

James D. Dana writes his "System of **Mineralogy:** Including an extended treatise of **Crystallography."** (30)

Ohio's first reported use of natural gas occurs on a farm near Findlay. The gas, encountered in digging a water well, is conveyed through wooden pipe to the farmhouse and lighted off the end of a gun barrel. (47)

Wilhelm Eduard Weber first uses earth-inductor for measuring the strength of terrestrial magnetic field at any point. (7)

1838

April 1—**Ruben Drake** drills 1011-foot brine well in Winn Parish, Louisiana, probably the first use of a very crude, wooden, **rotary drilling rig.** (Oil & Gas Journal)

Asphalt used on the roads of Paris, France. (39)

1839

February—The St. Louis Gas-Light Company chartered. The gas works was finally put into operation eight years later, in 1847. (38)

Along the Calcasieu River near **Lake Charles, Louisiana,** oil is sometimes collected and used. (21)

1840

Natural gas initially used in Pennsylvania for the evaporation of brine in the refining of salt by John Criswell, at Centerville, Butler County. This is the first recorded use of natural **gas** as a fuel **for manufacturing.** (47)

Gas meters begin to be used. The idea of selling gas by the measure —instead of flat rate—originates with the Chartered Gas Light Company of London, which also is the first company to employ **"cost of service"** elements of business with the inauguration of a rental charge to customers for gas meters. The usual charge is 10 percent of the cost of the meter, including fittings. (38)

1841

September 4—**Patent** on **drilling jars** granted to William Morris. (1)

J. D. Forbes, an Englishman, develops the **seismograph.** (35)

Some streets in **Philadelphia** are gas-lighted. (35)

John A. **Roebling's Sons Corporation** founded as John A. Roebling's

Sons Company in Saxonburg, Pennsylvania as manufacturers of wire rope and wire. (50)

In the Kanawha Valley of **West Virginia,** William Thompkins strikes a large flow of natural gas while boring a salt well. He pipes the gas to his salt works and uses it instead of coal to boil down brine. (47)

1842

Sir William Logan, director of the Geological Survey of Canada, notes that oil seepages on the hills at Gaspe, near the mouth of the St. Lawrence River, are located on **anticlines.** (22)

1843

Halifax, Nova Scotia, organizes a gas light company. (38)

James Hall publishes a geological quarto on the western section of New York. In pure science, it sets up what for years is known as the New York System and gives the first clear, logical account of America's early formations. (30)

Von Wrede first suggests that local variations in the earth's **magnetic field** might be used as a means of locating magnetic ore. (7)

William Smith, iron moulder, invents **iron pipe.** (79)

1844

May 24—First telegraph message—Washington to Baltimore.

July 12—English patent #10,258 issued to **Robert Beart** of Godmanchester, England for a **rotary drilling machine** using a rotating tool, hollow drill rods, and circulating fluid to remove cuttings. (1)

Kind's **core drill** is the earliest form known, having been employed in coal strata near Forbach, in Lorraine. (28)

Croll and Richards patent improved **dry gas meter** which is basis of present meter. (51)

1845

M. Fauvelle, a Frenchman, invents the "water-flush" system of **rotary drilling.** (35)

A simplified two diaphragm **gas meter** invented. (38)

Lewis Peterson, Sr., of Tarentum, Pa., enters into a contract with the Hope Cotton Factory at Pittsburgh, by which he is to supply two barrels of crude petroleum per week for use as a spindle **lubricant in** mixture with sperm oil. This mixed lubricant was used at the Hope Factory for 10 years. (37)

Ascanio Sobrero invents **nitroglycerin** in the University of Turin, Italy. (7)

Sperm oil costs $1.30 per gallon. Oil from salt well reported as "just as good a lubricant for spindles," and at a cost of 75 cents per gallon. (43)

1846

August—Abraham Gesner claims to have been the first to produce **illuminating oils** from bituminous materials in America. He is distilling it from Nova Scotia coal. (37)

American Chain & Cable Co., Inc., founded as Hazard Manufacturing Co., in Mauch Chunk (now Jim Thorpe), Pennsylvania as manufacturers of wire rope. (50)

Newark, N. J., and **Cleveland, Ohio,** gas light companies organized. (38)

Nitroglycerin invented by Professor **Ascanio Sobrero,** Italian chemist, and first successfully used by **Alfred Nobel,** Swedish engineer, at Helenborg, Sweden, demonstrating its power—13 times that of gun powder of similar bulk. (79)

1847

Dr. James Young builds Britain's first refinery in order to process crude oil seeping into the workings of a coal mine at Alfreton, Derbyshire. When this supply becomes exhausted, he discovers that oil can be obtained by the distillation of cannel coals and shale, and he founds the Scottish Shale Oil Industry in 1851. (45)

1848

January 24—Gold discovered in California.

April—**Louis Agassiz** becomes professor of natural history at the new scientific school at Harvard University. (30)

Robert Mallet first proposes to the Royal Irish Academy that an artificial earthquake be produced by exploding gunpowder "to set in motion an earthquake wave" to be recorded by suitable instruments miles distant, so as to survey and map "formations constituting the land . . . (and the) bottom of the great ocean." (**Seismic Mapping**). (7)

Platinum mantles for gas lights first used in Paris. (38)

Gas light company organized in **Washington, D. C.** (38)

Dayton, Ohio, Gas Company organized; first gas is made in 1849 from refuse grease obtained from slaughter houses, is distributed through mains made of stove pipe coated with 2½ inches of lime mortar. (38)

1849

Edwards granted a patent in England for his form of stove, called "Gas Fire," that consists of lumps of incombustible material heated to near incandescence by gas burners, so as to resemble a coal fire. (Very similar to our present-day gas-fired, charcoal-type broilers!) (38)

Robert Mallet constructs the first true **geophone.** It is a seismoscope, a bowl of mercury from the surface of which is reflected a spot of light observed through a telescope. The spot disappears when the surface of the bowl ripples. (7)

1850

August 28—The manufacturing of gas begins in **Chicago by the Chicago Gas Light & Coke Company** which has 125 private customers, 99 street lamps, and one public building on its lines. Gas sells for $3.00 per Mcf. (38)

La Compania de Kerosina Jujena finds oil at the Laguna de la Brea (Lake of Tar) east of Salta, **Argentina.** (10)

Oil from seepages in Ventura County, **California,** refined by Mexicans for illumination in missions. (66)

Luther and William Atwood, two Boston chemists, produce from coal tar the first **coal oil** made for sale in the United States. They mix it with animal and vegetable oils—for lubricating machinery—and call it **"Coup Oil."** (36)

Distillation in **Japan** first successfully accomplished. (World Petroleum)

Samuel Kier, a Pennsylvania canal boat operator, devises a process to distill petroleum. He obtains an excellent illuminant which he calls **"carbon oil."** (10)

Brewer, Watson and Company, and the Hyde Brothers, another firm engaged in the lumber business along **Oil Creek,** Pa., begin lighting their mills with petroleum. (36)

Baron Thorman of **Russia** engages the famous German chemist, Justus von Liebig, to furnish plans for a refinery and to provide one of his assistants to aid in its construction. (48)

Dr. James Young, a Scottish chemist, patents an invention for "obtaining paraffine oil, or an oil containing paraffine, and paraffine from bituminous coals" by slow **distillation.** (35)

Young, Meldrum and Bunney erect a plant at Bathgate, England, for the **distillation of Boghead** coal, and crude oil is produced at this plant in 1851. (37)

1851

Two **shale oil** works are in operation in Scotland. (37)

Dr. Pole's formula for calculating the flow of gas in pipes at low pressure developed and presented to the gas industry. (38)

Works established in **Germany** for producing **paraffin oil from shale,** the most important being the plant of A. Wiesmann and Company at Augustenhutte, near Bonn. (37)

Charles N. Tripp forms a company to make **asphalt** from "gum beds" and in 1855, wins an honorable mention for his asphalt at the Universal Exhibition held in Paris, France. (63)

First oil lease in history of U. S. petroleum industry on property of J. O. Angier, of Titusville, Pa., instigated by Dr. Francis Beattie Brewer, whose father owns a lumber company "lessee" in that area. (1)

1852

August 31—California's first gas company, **San Francisco Gas Company,** is formed. (38)

September 24—First successful airship flight.

For the first time, **gas lights** outnumber oil lamps in New York City. (38)

Mikolasch distills crude oil, treats the distillate with sulphuric acid and caustic soda, and obtains a burning fluid. (**Refining**) (35)

1853

Petroleum oil replaces **candles** for lighting Emperor Ferdinand's North Railway Station in Vienna. (35)

Dr. Abraham Gesner, a skilled chemist in Pittsburgh, is manufacturing an improved illuminating oil from coal and calling his product "kerosene," a name for which he acquires the trade rights. (35)

The United States Chemical Manufacturing Company begins working coal tar for the manufacture of **lubricating oil,** at Waltham, Mass. (37)

1854

November 10—First **deed of property** sold **for oil purposes.** Brewer, Watson and Company convey 105 acres of land in Cherrytree Township, Venango County, Pennsylvania, to George H. Bissell and Jonathan G. Eveleth for $5,000. Deed recorded January 1, 1855. Bissell and Eveleth are to ditch and develop surface oil. Idea of drilling comes in 1856 when Bissell sees Kier ad stating rock oil has come from a depth of 400 feet. (43)

December 30—Certificate of Incorporation of **Pennsylvania Rock Oil Company** of New York filed in Albany. Leased Hibbard farm near Titusville. Capital stock—$250,000; major stockholders upset at delays of company, organize the **Seneca Oil Company** in March of 1858 and hire **Col. Edwin L. Drake** to drill first well. Founders include **Dr. Francis B. Brewer,** George H. Bissell, **Dr. Dixi Crosby, Albert H. Crosby,** and **J. M. Townsend. George H. Bissell** given credit for first conceiving idea of boring for oil. (1)

Kind makes the first **core orientation.** (28)

Belcher Sugar Refinery deep salt well in St. Louis completed at 2193 feet. (It had been commenced in 1849.) (1)

In a little known book, "Schamyl: the Sultan Warrior, and Prophet of the Caucasus," translated from the German by Dr. F. Wagner and F. Bodenstedt, published in London, mention is made of the **explosive power of crude oil** when mixed with air. (35)

The first **water gas apparatus** patented in the U. S. by **John and Thomas Kirkman.** (38)

Roots-Connersville Blower Division founded as P.H. & F.M. Roots

Company in Connersville, Indiana, as manufacturers of rotary positive, impeller type air blowers. (50)

1855

February 12—Charter granted to **The Peoples Gas Light and Coke Company** of Chicago. The charter is the first to include provision establishing maximum rates to be charged—$2.00 per Mcf. for private customers. (38)

February—The **Harlem Gas Light Company** organized to serve areas of New York City above 79th Street. (38)

April 16—**Benjamin Silliman, Jr.,** in a report on samples of the Cherrytree Township, Venango County, Pa., oil gives results which he has obtained by a study of the "Rock oil or petroleum." His report gives important information on the **chemistry of petroleum** and determines its economic value. He also authors technochemical classic on California petroleum (1865 and 1867) and on the combustion of fuel (1860). (37)

September 18—Incorporation of the **Pennsylvania Rock Oil Company** of Connecticut. (4)

Robert Wilhelm Bunsen patents his famous gas **burner** designed to produce heat rather than light. (38)

George Bedell Airy announces his **theory** on **isostasy**: that at some depth below the earth's crust there is a change in density of the material, and that the lighter upper rigid part floats on the heavier lower fluid part. (33)

John Henry Pratt announces his **theory** of **isostasy**: that the upper material of the earth's crust is lighter than the lower material, but differs from that of Airy in assuming that the boundary at which the change in density occurs is essentially horizontal and at a uniform depth called "the **depth of compensation**." (33)

The **distillation of petroleum** by "high steam" proposed by **Benjamin Silliman, Jr.** (37)

Elizabethtown Consolidated Gas Company chartered as the Elizabethtown Gas Light Company by a special act of the legislature for the purpose of supplying gas to Elizabethtown, New Jersey. (50)

1856

LaRue and Miller report the presence of several **alkylbenzenes** in Burma petroleum. (26)

Sir Henry Bessemer develops and patents his process for manufacturing steel. (38)

Dr. Abraham Gesner's New York Kerosene Company on Long Island commences the manufacture of **kerosene,** as an illuminant, using cannel coal from England and the United States. It is advertised as costing 1/7th as much as sperm oil. (4)

John Shaw, an American, drills for oil in Enniskillen Township in southwestern Ontario, **Canada.** (10)

The firm of Peterson and Irwin buys a farm near **Tarentum,** Pennsylvania, on which is located a producing salt well. This well produces two and one half to five barrels of oil a day which is marketed in Baltimore, Maryland, by Mackeown, Nevin and Company of Pittsburgh. Its principal use is in oiling the wool processed in carding mills in Baltimore. (15)

1857

December 30—The Pennsylvania Rock Oil Company draws up a lease with Edwin L. Drake and E. B. Bowditch in which Drake & Bowditch agree to pay Company one-eighth **royalty,** in oil, with Company to furnish the barrels. The Lessees are given an option to purchase this royalty oil at 45 cents a gallon. This lease is, at first, for 15 years but is modified on February 12, 1858 to provide for 25 years and for the Lessees to pay a royalty of 12 cents a gallon in lieu of the one-eighth part. (Rock Oil by Thomas A. Gale—1860)

Sulphuric acid is employed in the "coal oil" industry. (37)

The first attempts made to use **albertite** as a source of illuminating and lubricating oil. (36)

The **Downer Kerosene Oil Company** first makes mineral oils from **albertite,** mined in New Brunswick. (37)

The lightest distillate obtained from albertite is termed **"keroselene."** This is first prepared by **Joshua Merrill** and is used in the automatic gas machines of that day. (37)

Joshua Merrill develops a fire and **oil-proof cement** for making tight and lasting joints on stills. (4)

A well drilled near **Petrolia,** Ontario, Canada, completed as a flowing oil well—although its objective is water. (1)

James M. Williams starts search for oil around seepages on banks of Thames River in Kent County near **Bothwell** in Ontario, **Canada.** He then moves his operations to the gum beds of **Enniskillen** in Lambton County, Ontario (Later named **Oil Springs**). Williams digs a 49-foot hole, with the walls seven by nine feet, cribbed with logs. He does not reach the rock, but obtains from 2 to 10 barrels of oil a day. He builds a retort in which he distills the oil. (63) (Rock Oil, 1860)

A patent granted for heating—by use of **gas—for irons in laundry work.** (38)

1858

March 23—Formation of **Seneca Oil Company.** Takes over Hibbard lease near Titusville. George Bissell given credit for conceiving idea of boring for oil. E. L. Drake sent there to drill. (1)

May 29—**Prof. Dr. G. Ch. K. Hunaus** discovers first oil well at Wietze, **Germany,** at a depth of about 200 feet. Wietze is located in the German "oil country" near Hanover. The Hunaus discovery does not in any way conflict with the honors bestowed upon Drake. Hunaus is looking for coal deposits and accidentally stumbles on oil. Drake is looking for oil—and finds it. (45)

A **deep salt well** completed at Louisville, Kentucky, at 2086 feet in 16 months. (1)

The introduction of steam into petroleum during its **distillation,** first practiced in the United States by the **Downer Kerosene Oil Company,** at the suggestion of **Joshua Merrill.** (37)

The **first** recorded **corporation** to serve **natural gas** to business and residential customers established in Fredonia, New York. (51)

In **Poland,** oil discovered at Kleczany. (40)

Rotary-drilling methods are discussed by Professor August Beer of the Pribam School of Mines in Austria, in a publication on drilling wells into the earth. (1)

A refinery built in **Trinidad** to make "coal oil" from a vast asphalt lake. (10)

"Under cutting drills" used by Captain John Pope in drilling for water in West Texas. (1)

Professor Sanders introduces the process of making **water gas.** (38)

1859

April 7—**Pennsylvania** adopts an Act of Assembly permitting the organization of companies for "the manufacturing of oils" from mineral coal. (3)

July 1—The first issue of the **American Gas Light Journal** (now the **American Gas Journal**) issued. It is the first publication to serve the gas industry and record its progress. (47)

August 27—On a stream called **Oil Creek,** near Titusville, Pa., **"Colonel" Edwin L. Drake** drills 69 feet, six inches, and discovers oil. The second day the well is producing from eight to ten barrels of oil. This is the first well ever deliberately drilled for the purpose of finding oil. (10)

October 7—The Drake well ignited by gas and destroyed; but soon thereafter, it is revived when the old equipment is replaced. **First oil well fire** on record. (Rock Oil—1860)

Samuel T. McDougal of New York advertises gas stoves and cooking apparatus. (**Advertising Gas Appliances**) (51)

Lynis T. Barrett, a Confederate veteran of the Civil War, acquires the first oil and gas lease in **Texas.** It covers the Skillern tract in Nacogdoches County. (44)

Near Dover, New Brunswick, **Canada,** during the late spring and

26

summer, **Dr. H. C. Tweedel** punch-drills four shallow wells, the deepest of which goes down 190 feet. He hits both gas and oil but not in commercial quantities. (63)

Six plants erected for **coal oil distilling** near Pittsburgh, Pa. One of these, the Lucesco Company, has a distilling capacity of 6000 gallons of crude oil per day. The company has $120,000 invested in its works, and in 1860 ten revolving retorts are in operation. (37)

The pressure governor (**gas regulator**) begins to be incorporated in street lighting assemblies. (38)

J. S. Newberry mentions marine plants as a probable source of petroleum. (**Organic theory**) (22)

The Louisville, Ky., Gas Works is **pipe coating** wrought iron pipe—internally and externally—with a coal tar mixture. (38)

G. Quincke discovers that when a liquid flows through a permeable material a potential difference is set up across the material. (7)
The first technical article on clay **retorts** appears. (38)

Total production for the 33 U. S. coal oil refineries is 20,000 gallons a day. (48)

The total production of the American petroleum industry, which is wholly obtained from **Oil Creek,** amounts to about 2000 bbl. (37)

Platinum wire being used to ignite—by electricity—**gas light burners** and relight them when they are accidentally blown out. (38)

Albert Potts patents a "**gas light mail station.**" (38)

1859-74—U. S. produces more than 90 percent of world oil. Until 1883, U. S. production is never less than 80 percent of world total. (2)

1860

April 7—the **first oil lease to mention gas,** recorded in Warren County, Pennsylvania, is from B. W. Lacy to the Warren Oil Co. (47)

April—**D. S. Stombs** of Kentucky and **Julius Brace** of Virginia patent the first semi-continuous system in a battery of stills. The **Stombs-Brace system** patented even before petroleum distillation has established itself. (4)

April—The steamer Venango carries the first load of petroleum to Pittsburgh. (36)

May 1—The Rathbone brothers complete a well at 303 feet, near the mouth of a small stream called Burning Springs Run in Wirt County, **West Virginia.** It flows 100 barrels a day. Later that year, a second well comes in flowing 40 to 50 barrels a day. (10)

May 13—**Luther Atwood** assigned a patent for "**cracking**" coal-oil or petroleum. (4)

May—**Charles Lockhart,** of Pittsburgh, goes abroad with samples of crude and refined oil, calling the attention of some of the European merchants to the value of petroleum. (36)

27

June 1—The first petroleum book, "Rock Oil, The Wonder of the Nineteenth Century, in Pennsylvania and Elsewhere," by Thomas Gale, an 80-page book published by Sloan and Griffeth at Erie, Pa. (40)

June—G. W. Brown, a newspaper editor, drills a four-inch hole to 100 feet near a spring eight miles northeast of Paola, Kansas. He finds small quantities of oil. He also drills to 275 feet southeast of Paola and manages to siphon off about a barrel of oil a day from the salt water. By 1884, after the Civil War, drilling was resumed. In 1886 a small refinery was erected at Paola to process the crude. This was the first well drilled west of the Mississippi. (10)

July 10—Rouse, Mitchell and Brown's Curtis well is the first flowing well. It is on the Buchanan farm near Rouseville, Pa., and is drilled with a springpole to a depth of 180 feet, from which depth it flows 5 to 10 barrels per day for from 15 to 18 months. No tubing is used and the well was flooded out with surface water. (79)

November 26—First Oil Men's Association formed in Titusville, Pennsylvania. Edwin L. Drake, who drilled the first oil well there in 1859, elected president. (54)

November—J. D. Karns brings in a well pumping 37-50 barrels daily, near Elizabeth, Virginia, but it does not result in a producing field. (4)

November—An oil pipeline suggested by S. D. Karns who said it would be a 6-inch gas pipeline from Burning Springs to Parkersburg, W. Va., in which oil would flow by gravitating down the Ohio 36 miles. Money was never raised and line never materialized. Later, J. L. Hutchinson, inventor of the rotary pump, conceived the idea of forcing oil through lines by hydraulic pressure. This was a theoretical success but a mechanical failure. (79)

December 21—A company organized in Erie, Pa., by Wilson M. Laird, associated with Clemens Busick and D. Kennedy, drills a well on Laird's farm on the shore of Lake Erie in West Mill Creek Township to a depth of 500 feet but finds neither oil nor gas. This is the first recorded 'dry hole.' (43)

December—56 plants engaged in coal-oil production, with possibly a dozen or more small distillers of crude coal oil unreported. Fifteen or more small plants operating exclusively on petroleum distillation, significantly located at points where petroleum does not have far to travel. (4)

The founders of The Atlantic Refining Company establish the oil exporting firm of Warden, Frew and Company in Philadelphia. In 1866, this firm merged with Peter Wright and Sons to become the Atlantic Petroleum Storage Company. On April 29, 1870, The Atlantic Petroleum Storage Company built a small refinery at its Philadelphia location and became incorporated under the laws of Pennsylvania as The Atlantic Refining Company. In 1874, The Atlantic Refining Company became an affiliate of the Standard Oil organization. In 1911, a Supreme Court order dissolved the Standard Oil Trust and Atlantic

Refining Company again became a completely independent company. It has remained an independent company since that date. (50)

In **Canada,** the first natural gas well drilled north of Trois Rivieres. (59)

Kidder's **gas regulator** (patented in 1852) is the first design to regulate the flow of gas into the meter. (38)

Germany's first productive oil well drilled on a **salt dome** at Hanigsen, near Hanover. It opens the Neinhagen-Hanigsen field, which until 1934 produced 60 per cent of Germany's petroleum. (10)

Houston, Texas, announces a plan to construct a "gas works." (38)

Natural gas development in **Kansas** starts with the drilling of several wells in Miami County near the town of Paola. (47)

Jean Joseph Etienne Lenoir, a Luxembourgian, produces a motor burning benzene, and it is supposed to develop three horsepower. It is a noncompressing, horizontal, double-acting reciprocating unit, with crank and fly wheel, working on a crude two-stroke cycle. (35)

Natural gas discovered around East Liverpool, **Ohio,** a city noted for its manufacture of pottery. (46)

James Dutton, Alden T. Warren and John Smithson complete a well at 50 feet, on the William Rayley farm, half a mile below the village of Macksburg, **Ohio.** The oil has a gravity of 28 degrees, and sells at the commanding price of $28 per barrel. (10)

With only two shallow wells competing with his, Colonel E. L. Drake thinks there is **overproduction.** (15)

The **Pennsylvania Railroad** begins using gas to light one of its passenger cars. (38)

Geologists suggest that the **porosity** of sandstones is sufficient for oil entrapment and oil well flow. (48)

The gas works at **Portland, Oregon,** is the first in the Pacific Northwest. (38)

H. D. Rogers first enunciates the **anticlinal theory.** Pennsylvania Geological Survey. First published in 1861 by **T. Sterry Hunt** and **Sir William Logan,** who developed the same theory independently. **Rogers** notes the gravitational **separation** of oil, gas and water in reservoir beds. (22)

Rodolphe Leschot, French civil engineer, uses a power-driven **rotary drill** with a diamond-studded bit. (1)

The first commercial well drilling in **Rumania** begins when oil wells are completed at Mosarele. (23)

First reference to **shooting wells** made when Henry Denis explodes a 3-foot copper tube filled with rifle powder in the bottom of a water-filled well at Tidioute. (7)

Hot water stove invented by Hunter-Keller & Company, of New York. (38)

"Washington" engine manufactured at Newburgh, N. Y., the first engine with a portable boiler to come into general use for drilling. (4)

J. M. Williams is experimenting with a **"cracking"** process. (35)

George Wilson patents an apparatus using superheated steam and vacuum similar to that used in refining sugar, for **refining petroleum.** (4)

Professor **Alexander Winchell,** of the University of Michigan, suggests that sandstones themselves are sufficiently porous to contain oil even without fracturing. (22)

240 wells drilled of which 201 were productive. Most of these drilled in the **Oil Creek** area. 500,000 barrels of oil produced this year. Value of production is $4 million. (Texas Business Review)

There are 53 coal oil distilling companies in operation in the United States. (37)

1861

January 22—The **Barnsdall and Abbott refinery,** which had been commenced November 6, 1860, completed and goes on stream at **Oil Creek,** Pa. Located one mile below **Titusville,** it is built at a cost of $15,000 and, comprising six stills and bleachers, is the earliest multiple still unit in the Pennsylvania oil region. (4) (57)

January—William Reynolds and J. J. Shryock of Meadville, Pa., send 12 barrels of oil to London to James McHenry, the chief contractor for the Atlantic and Great Western Railroad. He distributes samples to members of the Board of Trade in London and sends some to chemical experts in Paris. (36)

April 4—Southern Confederacy formed.

April 10—**Massachusetts** passes a law establishing the office of **"Inspector of Gas Meters and of Illuminating Gas"** to become effective July 1, 1861. (38)

April 17—The **first flowing well** in the oil region is on the Buchanan farm, near **Oil Creek,** Pa. It is drilled by Henry Rouse. (43)

April 17—Little & Merrick's well on the John Buchanan farm, at the lower end of Oil Creek, Pa., roars in and flows 3000 barrels of oil. It explodes, catches fire, and ultimately 19 persons lose their lives. This is the first recorded instance of such an explosion. (**Explosion and oil well fire**) (43)

May 12—Captain A. B. Funk's **"Fountain well"** on David McElhenny's farm on Oil Creek is both the first large flowing well and the first well to the Third Sand. It tops the third sand at 400 feet and drills into it 60 feet deeper when it starts to flow at the rate of 300 barrels per day. (79)

September 7—The Phillips #2 well located on the Tarr farm on Oil Creek, Pa., roars in at 4000 barrels per day. This **production record** stands for 23 years. Oil price falls to 10 cents per barrel. (43)

October 24—First transcontinental telegram message sent.

November 4—Landowners and operators of wells along the Oil Creek area come together to organize and take measures to improve the price of oil. At the next meeting, they organize the **"Oil Creek Association."** By January of 1862, the first great combination of producers has been organized, and they refuse to sell oil below $4 a barrel. (36)

November—Jacob Jay Vandergrift of Pittsburgh starts the **bulk boat business** when he tows two large coal boats with 4000 empty barrels to Oil City with his steamer, the Red Fox. (36)

November—The **first** shipload of petroleum to cross the Atlantic is the 224-ton sailing ship Elizabeth Watts. It is loaded at Philadelphia with 3,000 barrels of oil headed for London. The ship is chartered by Peter Wright and Sons of Philadelphia and marks the beginning of regular traffic in **full-cargo shipments of oil.** The shipping rate is one dollar a barrel plus a 5 per cent commission to the owners of the vessel. (4) (15)

December—W. W. Murphy, the United States Consul at Frankfurt, first introduces petroleum into **Germany.** (36)

E. B. Andrews, a professor of geology at Marietta College, Ohio, points out the occurrence of oil and gas along the axes of **anticlines** in Ohio and West Virginia. (22)

T. Sperry Hunt, a chemist and geologist, makes a clear, comprehensive statement of the **anticlinal theory** of oil migration and location. (48)

Lease **bonus payments** come into use with $200 to $600 being paid as incentives to sign leases, in addition to royalty payments. (4)

The **Columbia Oil Company** formed, with **Andrew Carnegie** as one of its principal stockholders. One of the first "model" oil villages built by this company on the Story Farm, a few miles above Rouseville, Pa. (17)

Samuel Downer is probably first major coal-oil refiner to convert to **petroleum refining.** (4)

A. N. Wood & Company of Eaton, N. Y., manufactures a small, **portable engine.** Mounted on a compact tubular boiler that is in turn attached to a light wooden frame, the unit would be put into operation at a new location immediately upon unloading from a wagon. (4)

First successful three-lift **gas holder** built in London. (38)

Dr. Henry Bigelow, a renowned Boston surgeon, introduces extensive use of Joshua Merrill's coal-oil distillate "keroselene" as a local **anesthetic.** (4)

Joshua Merrill makes a major **improvement in stills** when he substitutes a formed, seamless bottom cut from a single plate of flange iron or steel.

31

It replaces the conventional riveted bottom of cast or wrought iron. (4)

Joshua Merrill adds to his basic advances in still design by inventing an air chamber to insulate the still during heating and cooling periods and to effect better temperature control. (4)

Richard Glyde, of Pittsburgh, designs and builds an **oil barge** for use on the Allegheny, with several compartments, each holding 80-100 bbls. of oil. (4)

The "**boot leg**" **packer** is being used in Pennsylvania. (1)

The first wells dug in **Peru** for oil are excavated by hand near Zorritos. A Scotsman named Farrier is in charge of the work. (45)

Chiu Kou digs a well 10 feet deep in northern **Taiwan,** and recovers a few gallons of crude oil a day. (45)

The Chinese government of the Ching Dynasty starts to explore oil reserves in northern **Taiwan** by a primitive method. (45)

Earthen storage for oil used, following completion of Empire well on Oil Creek. Owners first build dam to hold flood of oil and later dig holes in ground and crib them with timber. (Early Days of Oil, Paul H. Giddens, Princeton University Press, 1948)

First round hooped **wood tank** built in oil field below Titusville, Pa., by a Mr. Akin; replaces ractangular wood boxes of varying sizes used, instead of individual barrels or casks, for storage of oil; round tanks hold from 6 to 12 barrels. (1)

A device developed in France, using a "telegraphic agent" to indicate pressure at a remote point, allowing an "engineer" to make changes in pressure. (38)

1862

January 12—First issue of **Oil City Weekly Register** at Oil City, Pa. (43)

January—**British** government places a one cent per gallon tariff on petroleum imported from the U. S. (**Tariff, first oil**) (43)

July 1—Congress passes a **federal duty** of 10 cents a gallon on **refined petroleum.** (36)

December 12—**Casing** first used, on well at Tidioute Island by Julius Hall. (43)

1,500,000 gallons of petroleum sold in **Belgium** during this year. (36)

J. Cutler, a novitiate refiner in Boston, turns out a suitable **burning oil** using A. C. Ferris' adequate acid-alkali treating method, without repeated distillation. (4)

Natural gas discovered in **California** near the Mattole River, in the Lower Mattole Valley. (38)

Hugh Nixon Shaw drills and brings in **Canada's** first 'gusher' at 165 feet at Black Creek (Oil Springs), Lambton County, Ontario. (63)

The first year of recorded oil production in **Canada.** (10)

Thomas Swinnerton, of England, granted a patent on a process to make **coal gas** by utilizing waste heat of blast furnaces in iron works. (38)

A. M. Cassedy, a pioneer Pennsylvania oil man, drills **Colorado's** first oil well six miles north of Canon City. It produces a barrel a day at 50 feet. He drills six more producers, some of them to 90 feet. Cassedy had opened the first pool of what came to be known, after extensions had been discovered and deeper pay horizons found, as the Florence field. (10)

James D. Dana writes his "Manual of **Geology.**" (30)

Alphonse Beau de Rochas, a Frenchman, suggests a **four-stroke cycle engine.** (35)

Two Americans, Shaw and Linton, patent a **furnace** in which **fuel oil** is conveyed into the interior in a gaseous stage. (35)

Professor T. S. C. Lowe reports making gas to inflate balloons that are used to make observations on Confederate batteries at Fair Oaks, Virginia. (**Gas in Warfare**) (38)

First oil refinery in Germany put on stream at Salzbergen. It is operated today by the Wintershall A. G. Oil Company. (45)

At the upper end of Cherry Run, Pa., near Plumer, John E. Bruns and the Ludovici brothers of New York City erect the **Humboldt refinery.** (36)

First recorded **mineral interest** sale by J. W. Sherman of Cleveland who sells 1/16 of his interest in lease on Foster farm on Oil Creek for an old horse with which to power his spring pole. He later sells other interest for other supplies and services. He almost sells all of his interest before the well comes in producing oil worth $1.7 million. (4)

Oil Well Supply (Division United States Steel Corporation) founded as **Jon Eaton** in Oil City, Pennsylvania, as manufacturers of bits, other cable tools, temper screws, bailers, bull wheels, derrick and rig fittings. (50)

Pennsylvania creates the first corporations "for the purpose of conveying oil through pipes or tubes." (3)

Stanley Hope, an English banker, introduces superheated steam into commercial **refining.** His process is a modification of one developed by Dr. Herbert W. C. Tweddle, an English chemist. (4)

Petroleum from the United States introduced in **Russia.** (36)

Col. E. A. L. Roberts conceives the idea of **shooting wells** by exploding torpedoes in oil wells to increase production. (1)

John Tagliabue, a renowned Italian-born instrument maker, introduces his famous **closed-cup testing** apparatus for determining the **flash-point** of kerosene.

Congress passes a **federal gas tax** of five to 15 cents per Mcf, effective September 1, 1862. A New York company proposes to pass the tax to its customers, and is greeted by editorial blasts of the New York City newspapers. Public pressure forces the company to withdraw and pay the tax itself. (38)

1862-63—Two wells are drilled for oil on Otter Creek in Crawford County, **Indiana.** Both were dry holes, but the deepest of the two was bored to 1180 ft., a surprising depth for that period. (**Deepest wells**) (10)

Pipeline legislation defeated in Pennsylvania by teamsters. It was proposed that the line run from Oil Creek to Kittannig. A later plan for a line down the Allegheny to Pittsburgh failed. (79)

1863

February 19—A 2.5 mile two-inch iron **pipeline** from the Tarr farm to the Humboldt refinery is being tested to determine whether or not powerful pumps will force the oil through the line. Barows & Company is already moving oil from Burning well to their refinery, about 1000 feet, by this means. No report of results leads to belief that it failed. (**Pipeline, first iron**) (43)

July 14—**J. R. Leschot** receives U. S. Patent #39,235 covering a rotary rock drill set with diamonds or other satisfactory hard material, and with hydraulic-flushing methods of removing cuttings. (**Diamond coring**) (1)

The discovery of **butadiene** announced. (25)

Etienne Lenoir invents the **gas engine.** (38)

Sir William Logan and his assistants publish "**Geology of Canada.**" (30)

Sir William Logan points out petroleum and solid bitumen in a greenstone dike at Tar Point, Gaspe, in the province of Quebec, **Canada.** (37)

Three of the largest refineries, located near the port of Marseilles, **France,** begin to process crude oil imported from America. (4)

Brydges Adams introduces into America an **oil-spray burner furnace.** (35)

Joshua Merrill begins the commercial production of gasoline at the **Downer plant** in Boston for the largest manufacturer of air-gas machines. (4)

Frederick Crocker's famed "**Oil ejector**" is a major break-through in eliminating oil well clogging. His first major success is in restoring two defunct Pennsylvania flowing wells to a production of many thousands of barrels. (4)

Pennsylvania Legislature passes the first **anti-pollution** bill to prevent running of tar and distillery refuse into certain creeks in producing districts. (3)

R. Weinberger describes severe **poisoning** of two workers engaged in cleaning out a vessel containing petroleum residuum. (37)

John D. Rockefeller and **Maurice B. Clark,** partners in a mercantile commission house, and two of Clark's brothers decide to join **Samuel Andrews,** a self-taught refiner, in manufacturing kerosene. (8A)

H. D. Rogers first announces the correlation between dynamic and temperature metamorphism, coal composition, and the **occurrence of oil and gas,** as revealed by his extensive field tests in Pennsylvania. (22)

Lockhart and Gracie introduce mechanical **scrapers** which operate on a rotating shaft so that the residuum in still bottoms can be dumped before it has time to cool and harden. (4)

William Reed, using electrical charges in **shooting wells,** explodes three charges in tin casings that withstood water pressure in the Criswell on Cherry Run, Pa. (4)

Iron tanks used to ship oil from Canada by rail to Portland, Maine, thence to Liverpool. (1)

American Meter Company formed with Samuel Downs as president; firm is consolidation of Downs and Merrifield; Code, Hopper and Company, and Robert H. Gratz and Company. Downs had opened a meter shop in New York in 1863. (38)

First refinery in Baku opened by Mirzoeff. (76)

Joshua Merrill makes a clean break-through to the best modern practice, when he begins giving all oil-burning **distillates** a final distillation after treating with acid and soda. (4)

1864

March—Death of the widow, Mrs. Culbertson McClintock of Venango County, Pa., leaves oil fortune to the adopted orphan, **John Washington Steele,** and starts his fantastic and profligate career as **Coal Oil Johnny.** He squanders a vast fortune in the most notorious spendthrift spree in history in less than a year. (Coal Oil Johnny, His Book, by John Washington Steele, Hill Publishing Company, NY, 1902).

April—Sale of a farm along **Oil Creek** for $650,000 in greenback currency remained the largest sum of cash ever paid for oil land only until November of this year, when a farm at **Oil City** sells for $750,000. (4)

June 30—A **federal tax** of $1.00 per barrel placed **on crude oil.** (36)

November 22—Patent to **T. B. Gurning** for **first air lift.** Gas compressor for taking gas from the production and conducting it to the well bottom through an inner string of tubing for assisting the flow of oil. (1)

John Wilkes Booth, Thomas Mears and John Ellser form the Dramatic Oil Company to drill for oil near Franklin, Pennsylvania. The well Booth had owned a share of, on Pithole Creek, came in a gusher six weeks after his capture and death, after Lincoln's assassination. (16)

35

Opening of a producing district several miles up **Cherry Run., Pa.,** marks first important departure from pioneer territory in Venago County and from flatlands along streams. (4)

The **United States Naval Board of Engineers** begins experimenting with petroleum as a substitute for coal on naval steamers. (36)

Bordeaux, France, adopts kerosene—in preference to gas—for lighting the new public gardens. (36)

First well on a hilltop. A venturesome operator, probably against the advice of experts, drills a well on a hilltop near Oil City, Pennsylvania. (GeoTimes)

The superintendent at the Ladies well on Watson's Flats near Titusville, Pa., turns to **gas fuel** with notable success. Pipes it through a barrel to the furnace and uses it to light the engine-house as well. (4)

The first **Kansas Geological Survey** authorized, and in 1866 the first report is made. (21)

So great is the demand for oil stocks in New York, that a **Petroleum Board** is organized in the fall of this year. (36)

In **shooting wells,** Frederick Crocker explodes a torpedo in the bottom of a well by means of a weight falling on a pistol cartridge inserted in the shell. (4)

A steamboat on the Hudson River is **lighted with gas;** it takes on its supply at Albany and stores the gas in tanks. (38)

The U. S. Petroleum Association approves and accepts as standard the Baume-type hydrometer of **Jarvis Arnabalde** and **C. J. Tagliabue** because of its "uniformity and accuracy." **Antoine Baume,** a French scientist, designed the linear **hydrometer** scale for liquids in 1768. (1)

As early as this date, R. G. Loftus claims a process of recovering the acid used in refining Pennsylvania petroleum. (37)

Colonel Gowan, an American, drills several shallow wells in search of petroleum in the **Crimea.** Some encounter only gas but others yield some oil. (80)

First carbon black made in U. S. by J. K. Wright, ink maker, in Philadelphia for use in printing ink, particularly for newspaper industry. Wright makes the carbon black on sheet iron cylinders which revolve over gas jets; it is removed by stationary scrapers. First carbon black patent issued to A. Millochan, New York, Dec. 19, 1867, but the first successful patent for carbon black was issued to **John Howarth** of Salem, Mass., in 1872. (79)

Gas works in several **Confederate states** report using **cottonseed to make gas** as coal is practically unavailable. (38)

Eagle Gas Stove Works of New York City introduces a **"gas stove."** Device is little more than a gas hot plate. (38)

George Westinghouse discovers airbrakes.

36

January 8—**Pithole Creek field** discovered by the United States Petroleum Company. Well located with a witch-hazel twig comes in as a gusher. It started flowing 250 barrels per day. (**Dowsing**) (43)

January—First recorded use of liquid nitroglycerine in **shooting wells** is in New York. **Col. E. A. L. Roberts** first demonstrates use of explosives to increase well flow. First instance was on the "Ladies Well" near Titusville—patented the process. First 39 wells shot increased production on the average from 125-200 barrels daily. (1)

March 7—Walter Hyde granted a patent for an **"Improved Well Borer."** He uses an oscillating lever and fulcrum, a double gear, two windlasses, and a suitable platform to effect this cable-tool drilling machine. (40)

April 9—Surrender at Appomattox.

April 14—Lincoln assassinated.

May 23—I. Y. Smith receives a patent for a rotary drill which is a **combination cable-tool and rotary device.** There is also a rotary table and gripper box which turns the drilling cable and "thus secured a round hole." (**Combination rig**) (40)

May 27—Producers and landowners of the Tarr farm meet at Tarrville, Pa., and decide every well should be cased down to the second sandstone and seedbagged at that point, taking the **first step toward conservation.** (15)

June 14—**Titusville Morning Herald** makes appearance—First daily newspaper published in oil regions. (43)

July—**Thomas A. Bard** spuds in his first well on the **Rancho Ojai,** north of San Buenaventura. It produces more water than oil. In 1866, he drills five more. Ojai No. 6 is considered **California's first commercial producer.** It is drilled to 550 feet with steam equipment. Its settled production is 15 to 20 barrels per day. Bard later becomes Union Oil Company's first president. (10)

September—Oil shipped by **tank car** from Pennsylvania to New York. A flat car, designed by **Amos Densmore,** carries two wooden tanks, each holding 42 to 45 barrels. (54)

October 10—**Oil Transportation Association** (composed of Charles Hickox, Charles W. Noble, Samuel Van Syckle, H. C. Ohlen, and the firm of Reed and Cogswell) completes and tests 32,000 feet of two-inch iron pipe laid from United States well to Miller Farm on the Oil Creek Railroad; three pumps used, two at Pithole and one at Little Pithole. A telegraph line is added to the equipment. The line is laid on top of the ground most of the way. (**Pipeline, first oil**) (43)

October 16—With the October 10 tests successful, **Samuel Van Syckle's** pipeline goes into service. It pumps 80 barrels of oil per hour, the equivalent of 300 teams working 10 hours. On this date, also, a six inch line is being constructed from Pithole Creek to the Island Well, seven miles, by the Pennsylvania Tubing Company. (43)

November 21—An oil exchange formed at Titusville, Pa. (36)

December—The **Reno Oil and Land Company** organized. It purchases 1200 acres of land on the Allegheny River, four miles from Oil City, and proceeds to lay out a model town—Reno—and drill wells. (36)

Robert Briggs, in a discussion at a Philadelphia meeting of the American Philosophical Society, describes petroleum as an intimate mixture of gases and liquids. (1)

Southern **California** oil hunters stake the first claims to the "oil springs" of **Pico Canyon.** (Standard Oil Company of California)

It is apparent from **John F. Carll's** discussion (1880) that accidental and perhaps intentional **water flooding** of the oil-producing zone occurring in the Pithole City area pointed out possible benefits of flooding. (1)

Small **casing,** 3¼ inch in size, first introduced. First used by Julius Hall at well on Tidioute Island (Pa.) also at Blood Farm—Oak Creek. (1)

Three Englishmen, Ayden, Wise and Field, introduce a **nozzle feeder oil burner furnace.** (35)

The first company to engage in the natural gas business formed in **Fredonia, N. Y.,** as the **Fredonia Gas Light and Water Works Co.** (38)

The first safe machine for making illuminating and heating **gas from gasoline** built. (54)

Charles N. Gilbert, an inventor, forms a partnership with machine designer John F. Barker, to manufacture a safe and efficient apparatus for generating an **illuminating gas** from high-gravity gasoline. (8A)

Charles Pratt, an early refiner, hires a German inventor, Herman Miller, to improve the **kerosene can.** Miller becomes known as "the father of the five-gallon tin." (Standard Oil Co. of New Jersey)

Natural gas, from a well near McCoy's Station, Pa., first used for manufacturing **lampblack.** (47)

Job Moses, a manufacturer of patent medicine, takes over a well from the Hall Farm Petroleum Company near Limestone village in Cattaraugus County, **New York.** He drills and finds oil at 1060 feet. The well produces 200 bbl. of oil per day, but is ruined by water. In 1871, Moses and some associates drill the first successful well on the Pennsylvania side of the county line and open up the rich **Bradford field.** In New York, a well called the John Braudel No. 1, drilled in September of 1877, is still producing. (10)

Two Americans, Cyrus Warren and Francis H. Storer, in laboratory work to test the **organic theory** of the **origin of oil,** obtain members of the methane, ethylene and benzene groups. (35)

Warren and Storer prepare a lime soap from fish oil, which, on destructive distillation, yields a mixture of hydrocarbons hardly distinguishable from coal oil. From this mixture they isolate and identify paraffins, olefins, and members of the **aromatics series.** A true **artificial petroleum** has therefore been prepared. (37)

The **"seed bag"** packer in use in the oil fields. (1)

J. H. A. Bone publishes book entitled **"Petroleum and Petroleum Wells,"** in which he describes much of the equipment used in the early fields. (1)

Opening of **Pioneer Run and Bennehoff Run,** with important strikes on hilly terrain, definitely explodes notions that paying territory is confined to flats bordering streams. (4)

At **Pithole,** the productive third sands require drilling to more than 600 feet. (4)

A **refinery** capable of handling 2000 gallons of crude petroleum per day **costs** about $11,230. (37)

The **first separator** introduced to the oil industry at Oil Creek, Pennsylvania. (48)

J. F. Keeler, of Pittsburgh, builds a predecessor of the modern type **tank car,** twenty-five feet long, eight feet wide, shaped like a box car with the bottom rounded like a "U." (4)

The earliest patent bearing directly on the subject is one granted to **James Young** "for certain improvements in **treating hydrocarbon oils."** (37)

Producing wells have been drilled in Kentucky, New York, Ohio, Tennessee and West Virginia. Total production amounts to 2,498,000 barrels valued at an average price of $6.59 a barrel at the wellhead. (Texas Business Review)

1865-66—**Robert Chesebrough** granted a series of patents covering all phases of filtration through animal charcoal or bone black, of coal oil or petroleum, both crude and refined, either cold or passed through a steam-heated filter. This was the basic process through which he eventually produced the famous **"Vaseline"** petroleum jelly. (4)

First experimental **water flooding** conducted in a few wells in Pithole field, Pennsylvania. (1)

John D. Rockefeller and Samuel Andrews buy out Maurice B. Clark's share in their Cleveland refinery and form the firm of **Rockefeller and Andrews.** (Standard Oil Company, New Jersey)

1866

January 2—P. Sweeney receives patent #51,902. It covers a stone drill with a bit using **rolling cutters** as the cutting elements, which is the forerunner of the modern **rock bit.** In addition, he uses a hollow drill shaft and circulating fluid to remove cuttings. (1)

March 17—Well known as the "Alpha" well drilled to 300 feet, without production, by Smith, Scott, Ross and Carter and Company in Monturoa, **New Zealand.** Well was dry—but on what is now known as the Egmont oil field. (1)

April 9—Dr. Henry Bigelow, after research by Joshua Merrill, announces a great advance in local **anesthesia:** Petroleum product which he calls **"rhigolene."** Modern nomenclature: a mixture of **pentane and butane.** (4)

July 10—West Bridgewater, **Massachusetts,** citizens organize $20,000 corporation to explore for oil after indications report it nearby. (43)

July 26—Kaiser's office in Germany issues patent on Carl Schwend's **electrodrill,** "a deep drilling method through application of electrical power transmission with the elimination of the drill stem." Patent issued **C. W. Van Wormer** of Houston Aug. 8, 1944 for electrodrill. Russia started using electrodrill 1947, apparently based on Van Wormer patent which was not adopted in U. S. By 1962 Russians had drilled 16,000 feet successfully with this type of drill. (German and U. S. Patent Offices, World Oil)

August 1—A patent for a method of **shooting wells** by exploding torpedoes at the bottom of wells granted to **E. A. L. Roberts.** (54)

Summer—Alfred W. Smiley and George E. Coutant build the first **"accommodation pipeline"** to connect Pithole well tanks with dump tanks of the pipelines. It is a two-inch line, four miles long and brings the price of moving crude to pipeline dumps down from 50 cents-$1.00 a barrel to 25 cents a barrel. Other pipelines quickly adopted accommodation lines. (4)

September 4—Patent to **J. Jann.** Gasoline, sweet oil and sulphuric acid are mixed, and the separated layer is decanted and used as a burning oil. (29)

September 12—The first concessions granted in **Venezuela** for exploration and exploitation in Sucre, Monagas and Trujillo states. (45)

October 4—**Vacuum Oil Company,** a New York corporation, organized in Rochester, New York. (50)

Dec. 18—Patent issued to **W. B. Snow** for his pump with a close-fitting metal plunger and metal barrel. This is a grooved metal **packing collar** with a tubular plunger and with no packing or cups. (1)

December—Col. **E. A. L. Roberts** explodes torpedo in Woodin well on Blood Farm—a dry hole that has never produced. It immediately starts flowing 20 barrels daily. A second torpedo in January, 1867, steps flow up to 80 barrels daily, establishing for the torpedo all Roberts had claimed. Roberts had filed for a patent in 1865 and, after several lawsuits, had won out in 1866. (79)

Dr. M. C. Eghert of Rouseville, Pa. (his brother was A. G.), and some twenty other producers at Oil Creek, Pa., post notice that selling crude oil by the barrel without regard to size is "injurious to the oil trade."

For every forty gallons sold they made an allowance of two gallons in favor of the buyers. Virtually established forty-two gallons as the standard of measurement for **crude oil barrel.** (1)

The first important oil flow found with the drill, in the **Kuban** (Russia). (80)

F. H. Wenham, an Englishman, patents the first **biplane,** building his gliders with two or more surfaces. (35)

A well on the island of Lahuan, off the northeast coast of **British Borneo,** is drilled to the depth of 19½ feet and flows a small quantity of oil for many years. (20)

Dr. P. H. Van der Weyde announces the discovery of "Chimogene," later "Cymogene." Modern nomenclature: **butane.** (4)

Alfred Nobel invents **dynamite** by mixing nitroglycerine with finely powdered earth. Dynamite, first manageable explosive, makes commercial seismic work possible. (65)

George Smith of Rouseville, Pa., introduces a major improvement in drilling tools when he brings out the first **steel-lined jars.** (4)

The **Pechelbronn field** in France starts producing oil. (45)

A direct railroad connection established in the Spring, between **Pithole** and the Atlantic & Great Western RR at Oil City, and through shipments can now be made to New York and elsewhere. (36)

Robert Cornelius invents and patents a **gas displacement pump.** (1)

The **Wheland Company** founded in Athens, Tennessee, as manufacturers of saw mill equipment. In 1926, they start the manufacture of **slush pumps.** (50)

Alexis Thirault, of New York City, develops a **three-unit single still** divided into three units. It is designed to produce kerosene only and is much more practical than the earlier Stombs-Brase still. (4)

Edward Orton first explains and illustrates the effect of **terrace structure.** (37)

The **federal tax** of $1.00 per barrel on **crude oil** repealed. (36)

The first commercial production in **Tennessee** comes from the Spring Creek pool in southern Overton County—near old oil spring. (10)

The first **Texas** oil well completed by **Lynis T. Barrett** near Oil Spring, Nacogdoches County. The well is completed at 106 feet with a reported capacity of 10 barrels per day. (44)

The **Titusville Pipe Company** organized to build a two-mile double line of two-inch pipe from Titusville to Pithole. When completed in March, the line has a capacity of 3000 barrels a day. (36)

The first well in **Trinidad** drilled near Pitch Lake by the Trinidad Petroleum Company. It does not produce in commercial quantities. (10)

California—The **Stanford brothers** complete an 80-foot up-sloping tunnel into the side of Sulphur Mountain north of **Ventura.** Production is one to 20 bbl. a day. Tunneling continues off and on for the next 25 years. 31 tunnels dug. Longest 1600 feet. **(Oil mining)** (6)

There are 58 refineries in Pittsburgh, 30 in Cleveland, and numerous others along the East Coast. (Texas Business Review)

1867

June—**U. S. Navy gunboat Palos, using petroleum as fuel,** steams 25 nautical miles at a remarkable speed of 14 miles an hour. Less than four barrels of petroleum does the work of six to eight tons of coal with a 50 per cent gain in speed. Congress had appropriated $5000 for the tests. (4)

July 15—Successful experiments with **oil as fuel for a locomotive** conducted by the Warren and Franklin Railroad of Pennsylvania. (54)

Otto and Langen exhibit their free-piston **atmospheric engine** at Paris. (38)

Baltimore Refinery of Standard Oil Trust starts operations. (50)

A. H. Tait and J. W. Avis receive a patent which pertains to "improvements in apparatus for **distilling petroleum.**" (37)

Two significant **gas appliances** introduced into the U. S.: The Etna combined gas stove and heater, and Dr. Musgrove's gas stove. (38)

A. C. Rand introduces his **"pneumatic gas machine,"** a portable unit for carburating gasoline that embraces several patented improvements to improve distribution of the gas by pipes. (4)

The **"Portable Gas Light Machine"** introduced. (38)

Oil discovered on Richland Creek, **Kentucky,** on the Hughes farm in Knox County, five miles northeast of Barbaursville, at 400 feet. (10)

Chas. Martin & Company, **oil inspectors,** is the outgrowth of a business that was established shortly after the Drake discovery well at Titusville, Pa. (50)

Peru—A. E. Prentice, a wandering Pennsylvania oil man, using a diamond drill, discovers oil at 146 feet in the Zorritos field north of La Brea—Parinas. It produces 60 barrels of oil a day. (10)

Vitreous coatings (porcelain) reported being used on various types of gas apparatus, is called a "new act." (38)

Rockefeller, Andrews and Flagler merge with the refineries of **William Rockefeller & Co., Rockefeller & Andrews, Rockefeller & Co., S. V. Harkness,** and **H. M. Flagler,** "to unite skill and capital in order to carry on a business of some magnitude and importance." (49)

Alfred Nobel licenses Colonel E. A. L. Roberts to use dynamite in **shooting wells** for greater production. (Baroid Division National Lead Company)

The Robinson brothers design the **"snap thief"** for the purpose of obtaining samples at various levels in a tank. Such samples are combined to form a composite sample. (1)

Riveted **iron tanks** begin to replace wooden tanks for oil storage. (1)

Eghest and Brown build the **largest iron storage tank** in the world—80 feet diameter by 22 feet three inches high, on the Jersey shore at Bellows Island, N. Y. (43)

Patent #68,350, entitled "Improvement in Apparatus for Testing Deep Wells," granted to T. Burr and T. Wakelee by U. S. Patent office. Significant development in **testing packers.** (1)

Jonathon Watson drills **deepest well** to depth of 2130 feet in **Titusville,** Pa. (1)

The first **tubing** designed expressly for oilfield service made for **John Eaton** in the early 1860's. In 1867 **Eaton** introduces standardized casing and tubing to the petroleum industry. (Oil Well Supply)

Hiram B. Everest, of Rochester, N.Y., becomes interested in a proposition posed by Matthew P. Ewing for recovering more kerosene from crude oil by **vacuum distillation.** Starting with an original patent issued in 1866, they progress to an improved design incorporating the use of steam. (40)

Nikolaus August Otto, German technician, invents (with **Eugen Langen**) early form of **internal combustion engine.** (65)

1868

February 1—**First** records of **price quotations based on gravity.** Oil at Pioneer, Titusville, Petroleum Center and Miller Farm quoted at $2.00 to $2.15 per barrel for 40° to 49° gravity oil delivered on tank cars. (1)

February—Abram James, an ardent spiritualist, digs for oil on the William Porter farm a mile south of Pleasantville. He strikes oil and calls his well the Harmonial, in honor of the spiritual philosophy. By the end of the year the ensuing **"Pleasantville Boom"** has collapsed. (36)

The **aerated flame burner** with platinum mantle invented. (38)

Binney and Talbot describe a peculiar occurrence of petroleum in a peat bed on Down Holland Moss, not far from Liverpool, **England.** (37)

Helium first identified in the **sun's atmosphere.** (64)

A Kokomo, **Indiana** man discovers gas while boring a well in his cellar. He "tubes" the well and uses the gas to light his house. (38)

An American engineer, J. B. Chichester, introduces gas to **Mexico City** after successfully converting a long-idle and never-used gas plant to the new process. (38)

The **"right of way"** problem eased by a Pennsylvania law giving free right-of-way to any pipeline in eight counties in the Oil Region. But, because of railroad opposition, this law prohibits pipelines from reaching Pittsburgh. (40)

Standard Oil Company (**Pennsylvania**) organized. This corporation was the first to bear the Standard Oil name. (8A)

Christopher Latham Sholes invents **typewriter.**

Gas main explodes at U.S. Capitol in Washington, D. C., "under the dome;" no one injured, damage extensive but not serious. (38)

The **first general industrial use of natural gas** recorded in the United States by an oil well supply firm, **Jarecki Mfg. Co.,** in its plant at Erie, Pa. (46)

1869

February—At Titusville, Pa., the first **Petroleum Producers' Association** formed. (36)

May 1—T. F. Rowland granted a patent for **offshore drilling rig.** Patent #89,794. (1)

May 10—**Transcontinental railway completed** when a golden spike is driven at Promontory, Utah, marking the junction of the Central Pacific and Union Pacific lines. (54)

May—An accident leads **Joshua Merrill** to a patent on deodorized neutral oil and its distilling process. He had placed his oil on the market in 1868 with sales of 276,000 gallons. By 1869, sales had gone over 465,000 gallons. (4)

September 24—**Black Friday** (first) as Jay Gould and James Fisk, Jr., try to corner gold market.

November 17—**Suez Canal** opened.

Compressed **rock asphalt** employed on roads in London, England. (39)

A diamond drill sent to and first used in the United States in Vermont stone quarries. (1)

George Machlet arrives in the U. S. from Germany; he is later to perfect a greatly improved gas burner system using positive air pressure, known as the "**Little giant melter.**" (38)

Flagler Brothers, of Boston, Mass., incorporate to manufacture tubular products. Later became the **National Tube Company** which was the first to hydraulically test pipe to 300-350 psi as standard practice. (38)

Oil well drilling commences in **Punjab** but appreciable production is not obtained until 1915. (23)

Lord Kelvin measures **temperature** down to a depth of 347 feet in the Blythswood well, using for the purpose an electric thermometer. (1)

"**Cambridge**" **gas stoves** introduced. (38)

1870

January 10—**The Standard Oil Company of Ohio** formed in Cleveland, with a capital of $1,000,000. This firm absorbs the firm of Rockefeller, Andrews and Flagler. (16)

May 4—The SS Charles, first vessel fitted for bulk shipment of oil, loads in New York. She has 59 iron tanks with a total capacity of 794 tons. (54)

Asphalt, as a material for paving, introduced to America when a street is paved in front of the Newark, New Jersey, City Hall. (54)

Cyrus S. Anzell's demonstrations of the validity of his "belt" theory of locating oil wells causes operators to flock into Pennsylvania's Lower Region. (4)

John F. Carll reports production techniques being practiced in Pennsylvania such as the flushing action of benzene, the use of a wire brush to clean the face of the sand, and a chemical action set off by an electric spark which he terms the "volcano." (Secondary recovery) (1)

M. C. Bullock introduces new fluid-circulating diamond core drill into coal fields near Pottsville, Pa., after purchasing rights to Leschot patents on diamond drilling equipment. He had used machine in 1869 in Michigan. (1)

S. A. Hill and C. F. Thumm receive a patent for "improvements in apparatus for distilling hydrocarbon oils." (37)

"Oil gas" process at Saratoga, N. Y., reported successful in operation, uses naphtha or "light oils" to produce improved grade of gas for lighting. (38)

Japan first officially records crude oil production in the statistical data of the government. (World Petroleum)

A natural gas line 25 miles long, constructed of white pine, having eight-inch ID and 12½-inch OD, begun between West Bloomfield and Rochester, N. Y. (38)

Emerson McMillin invents the iron-oxide process for purifying manufactured gas. (38)

Kerosene first introduced into Japan. (4)

Charles Miller of Franklin, Pa., introduces Galena oil as a solid lubricant. It is lead oxide kept in suspension in reduced Franklin-district crude. (4)

Thalen and Tiberg construct first magnetometer, a dip needle combined with a compass. (7)

The mechanical joint for cast iron pipe invented by Clark and installed in the lines of the Elizabethtown, N. J., Consolidated Gas Company. (38)

Julius Hock builds a petroleum engine of non-compression type in Vienna. (35)

A. A. Potylitsyn begins studies of the composition of waters from oil-bearing strata. (27)

The Stevens Institute, of Hoboken, N. J., established. It is later to supply the gas industry with many talented individuals. (38)

45

Improved "wet type" **gas meter** patented by **Trumbore,** provides a means of keeping a constant fluid level in meter, thus assuring its "efficient functioning." (38)

1871

March 13—One hundred and sixteen dealers, producers, refiners and brokers along Oil Creek hold the first formal meeting of the **Titusville Oil Exchange.** (36)

March 14—John R. Hill patents method for closing water courses in wells by **cementing.** (1)

April—The **Franklin,** Pa., **Oil Exchange** opened. (36)

May 1—**South Improvement Company** created by an act of Pennsylvania Legislature. It is empowered to "to construct and operate any work or works, public or private, designed to include, increase, facilitate, or develop trade, travel, or transportation of freight, livestock, passengers or any traffic by land or water, from or to any part of the U. S." Nine hundred of the 2000 shares are owned by Messrs. H. M. Flagler, O. H. Payne, William Rockefeller, H. Bostwick, and J. D. Rockefeller, later to become prominent in the Standard Oil Company. (49)

May 16—**AIME** founded as the American Institute of Mining Engineers. Along with **ASCE, ASME** & **AIEE,** it is one of the original four "Founder" societies for the engineering profession in the U. S. (57)

October 31—A patent issued on a **fractionating tower** still to **Henry Rogers** of New York. Rogers' fractionating tower embodies many features of a modern fractionater. (4)

October—The great **Chicago fire** rages for 27 hours, destroying 18,000 buildings over an area of more than 1688 acres. Peoples Gas Light and Coke Company's North Station is saved, although every other building to the north, south, and east has been destroyed. (38)

Bradford, Pa., **field** discovered. (11)

Cubic foot bottle for measuring gas—invention of Hartley & Glover—described. (51)

The **Hyde Park Gas Company** in Chicago reported to have laid three-, four-, six- and eight-inch wooden mains. (38)

T. Sperry Hunt states that a well sunk at Terre Haute, **Indiana,** for water was carried to a depth of 1900 feet and yielded about seven gallons of oil daily. A second well yielded 25 barrels daily, at a depth of 1625 feet. (37)

Railroad tank cars, consisting of a horizontal cylindrical tank of boiler plate, mounted on a four-wheel platform or railroad truck appear. (37)

Buffalo, New York, drills gas wells for city use. (38)

1872

January 18—**South Improvement Company** enters into contracts with

Pennsylvania, New York Central, and Erie Railroads granting the company **rebates** on all petroleum and products carried by them. (49)

February 27—Beginning of the **"oil war"** between the producers and refiners in the Pennsylvania Region and the interests promoting the **South Improvement Company.** The war ends March 25, 1872, after an embargo on crude shipments by the Petroleum Producers Union forces the railroads to cancel contracts with the South Improvement Company. (4)

March 25—Railroads publicly abrogate contract with **South Improvement Company.** (49)

April 2—Pennsylvania Legislature revokes the **South Improvement Company**'s charter, and also passes a free pipeline bill, conferring upon pipeline companies the **right of eminent domain.** (4)

April—**Early natural gas line fails** when difficulty arises in maintaining adequate flow in gas pipe line from West Bloomfield to Rochester, New York. When customers complain gas is not equal to manufactured gas **Rochester Gas Company** refuses to use natural gas, wrecking the **Bloomfield Company.** (38)

August 1—The first iron **pipe line** to bring **waste gas** from nearby oil wells completed to **Titusville,** Pennsylvania. It delivers 4,000,000 cubic feet of gas a day to 250 domestic and industrial customers. (47)

August—The **Petroleum Refiners' Association,** better known as the **National Refiners' Association,** formed with John D. Rockefeller as president. (4)

September—**The Gas Light Association of the United States,** first national gas association to be formed in this country, created at a meeting held in Cleveland, Ohio. (38)

December 19—**"Treaty of Titusville"** signed between **Petroleum Refiners' Association** and **Petroleum Producers' Agency.** The compact called for the Refiners' Association to buy crude from the Producers' group at prices to be fixed by the latter. (4)

Baku oil field development begins in full. 415 wells, all dug by hand. (1)

A **42-gallon measure** for crude oil adopted by the Petroleum Producers' Association as the **standard barrel.** It is approved by the United States Congress in 1916. (63)

George Brayton, a Yankee, patents an engine burning an **air-gas** mixture at constant pressure. (35)

Baron Julius de Reuter obtains concession to explore for oil and other minerals in Persia (**Iran**). Later cancelled due to Russian pressure on Persia. In 1889, obtains new concession and drills three dry holes. (55)

Patent to H. W. Faucett. Oil pumping engine, steam operated, discharges its steam into well. **Bottom hole steam pump.** (1)

Two hundred producers of Parker's Landing, Pa., "signed a pledge" to stop drilling for a period of six months after September 1 of that year. As a result of this "shut in" of approximately ⅔ of the volume of production of the "oil region" of Pennsylvania at that time, the price of Oil City crude oil per bbl. increases from a low of $3.10 on September 18 to $4.60 on November 1, 1872. (**First shutdown days**) (1)

The first **tank steamer,** the 2748-ton Belgian ship Vaderland, slides down the ways. (40)

First known **gas production in Texas,** from well owned by the Graham brothers and located near Graham, Young County, Texas. (58)

1873

March—The **Medoc district** in Butler County, Pa., opened up with a third-sand flowing well at 1440 feet. (4)

April 10—**"Colonel" Edwin L. Drake,** driller of the first oil well at Titusville, Pennsylvania, in 1859, granted a pension by the state of Pennsylvania. (54)

September 19—**Black Friday.** Failures in NY stock exchange precipitate panic.

October 15—The first meeting of the **"Gas Light Association of the United States"** held in New York City. Charles Roome of the Manhattan Gas Company elected president of the "national" gas association. (38)

November—First recognized **fourth-sand flowing wells** brought in near Karns City, Pa., at approximately 1440 feet. (4)

Munzinger introduces an **"electric gas governor** and **pressure regulator"** that indicates pressure in mains and provides means for controlling it by raising or lowering pressure. (38)

J. T. Henry publishes **History of Petroleum.** (43)

Natural gas found at Iola, **Kansas,** and used for illuminating purposes at a neighboring sanitarium, which also investigates its possible medicinal value. (38)

The **machine stoker,** or charger, brings mechanization to gas making. This device invented by **Alomo Haven** of the **Brooklyn Gas Light Company.** (38)

J. S. Newberry advances the **organic theory** of the **origin of petroleum.** (35)

Prentice deepens one of his pumping wells and gets flowing production. Soon after, another field—Lobitos—is found between Zorritos field and La Brea—Parinas **Peru.** (10)

Stowell's Petroleum Reporter of Pittsburgh, Pennsylvania begins publication and continues until 1901. (48)

Professor **Thaddeus S. C. Lowe,** of Baltimore, obtains the first **water-gas patent.** (35)

New **"Gwynne-Harris" water-gas apparatus** put into operation at Citizen's Gas Light Company of Brooklyn. (38)

1874

October—**A. O. Smith Corporation** founded in Milwaukee, Wisconsin, by C. J. Smith as a machine shop. (50)

David Hostetter builds a pipeline from the Butler County, Pa., fields, to connect with a branch of the Baltimore & Ohio Railroad. His pipeline is called the **Columbia Conduit.** (16)

Fifteen years after the first oil well was drilled, Pennsylvania's State Geologist Wrigley estimates that the United States has enough petroleum to keep its kerosene lamps burning for only four years, becoming the first doom **forecaster.** (32)

Holten perfects method for measuring **inclination** of holes. (1)

Second Geological Survey of Pennsylvania starts scientific work in oil regions and publishes **first oilfield structure map** by **John F. Carll.** (GeoTimes)

The first iron and steel firm to use **natural gas in puddling and heating furnaces** is Rogers and Burchfield at Leechburg, Pa. (38)

C. Hell and E. Medinger conduct perhaps the first scientific investigation of **sludge acids** and **alkali residues.** (37)

Captain Vandergrift, in association with George W. Foreneau, completes the **first oil trunk line** from the oil regions direct to the Pittsburgh refinery. It is 60 miles long, four inches in diameter and delivers 7500 barrels of oil per day. (35)

Wietze field, in the district of Hanover, Germany is listed as a discovery. (70)

The Gas Light Association of the United States changes its name to **American Gas Light Association.** (38)

Great value of gas as a manufacturing fuel demonstrated when **Rogers and Burchfield** begin to burn it under boilers and for all puddling and heating furnaces at their steel plant at Leechburg, Armstrong County, Pennsylvania. By 1887, a total of 96 rolling mills and steel mills were either wholly or partly using natural gas for fuel. By 1890, it had displaced 10 million tons of coal annually. In 1885, gas waste was depleting fields and the commodity became more valuable and meters and other conservation appliances were employed. (79)

Natural gas discovered at **Mattoon, Illinois,** in a well drilled for water. (38)

1875

March 15-21—First traces of oil in the Djebel Tselfat (southwest **Morocco**) area discovered by an Englishman, **A. S. Pearson,** and his son, **L. D. Pearson.** (45)

April 20—Patent to A. E. Nickerson and L. C. Streeter; proposes operations of number of wells from more-or-less conventional standard end pumping unit by transmitting motion from walking beam of standard end through wooden shackle lines. (**Multiple well pumping**) (1)

The **Central Refiners Association** formed. John D. Rockefeller, president. (4)

Continental Oil Company founded as Continental Oil and Transportation Company devoted to the distribution of petroleum products to the pioneers of the West. (50)

Robert Magee Downie, founder of Keystone Driller Co., conceives idea of **portable drilling machine.** Built about 1878 in Butler Co., Pa. Spring pole is still used but motion is applied to the pole by a steam engine. (1)

S. P. Stadtler, of the Second Pennsylvania Survey, **analyzes natural gas** and shows that no "olefines" were present. (48)

M. C. Ommegauck proposes that chloroform be used for extinguishing **oil fires.** (37)

The process of producing a "carburretted" **water gas** by the use of a "super-heater" patented by **Thaddeus Lowe.** The principal advantage of the process comes from the successful utilization of heavy petroleum fractions to produce a water gas with excellent heating and illuminating qualities on a large scale. (4)

Alexander Graham Bell invents the telephone. (54)

Bayonne Refinery started by Frederic Prentice. Later sold to Ohio Standard and then acquired by Standard Oil Company of New Jersey, when it began operations on August 30, 1882. (8A) By 1883, Bayonne Refinery was the leader in the nation, annual run of 2.3 million barrels. (The Lamp)

Pico Canyon field in California is discovered by C. C. Mentrey's No. 1 Pico well. (74)

Old salt well drilled in 1820, near **Sciotoville, Ohio,** reopened and used for gas by Scioto Firebrick Company. Well had produced petroleum and natural gas since 1820, but no one knew what to do with it. (38)

1876

March 7—**Telephone** patented.

Roads surfaced with Trinidad Lake **asphalt** laid in Washington, D. C. (39)

Robert Nobel puts a refinery into operation in the **Baku,** Russia oilfields. (4)

Broderick & Bascom Rope Company founded in St. Louis, Missouri as manufacturers of wire rope. (50)

The first commercial oil refinery built in **California** by California Star Oil Works near Newhall. (40)

Isaac Canfield drills a well to a depth of 1187 feet a short distance south of the present site of the city of Florence, **Colorado.** Oil found in joints and fissures in the Pierre Shale. (10)

An **internal combustion engine** using gasoline vapor completed by **Dr. N. A. Otto** of Cologne, Germany. His motors are too heavy for use in road vehicles; they are stationary engines used mostly in factories. (4)

Mexico—An unidentified American sea captain finds oil at Tuxpan, refines and sells it locally as kerosene for a brief period. (10)

General H. L. Abbot, U. S. Army Corps of Engineers, measures used **velocity of seismic waves.** Explodes 50,000 pounds of dynamite, using Mallet's seismoscope. Measures velocities up to 10,000 ft. per second. Though apparatus not sensitive enough, velocities indicate Abbot may have measured first **artificially produced compression waves.** (7)

1877

April—Earliest patent for a **well jack** issued to W. F. Plockrass. (1)

Ajax Iron Works founded in Corry, Pennsylvania, as manufacturers of steam engines for drilling oil wells, and gas engines for drilling and pumping oil. (50)

The first large water-gas plant is built in **Baltimore.** (35)

Standard's **Bayonne (N. J.) Refinery** goes on stream. (50)

Col. John J. Carter sells his clothing store and forms the **Carter Oil Company.** In 1893 he incorporates and a year later sells 60 percent interest in his company to a Standard Oil Company affiliate. Later the remaining interest is acquired by Standard Oil. At the time of dissolution in 1911 Carter is the only producing company left to Standard Oil Company (N. J.) (50)

Robert Locke drills an oil well for the Chinese government among the headhunters of **Formosa.** (36)

Herman Frasch, a chemist, receives a patent for an improved method of refining **paraffin.** In addition to his work in the petroleum industry, Frasch also has patents for making oil lamps, white lead, salt, carbonate of soda, carbon for use in electric lights and thermal electric generators, waxed paper (1884), and for the **extraction and manufacture of sulphur.** (8A)

O. Silvestri finds both liquid oils and a solid paraffin in basaltic lavas from near **Mt. Etna.** (22)

The **Retort Gas Stove** Company introduces a stove constructed on a "new principle"—superheating the gas before it is mixed with air. (38)

Samuel Van Syckel receives a patent for **automatically supplied stills.** The first yields naphtha; the other two yield illuminating oil. (37)

The **Nobel brothers** order a special tank ship built in Sweden. It is the **first tanker** in the world built especially for the purpose of carrying oil. (Baroid Division—National Lead Co.)

The first tiny **prototype** of the modern tanker appears on the Caspian Sea, and before long, fleets of tankers ply the Caspian, the Volga River and the Baltic Sea. (40)

Western Gas Association organized. (47)

1878

January 28—First commercial **telephone exchange** opened at New Haven, Connecticut. (54)

May 21—H. W. Faucett patents a steam **power cylinder** to be lowered to the bottom of a well, and connected directly to the **oil-well pump** itself. (40)

May 22—A very comprehensive statute, for the **regulation of pipeline** transportation, requiring reports, statements, and the appointment of examiners, enacted in **Pennsylvania** and remains effective. (3)

November 3—The Haymaker well near Murraysville, Westmoreland County, Pennsylvania, comes in as a gas well. (Pennsylvania Natural Gas Men's Association)

November 22—The **Tidewater Pipe Company, Limited,** organized. It builds the **first trunk** (longline) **pipeline over the mountains;** the pipe reaches Philadelphia & Reading Railroad at Williamsport, Pa., and breaks the near-monopoly of Standard Oil in gathering oil and the dominance of the railroads in transporting petroleum to the sea. Starts pumping 10,000 barrels of oil daily over 110 miles from Bradford field. (8A)

Sixty-six percent of the U. S. production exported, primarily as products. Eighty-five percent of these **exports** are illuminating oil or kerosene. (48)

Larkin and Company, Inc., founded as Larkin's Shop in Chicora, Pennsylvania as a repair shop for steam engines, steam pumps, gas pumps and pumping equipment for oil wells. (50)

The **Nobel Brothers Naphtha Company** incorporated. (4)

Pennsylvania passes an Act requiring that all **statements of bulk petroleum** be given in barrels of 42 gallons. (3)

The first concession exploited commercially in **Venezuela,** given to Manuel Antonio Pulido and his Compania Petrolia del Tachira, in the town of Rubio, Tachira State. (45)

Pennsylvania passes a law compelling the **plugging of wells.** (3)

1879

Feb. 19—**Pacific Coast Oil Company** incorporated in California with capital stock of $1 million as part of **Standard Oil Trust.** (79)

April 16—Miss M. S. Dodd gives a series of free public lectures on the use of gas for cooking and demonstrates cooking techniques, introducing "home service" to the gas industry. Natural **gas, home demonstrations.** (38)

September 10—**Pacific Coast Oil Co.** incorporated. On July 23, 1906, name was changed to Standard Oil Company. On October 15, 1906, business and assets of **Standard Oil Company (Iowa)** purchased. (See 1926—Standard Oil Company of California) (50)

October 18—The Norwegian steamship Stat leaves Philadelphia for Rouen with the first cargo of petroleum ever loaded in a **tank steamer bound east.** (4)

The **Alleghany County field, New York,** discovered by the Triangle No. 1 of O. P. Taylor; although its initial production is only about 10 barrels per day, the well was still being pumped more than 48 years later. (68)

American Meter Co. sends representative "to select and import for them the best makes of French and English gas cooking stoves adapted for use in the United States." (51)

The **Bovaird Supply Co.,** founded as the Bovaird & Seyfang Manufacturing Co., in Shamburg, Pennsylvania as manufacturers of cable drilling and fishing tools such as bits, jars, stems, bailers, rope sockets, slip sockets, rope spears and tool wrenches. (50)

Thomas Alva Edison invents the incandescent lamp. (54)

George B. Selden, of Rochester, New York, applies for a patent for a **gasoline motor** like that used as a stationary engine, to drive a road vehicle. (13)

Fletcher's gas range, imported from England, used in Oakland, California. (51)

W. Goodwin & Company, of Philadelphia, introduces the **first gas range designed especially for hotel and restaurant purposes.** (38)

A Russian, **Dimitri Mendeleef,** publishes a notable paper on the inorganic origin of petroleum. (**Inorganic theory**) (35)

Thalen publishes his work "On the Examination of Iron Ore Deposits by **Magnetic Measurement.**" (7)

George Saybolt develops his electric flash and fire tester, which is adopted for standard use by the **New York Produce Exchange,** then a clearing house for the sales of petroleum oils. (35)

State of New York enacts legislation with regard to **plugging of abandoned wells.** (3)

Charles Francis Brush, American scientist, invents Brush electric **arc light.** (65)

1880

February 19—A Mr. McDougall of Hornellsville (Hornell, N. Y.) reads what is probably the **first paper** on **natural gas** presented before a convention—that of Central New York Gas Engineers Association held at Rochester, N. Y. (38)

May 21—First report of **wire rope** used in drilling. (Colorado Fuel and Iron Corporation)

September 8—The **Imperial Oil Company Ltd.,** formed in London, Ontario, Canada. (63)

September 14—Stock of oil companies called on the floor of the **Oil City, Pennsylvania Oil Exchange** for the first time. (54)

November 8—"Colonel" **Edwin L. Drake** dies in Bethlehem, Pennsylvania, at the age of 61. (54)

Clark Bros. Co., founded in Belmont, New York as manufacturers of steam engines and gas engines. (50)

The **first natural gas compressor station** put into operation by the **Bradford Gas Company** at Rixford, Pa. The plant has a duplex compressor driven by a 580-horsepower steam engine with a compressing capacity of 5,000,000 cubic feet a day and a discharge pressure of 60 pounds. (38)

A big step in **dewaxing** comes with the invention of the horizontal frame and plate presses which first see use in this year. It means that for the first time, low-cold-test lubes can be made for a price which opens vast new markets. (40)

Dresser Manufacturing Division founded as S. R. Dresser in Bradford, Pennsylvania, as manufacturers of oil well packers, wall fasteners, casing heads, rubber plugs, pipe couplings, pipe repair sleeves and clamps. (50)

John F. Carll reports on the stimulative effects of "**gas pumping,**" or the application of partial vacuum to the casingheads of wells that were producing ever-declining quantities of oil. He also reports that the head of water from shallow sands in a hole retarded the appearance of oil in the well bore until the pressure exerted by the column of water was relieved by bailing. (**Water encroachment**) (1)

E. O. Yates issued a patent on a push-pull central power. His ideas include use of **pull rods** and rod-holddown devices. (40)

A simple form of **pressure regulator** introduced in domestic lighting burners. (38)

The **first** record of an **American refining enterprise abroad.** Oil refined in Galicia, then a part of Austria-Hungary, with equipment imported from the United States. (32)

Standard Oil Company of California constructs a 500-barrel-a-day refinery at Alameda, California, the largest refinery west of Cleveland, and lays the West's first pipeline from Pico to Newhall, a two-inch line five miles in length. (50)

United States Government appoints American Gas Journal Editor Dresser to conduct the first official **census of the gas industry.** (38)

1881

January 1—Pennsylvania oil fields have produced 156,890,931 barrels of oil, about 95 percent of U. S. production. (15)

March 8—National Transit Company buys Pennsylvania Company for $16,250. In 1895, the trust purchased **W. L. Mellon Pipe Line Company.** (79)

November 15—**American Federation of Labor** organized in Pittsburgh as the Federation of Organized Trades and Labor Unions. Took name of AF of L in 1886 when Knights of Labor dissolved after Haymarket bomb episode in Chicago. (52)

December—Natural gas discovered in **Cincinnati, Ohio,** causing a sensation in that city. (38)

Kendall Refining Company, Bradford, Pa., founded to refine lamp and cylinder oil at rate of 10 barrels a day. Present name adopted 1913. (50)

1882

January 2—The **Standard Oil Trust** Agreement drawn up and signed. The word **"trust"** as applied to a business syndicate originates with Standard Oil when stock of 29 companies placed in safe keeping and management of nine trustees duly elected to manage the Standard Oil Trust and the dividend profit sharing plan. (79)

January—The Rockefeller interests become known as the **Standard Oil Trust.** (Standard Oil Co. of New Jersey)

August 5—**Standard Oil Co. of New Jersey** receives a charter and acquires a refinery, barrel factory and paraffin works at Bayonne, New Jersey, a refinery at Communipaw and docks at Weehawken. The firm is part of the Standard Oil Trust. (50)

August 10.—**Standard Oil Company of New York** organized and incorporated. (50)

August 29—B. Franklin invents a testing device used in controlling and **regulating the flow of oil wells.** (1)

Rye flour used to retard **cement-setting** time. (1)

A commercial gas well brought in three miles south of Litchfield, in Montgomery County, **Illinois.** (10)

The **first commercial gas well west of the Mississippi** completed in **Kansas.** (9)

The **United States Geological Survey** publishes its first annual volume entitled "**Mineral Resources of the United States.**" (48)

United Gas Improvement Company, one of the first holding companies in the gas industry, formed in Philadelphia, Pennsylvania. (38)

The use of ammonia for extinguishing **oil well fires** is under the consideration of a committee of the Polytechnic Society of Munich, Germany. (37)

The first oil well drilled in the **Pechelbronn** field, France. It produces a considerable quantity of light oil from 139 meters. (10)

New York Act of 1879 amended to particularize the method of **plugging wells** before withdrawing casing. (3)

Rotary drilling, destined to play an important role in developing oil fields, used for drilling water wells in Dakota Territory. (44)

Standard Oil Trust engages a chemist, Professor F. W. Arvine, to test lubricating oils. (Standard Oil Co. of New Jersey)

The **structural theory** revived and applied to gas by **I. C. White.** (GeoTimes)

1883

February—**"Gas Age"** founded as Water Gas Journal, a monthly publication. (51)

July 5—**Pennsylvania**—A law enacted, and still current, provides for gauging petroleum in the custody of oil transportation and storage companies, and for inspection of the oil and examination of books and accounts, by persons appointed by the court, upon application of owners of two percent of the oil in the company's custody. (3)

V. Markovnikoff and V. N. Oglobin establish that acid substances in petroleum contain **carboxyl groups** and are indeed real **acids.** (26)

The **Baku-Batum railroad** completed, permitting Russian oil to reach the Black Sea. (40)

Hardison & Stewart are reported to have put **cement** in a well in Pico, California. (1)

The system of **continuous distillation** adopted by the **Nobel Brothers,** owners of one of the most important of the **Baku** refineries, in the production of illuminating oil, and is used later by the same firm in the manufacturing of lubricating oil. (37)

First platinum basket gas mantle. (51)

Ohio legislature enacts a law entitled, "An Act Regulating the Casing of Oil Wells and the Mode of Plugging the Same When Abandoned." (3)

A Russian scientist, **N. Petroff,** is probably the first to demonstrate scientifically the value of **petroleum oils as lubricants.** (35)

A central inspection laboratory, to make certain that all tests are standardized, set up under **George M. Saybolt,** whose name is given to **testing procedures** still used all over the world. (Standard Oil Co. of New Jersey)

A. J. Zijlker, a Dutch tobacco planter, discovers natural outcroppings of oil in the wilds of northern **Sumatra.** (Shell Oil Company)

Fred Brown first proposes to find mineral deposits by the measurement of the resistance of the earth between two electrodes. (The **two electrode method.**) (7)

1883-85—Beauchamp Tower, for the British Institution of Mechanical Engineers, reports that, when applied to bearings, **oil bath** would give the best degree of lubrication. (35)

Chartier Valley Gas Company formed by manufacturers to bring natural gas to their glass and steel plants in Pittsburgh; gas is piped in from Murraysville in Westmoreland County, Pa. (38)

1884

March 18—J. G. Martin granted patent No. 295,413 on a **walking-beam** type drilling machine mounted on wheels. (1)

November 11—The **Consolidated Gas Company of New York** formed by merger of six existing (and often competing) gas light companies—the New York, Manhattan, Metropolitan, Municipal, Knickerbocker, and Harlem companies. It was then the biggest gas utility in the nation. (38)

Haddow, at Younger's Holywood Brewery, Edinburgh, makes the earliest use of a magnetic compass in a **borehole survey.** (28)

Andrew Carnegie states that one natural gas company has 335 miles of pipelines within the city of Pittsburgh, and is supplying a quantity of natural gas that would displace 10,000 tons of coal a day. (46)

Hot air house-heating furnace, designed by Professor T. S. C. Lowe, uses gas as fuel and is suspended from ceiling joists. (**Ceiling gas heaters**) (38)

E. F. MacGeorge invents a **core orientation** device which obtains the inclination of the core at the time of orientation. (28)

Natural gas discovered in Frankfort, **Dakota Territory,** at a depth of 85 feet. (38)

Carl Auer von Welsbach, working in the R. W. Bunsen laboratory in Germany, develops a practical **gas mantle,** which is patented. In 1885, he markets the lamp. (4)

Richards and Cross patent the "dry" type **gas meter** that, as far as basic principle is concerned, is almost unchanged in the meters used universally today for gas measurement to customers. (38)

Natural gas from the **Haymaker well** near Murrysville, Pennsylvania, piped into Pittsburgh, Pa., by Pew & Emerson Co. Ltd., the first time that **gas is transported** to a metropolitan city by a corporation organized to produce and transport natural gas. (Pennsylvania Natural Gas Men's Association)

The Cherokee and Choctaw Indian nations approve the organization of Indian companies that are to induce oil firms to enter the **Indian Territory.** (21)

Kansas—Area surrounding Paola being drilled. Heavy, dark crude sells as a lubricant at $3 to $5 per barrel. Small refinery built in 1886 to process oil. Still considered non-commercial. (10)

The Mining Law of **Mexico** made petroleum and other resources the exclusive property of the owner of the land. (14)

Natural gas, near Wheeling, W. Virginia, reported to have been used for **glass manufacture.** (38)

Edward Orton, State Geologist for **Ohio,** determines that oil accumulation in Ohio is related to a broad, flattened anticline. (35)

Oil Well Supply Catalogue shows two "Iron Gas tanks." One of these, "Ashton's Patent," seems to provide the basic features to be found in later **separator** improvements. (1)

Thomas Urquhart, an American connected with the Russian railways, perfects a method of **spraying oil with steam,** and this is used as a pattern by other inventors for some years. (35)

Wyoming—The Atlantic Pacific Oil Company drills the state's first commercial producer. It is near a spring on the Little Popo Agie River and flows oil and gas spasmodically from 300 feet. The field, first known as Popo Agie, is now called the **Dallas Dome field.** (10)

Chaplin-Fulton Company established. (38)

Pratt Manufacturing Co., a unit of the Standard Oil Trust, buys control of Gilbert & Barker Manufacturing Co., a Springfield, Mass., firm which builds machines to generate illuminating gas from gasoline, makes metal barrels and tanks and also sells large quantities of gasoline for its machines. (Standard Oil Co. of New Jersey)

George Westinghouse, having found gas on his property in Pittsburgh, organizes the **Philadelphia Company** (and later the **Equitable Gas Company** as a subsidiary) to serve Pittsburgh. (38)

1885

May 29—The **Pennsylvania** legislature makes its political climate much more conducive to the growth of the industry by authorizing the incorporation of natural gas companies and conferring upon them the **"right of eminent domain,"** subject only to such regulations as the councils of cities and towns might adopt by ordinance. (8A)

June 15—**Standard Oil Company** of Iowa incorporated in Iowa with capital stock of $1 million as part of **Standard Oil Trust.** (79)

June 26—The **Peoples Natural Gas Company** incorporates and is the first natural gas company to be chartered under legislation passed in Pennsylvania for that purpose. (50)

June—**Indonesia**—The first well drilled in the Langkat district of **Sumatra,** by Aeilco Janz Zijlker. It only flows five barrels per day, but it is the foundation stone of the mighty **Royal Dutch-Shell.** In June, 1885, the second well, Telaga Toenggal No. 1 is completed at a total depth of 72 feet. (10)

July 11—The first law passed in any state placing **gas companies,** and later electric companies, **under state supervision** passed by the **Massachusetts** legislature and approved by the governor. (**First**) (38)

I. C. White is the first geologist to demonstrate the truth of the **anticlinical theory** for the accumulation of oil and gas. He locates the Grapeville, Belleveron, and Washington oil fields in Pennsylvania on anticlinal axes. (22)

Atlas Refining Company is the first to list **fuel oil** among its products. (8A)

Natural gas discovered in **Canada,** in a shallow well in the Point-Aux-Trembles township. (38)

The first **carbon black** factory using the **channel process** built by Peter Neff at Gambier, Ohio. (47)

Continental Oil and Transportation Company reorganized as Continental Oil Company. (50)

More than one thousand vessels engage in the American **export** oil trade and movement underway to handle it in bulk with a capacity of 2500 to 14,000 barrels per voyage. (15)

Incandescent gas mantle invented by Welsbach, and introduced in 1890. (51)

The tanker Crusader, a converted wooden sailing ship owned by L. U. Sone of New York, sails from Philadelphia to London with the first **trans-Atlantic cargo of kerosene** to be shipped in bulk. (4)

The discovery of oil at **Lima,** Ohio, brings a problem in the form of hydrogen sulfide and sulphur in the Lima crude. (48)

American oil supremacy in the **Middle East** is threatened when Russian oil is shipped to Beirut, Lebanon. The Russian advantage comes from transportation: Russian cost is less than half the American. (4)

The **Nobel brothers** convert the steam cargo vessel, The Fergusons, into a tanker and haul a cargo of refined oil from Batum to Antwerp. Continues in bulk petroleum service until 1889, when she is destroyed by an explosion at Rouen. (4)

The first suggestion of **odorizing natural gas** to assist in leak detection made by Irvin Butterworth, of Columbus, at a meeting of the Ohio Gas Light Association. (47)

Milne and Gray first use a falling weight, or **"thumper,"** in Japan to generate seismic waves and apparently are the first to use mechanical **seismographs** recording on moving smoked glass plates. They also record the different components of waves produced by explosives and they record simultaneously with two seismographs in line. These were probably the first refraction profiles ever shot. (7)

The **first "high pressure" manufactured gas transmission** line installed under San Francisco Bay, between Oakland and Alameda; the line carries 10 psi. (38)

H. A. Toby patents an instantaneous **automatic gas water heater** with thermostatic control. (51)

1885-86—Gottlieb Daimler develops a lighter **gasoline vapor engine** and is able to use one in a **motorcycle.** (16)

Karl Benz, German engineer, builds first **internal combustion engine vehicle,** a three wheeler, which he drives through streets of Munich in 1886. Later founded Benz & Co. in Mannheim to manufacture cars. (65)

First mention made of the possibility of **metering natural gas.** Heretofore, it was contracted by the year because natural gas was thought to give inaccurate readings in meters of the day. (38)

1886

July 21—**California Gas Light and Fuel Company** incorporated in San Francisco. (38)

August 24—**Pacific Lighting Corporation** organized. (38)

Levassor secures the French rights to the Daimler patents, and in a few years brings out the first **Panhard-Levassor automobile.** (35)

Karl Benz, of Mannheim, Germany, patents a frail automobile. It is said to be the first in Germany for a light, **oil-fueled motor vehicle.** (35)

Oil discovered three miles south of Litchfield, **Illinois,** following gas find in 1882. Only 6576 barrels produced until flow stopped in 1902. (10)

The first Russian kerosene reaches the west coast of **India** when Frank Lane of Lane & McAndrews begins shipping oil consigned to merchants in Bombay. (4)

The **Pennsylvania Railroad** sends Dr. Charles P. Dudley to the Caucasus to study Russian use of fuel oil in **locomotives.** His experimental runs prove that the method of burning the **oil as a fuel** is a success but that coal is less expensive. Among other railroads trying the method are the Rockaway Beach and the Manhattan **Elevated.** In California, the Central Pacific burns **oil as fuel in ferry steamers** on San Francisco Bay as early as 1885, and other freight and river steamers in the area also use it. (8A)

C. A. Bailey drills three wells at Port Huron, St. Clair County, **Michigan.** The wells produce from two to three bbl. per day and are considered the state's first oil wells. (10)

Osborne Reynolds, an English scientist, explains further the load-carrying power of an **oil film.** (35)

Oklahoma's first well, a dry hole, is sunk in Atoka and fails at 1414 feet. (10)

The **prepayment meter** introduced to the gas industry; the device is first called an "automatic meter" and is invented by R. W. Brownhills, of Birmingham, England. (38)

The first ocean-going ship built as a tanker is the steamer Gluckauf, built for Wilhelm Riedemann, a Standard Oil importer in Germany. (Standard Oil Co. of New Jersey)

The under-reamer introduced to the oil fields of the United States by John Eaton, following a visit to Rumania and Russia where the tool was first used. (Oil Well Supply Company)

The first great oil well in the Baku area comes in at 714 feet. (80)

The organization that is now Sun Oil Company founded when Joseph Newton Pew and E. O. Emerson become active in petroleum exploration and production activities in the state of Ohio. They had started together by piping gas from the Haymaker well to Pittsburgh. (Sun Oil Company)

1887

February 21—Herman Frasch applies for a patent for eliminating sulphur from "skunk-bearing oils." The essence of his process is to distill crude oil in the presence of copper oxide, which reacts with the sulphur, forms sulphide of copper, and leaves the oil odorless and sweet. (13)

April 16—An article describes the use of the Otto gas engine and a Lightfoot (compressor) refrigerator. This is possibly the first gas refrigerator. (38)

May 13—Toledo, Ohio, illuminated by natural gas for the first time. (8A)

August 1—Ohio Oil Company (now Marathon) incorporated with capital stock of $2 million as part of Standard Oil Trust. (79)

First production in Argentina secured in the province of Mendoza, on the Chilean frontier and some 55,000 barrels produced; commercial production begins December 13, 1907, when well near Comodora Rivadavia encounters oil at 530 meters. (10)

Gottlieb Daimler, German inventor, engineer and pioneer automobile manufacturer, patents small high-speed internal combustion engine (Daimler engine), important in development of the automobile. In 1890 forms Daimler Motor Co. which produced Mercedes automobile (1890) and in 1926 joined Firma Benz & Co. to form Daimler-Benz & Co. (65)

The Droojba gusher, in the Baku region, begins flowing at the rate of 50,000 barrels a day. This is the first of the big fountain wells in the field. (43)

M. T. Chapman files a patent application covering the addition of clay, bran, grain, cement, and other materials to drilling fluids. He is concerned with building up or plastering the walls of drilled holes. (40)

American Gas Furnace Company incorporated. (38)

Dearborn Chemical Company established. (38)

First **motorboat** demonstrated by Gottlieb Daimler at Wurtenberg. It is a single horsepower motor launch which first applies internal combustion power for the propulsion of a boat. (55)

Company formed by popular subscription to pipe natural gas to **St. Louis, Missouri,** from Edwardsville, Illinois, a distance of 30 miles. Pressure at the wells from which the supply is to be derived said to be 300 psi. (38)

Shows of oil found some miles south of Jabal Zait, in the Gemsah area of **Egypt.** (10)

Von Sterneck first develops a half-second portable pendulum suitable for relative **gravity measurements.** (7)

Providence, Rhode Island, opens first distinctive **gas appliance store.** (51)

The U. S. Congress passes the **Interstate Commerce Act** which eliminates rebates and other practices which had given Standard and other big shippers special advantages. (40)

McKittrick, Kern County, California **field** discovered. Heavy oil has been mined from open pits and shafts since 1861. (11)

L. Lewin refers to cases of severe **poisoning** with fatal issue among American workers employed in petroleum tanks. (37)

Kray devises a **pressure-distillation process,** but he is chiefly concerned with obtaining lighting oil from tar and the residue in petroleum stills after the last drop of valuable vapors have passed over and have been condensed. (35)

The **recording pressure gauge** made by Richard Brothers Company introduces charts and makes possible permanent records. (38)

S. R. Dresser secures a patent on the use of rubber in pipe joints, a form of **slip coupling.** (38)

Steel pipe for pipelines becomes available. (40)

The **Wellsbach Incandescent Light Company,** a subsidiary of U. G. I., acquires U. S. patent rights to the Welsbach mantle. A factory is established at Gloucester, N. J. in 1890 to manufacture the incandescent mantles. (38)

1887-91—Union Oil of California operates tunnels into oil sands at **Sulphur Mountain,** California. (**Oil Mining**) (1)

1888

April—Standard Trust organizes a wholly-owned subsidiary, the **Anglo-American Petroleum Company, Limited.** The company formed to stem the tide of competition from the Rothschilds and Nobels. (4)

May—**Sea level gas theory** disproved with drilling of deeper wells.

Previously it was not believed gas could be found below sea level. (38)

May—Standard Oil Company buys **Herman Frasch's** Canadian plant and patents, then puts him to work at their Cleveland, Ohio, refinery. (50)

Gas first discovered at Fort Smith, Sebastian County, **Arkansas**—but not in quantities commercially profitable. (9)

James D. Dinsmoor reportedly observes that when gas from one formation in a well bore is permitted to enter an oil-bearing sand in the same well, the offset wells are affected by increased rates of oil production which continue until source of gas is shut off. (**Well interference**) (1)

Drilling rigs become **self-propelled,** with power supplied by their own engines. (1)

Baron Roland von Eotvos, professor of physics in the University of Budapest, demonstrates first how the Coulomb **torsion balance** can be used for more extensive studies of gravity variation than that possible by the use of pendulum stations. (7)

First **German pipeline** laid between Oelheim and Peine and is of cast iron. It no longer exists. Oelheim and Peine are in the **German** oil country in the Hanover area. (45)

Prof. **T. S. C. Lowe** perfects the three-shell or **"improved double super-heater"** type of water gas set. (38)

India—The first commercial oil well drilled near Digboi in the state of Assam. The well is drilled by the Assam Oil Company, Limited, a subsidiary of Burmah Oil Company, Limited. (10)

Indiana—The state's discovery well drilled in Terre Haute, Vigo County. By 1889 oil is being produced commercially and the state's yield for the year is 33,000 bbl. One of the Terre Haute wells produced for more than 30 years. (10)

The first **iron-case meter,** made by Metric Metal Works, developed to measure natural gas. (38)

First known application of **secondary-recovery** methods in U. S., William Hill property in Venango County, Pa. (1)

A. Schmidt proposes the study of time-distance records of artificial disturbances to determine the variation of the speed of **seismic waves** with depth. (33)

America gets its first **tank steamer,** the Standard, which has a 162-ft. hull compared with the 320-ft. Vaderland. (40)

Texas Pacific Coal and Oil Company established by Colonel R. D. Hunter and his son-in-law, E. L. Marston. (50)

Tide Water Oil Company organized by Tide-Water Pipe Company, Ltd., to handle refining. The first refinery is built in Chester, Pennsylvania. (50)

First steel gasholder of large size designed and built for Consolidated Gas Company of New York by Continental Iron Works of Brooklyn. (38)

Philadelphia Company at Pittsburgh, Pennsylvania, places all its natural gas service on **meters.** (38)

1889

January 7—The Sun Oil Line Company incorporated in Ohio. On March 17, 1890, The Sun Oil Company incorporated in Ohio. On May 2, 1901; Sun Company incorporated in New Jersey. On December 15, 1922, the present corporate name, **Sun Oil Company**, adopted. (50)

February 19—**Ohio** enacts H. R. 813, "An Act to Prevent the Wasting of Natural Gas and to Provide for the Plugging of all Abandoned Wells." This law could properly be called Ohio's first conservation measure. (3)

April 23—Standard Oil Company acquires control of The **Ohio Oil Company** as its producing subsidiary. (50)

May 5—Construction started on Standard Oil Company's refinery at **Whiting, Indiana.** (50)

May 27—South Penn Oil Company incorporated under laws of West Virginia with capital stock of $2 million as part of **Standard Oil Trust.** (50)

June 18—**Standard Oil Company of Indiana** incorporated. (50)

June—The "W. L. Hardison," the **first oil tanker** ever built. Capacity, 6500 barrels of oil in steel tanks. Launched by oilmen Stewart, Hardison and Bard. (Black Bonanza)

Alten Foundry & Machine Works, Inc., founded as Alten's Foundry & Machine Works in Lancaster, Ohio as manufacturers of valve rods, derrick anvils, drilling stems, tool joints, surface equipment, power pumps and plug valves. (50)

Brea-Olinda field discovered in California. (11)

In **Burma,** oil discovered at Yenangyaung. (40)

Dr. **William M. Burton,** chemist, starts his career in the oil industry on an assignment to find out what causes pinholes in oil cans. (1)

Edward Orton issues his classical report on **Trenton limestone** as a source of petroleum and natural gas. In this work he introduces the use of contours on his map. (**contour map**) (35)

Martin Hans Boye makes a careful determination of the **gravitational constant** of the earth by a modified Cavendish balance. (33)

S. H. Roper of Roxbury, Mass., builds a light steam carriage and sells it to his family doctor. It is the first recorded **sale** of a **horseless vehicle.** (35)

Indiana legislature passes act establishing a Department of Geology and Natural Resources. (3)

64

First **Kansas** state legislation with respect to oil and gas. (9)

Pennsylvania Supreme Court in the case of Westmoreland Natural Gas Co. versus DeWitt, applies to oil in the earth the old English common law—the **law of capture.** The decision establishes a precedent that is universally followed in the United States. (12)

Detroit served with natural gas brought in by a 92-mile pipeline from fields in Ohio near Findlay. In November, 1888, James M. Clark, representing the Standard Oil Company, made application for the franchise, agreeing to lay parallel lines and to supply artificial gas in the event of failure of the natural gas line to Detroit. (38)

Twin-cylinder piston-valve steam engines for **oil well drilling** introduced by Innis Engine Works. (Oil Well Supply Division of United States Steel Corporation)

Equitable Gas Company of Pittsburgh, Pennsylvania, fabricates a 21½-mile, 36-inch pipe line from ¼-inch steel plate, riveted together, and calked to prevent leakage. (American Gas Journal—10/1959)

Missouri—Although there had been wells drilled as far back as the late 1860's, the first commercial well was drilled by accident near the town of Boone in Bates County. The state produces 20 barrels of oil, and gas from other discovery wells sold for $35,587. (10)

Oklahoma—A producing well sunk to 36 feet on Spencer Creek near Chelsea, by the United States Oil and Gas Company. It produces less than a barrel a day. (10)

Peru's largest oil field discovered. It is near the oil springs of Punta Parina and is called **LaBrea-Parinas field.** (10)

M. T. Chapman receives patent #409,272 covering a **rotary-drilling machine** incorporating all basic principles of modern rigs, including mud-laden circulating fluid. (1)

Shallow production discovered at **Salt Creek,** Wyoming. (70)

F. Fouque and Michel Levy, working in mines, make the first photographic record, that of a **seismoscope.** (7)

Tide Water Company, Ltd., extends its pipe line to Bayonne, New Jersey, reaching the Atlantic seaboard. (50)

Subsurface hydraulic turbine invented and patented by **George Westinghouse.** (1)

The first **automatic gas water heater** manufactured by Fuel Gas and Electric Engineering Company. It was developed by **Edwin Ruud.** (38)

Wyoming constitution creates a Board of Land Commissioners. (3)

1890

January 15—**Coalinga oil field** discovered in Fresno County, California, by Coast Range Oil Company, making 10 barrels per day at 163 feet. (74)

April 22—Sir Boveston Redwood and James Dewar are the first to patent a **pressure distillation process** for the purpose of increasing the yield of kerosene from Russian crude oil, but it never has been applied industrially or on a large scale. (13)

May 8—The **Royal Dutch Petroleum Company** founded as the "Royal Dutch Company for the Working of Petroleum Wells in the Netherlands Indies" to take over and operate the oil properties which A. J. Zijlker had assembled. (50)

September 2—The first 600-barrel still of the **American Oil Company** refinery charged with Lima, Ohio, crude. On Thanksgiving Day, the first shipment of kerosene made by the Frasch process leaves the refinery. (American Oil Company)

Sept. 3—Kern County Land Company incorporated in California with headquarters in San Francisco. The company had its beginnings in the 1870's when J. B. Haggin and Lloyd Tevis began purchasing land in Kern and other California counties. (50)

Oct. 17—**Union Oil Company of California** organized. (50)

Patent for **bottom hole control** granted to John D. Rockefeller. (1)

S. R. Dresser invents pipe **couplings** for absolutely tight joints on pipe lines. (46)

Among the more successful pioneer **gas-injection** projects are those conducted by **James D. Dinsmoor** in Pennsylvania and West Virginia fields. (1)

Jaccard maintains that liquid oils are derived from marine plants, while viscous bitumens might have originated from mollusks, etc. (**organic theory**) (37)

The **Sherman Anti-Trust Act** becomes United States law. (Standard Oil Company of New Jersey)

Baron Roland von Eotvos completes his first instrument. (**Torsion Balance**) (7)

The American rights to Welsbach gas mantle purchased by the **United Gas Improvement Company** of Philadelphia. (4)

George Saybolt designs and builds a brass tube which he places in a bath of oil or water so that the temperature can be carefully controlled; this is the Saybolt **viscometer**, still the accepted instrument for commercial measurements of viscosity. (35)

Standard Oil Co. of New York acquires 40 per cent interest in a new German company, DAPG—predecessor of **Esso A.G.** and the first Standard Oil affiliate in continental Europe. (Standard Oil Co. of New Jersey)

1891

February—The **Pitot tube** advocated for natural gas measurements. (38)

April 3—The **Texas Railroad Commission** organized; holds its first meeting on June 10, 1891. (44)

November 18—**California Ink Co.** founded by **Lyman Stewart** (Union Oil). The ink company is the enthusiam of Stewart's partner, **W. L. Hardison,** who invented a process for making **printer's ink from petroleum.** (Black Bonanza)

William Morrison, of Des Moines, Iowa, builds an **electric automobile** and drives it through the streets of Chicago in 1892. (35)

Congress passes first general authorization for **Indian tribal leasing.** (3)

Indiana—First legislative act devoted solely to conservation of petroleum passed, forbidding the burning of natural gas in flambeau lights. (3)

Kansas legislature passes an act requiring the casing of oil and gas wells and establishing a method of plugging them when abandoned. (9)

Chicago is the destination for the **first high-pressure** (525 psi) **"long-distance" oil pipeline.** The 120-mile, eight-inch wrought-iron line originates at Greentown, Indiana. (40)

Samuel M. Jones, founder of the **S. M. Jones Company,** receives a patent on the **first** all-metal **iron sucker rod.** (50)

The Bamberger and Mills Company drills the first oil prospect, in Grand County, **Utah,** but it is not a true commercial producer. (10)

W. Virginia—Act passed requiring that gas from unutilized wells be shut-in, authorizing adjoining owners to enter and shut-in gas wasted from adjacent wells, provides briefly for casing and plugging of wells, and prescribes penalties for violation. (3)

The Hugh McMurray No. 1 in Allen Township, Hancock County, Ohio, brought in by the Ohio Oil Company (now Marathon). This gusher holds early record as the **world's largest oil well,** producing at the rate of 42,000 barrels a day from a depth of 1200 feet. (50)

1892

January 7—First recorded union of oil workers formed at Hammansburg, Ohio, as **Oil Workers Local 5612, AFL.** (71)

February 28—Royal Dutch oil begins to move under natural gas pressure from the well at Talaga Said, **Sumatra,** to the refinery at Pangkalan Brandan. At full capacity, the refinery can turn out about 1600 five-gallon cans a day. (4)

February—**Axelson Manufacturing Company** Division of U. S. Industries, Inc., founded as Acme Iron Works in Santa Ana, California, for repair work of almost every type. (50)

March 2—The Ohio Supreme Court orders the **Standard Oil Company of Ohio** to dissolve its trust agreement of 1879. (American Oil Company)

July—The Murex, a 4200-ton tanker, first of the **Tank Syndicates** fleet, revolutionizes Eastern marketing when she passes through the Suez Canal with a cargo of bulk kerosene bound for the Far East. (4)

August 24—The **Gladys City Oil, Gas and Manufacturing Company** organized by **Pattillo Higgins.** (44)

November 28—The first commercial oil well in **Kansas,** the Norman No. 1 comes in at Neodesha, Wilson County, from a depth of 832 feet. (54)

First exploratory oil bore drilled at Coorong, South **Australia** is a dry hole. (45)

The first **all-steel standard rig including derrick** sent to **Australia** for use in a section where wood decayed rapidly. (Oil Well Supply)

First American Car built by the Duryea Bros., and Charles M. Franklin. (Review)

Dr. Rudolf Diesel patents **internal combustion engine** operating with pulverized fuel and air compression. He built the engine in 1895. (65)

Chemistry of natural gas described in **Schorlemmer's Handbook of Chemistry** and in a paper by Prof. F. C. Phillips, published by the Pennsylvania Geological Survey. (79)

Reynolds Gas Regulator Company formed. (38)

Tobey meter introduced—a three-diaphragm meter using a three-port valve seat, which can be adjusted by changing gear wheels in back of index. (38)

Production and use of natural gas begins in **Colorado,** when the **Florence Oil and Refining Co.,** supplies several homes in Florence with the gas output of one of its wells. (47)

Jones & Laughlin Steel Corp., Supply Division founded as Frick & Lindsay Company in Pittsburgh, Pennsylvania, as jobbers. (50)

Kentucky—Legislation enacted pertaining to oil, gas or salt water. Allows gas produced with oil or water to be permitted to escape. (3)

Mexico—The Mining Law of this year restricts the surface owner's right to exploit freely certain minerals, but permits free exploitation of combustible minerals, including petroleum, without special concessions. (14)

The first annual "**The Mineral Industry, Its Statistics, Technology, and Trade**" published. (48)

Geared powers for **multiple-well pumping** manufactured by Oil Well Supply. (50)

The word "steel" first mentioned in connection with oil field tanks in the **Oil Well Supply Company** Catalogue. (1)

The Standard Oil Trust reorganizes, and **Standard of New Jersey** becomes the operator of refineries at Baltimore, Maryland, and Parkersburg, West Virginia, and holder of shares in twenty-one other companies. The company name is now plain "Standard Oil Company," with "(New Jersey)" commonly added to distinguish it from other "Standards." (50)

First steel derrick, 72 ft. in height, constructed and made available to industry. (1)

The Case Company introduces **gasoline-powered tractors.** (54)

Utah statute (unamended, still on books) calls for the plugging of abandoned gas wells and sets out in great detail the method to be employed. (3)

1893

April 1—**Ohio** passes "An Act to Regulate Drilling, Operation and Abandonment of Petroleum Oil, Natural Gas and Mineral Water Wells, and to Prevent Certain Abuses Connected Therewith." Repeals acts of 1883 and 1889. (3)

April 19—**Charles E. and J. Frank Duryea** successfully operate a "**gasoline buggy**" in Springfield, Massachusetts. (Standard Oil Co. of New Jersey)

June 24—The **United States Pipeline Company** delivers its first throughput of both crude and refined oil to Wilkesbarre, Pa. It is a major event since the company proves that finished products can be moved over long distances without damage. **Products Line.** (4)

November 12—The "**largest gas well in the world**," the Swagler No. 1, brought in 12 miles east of Washington, Pa. Its roar heard for 15 miles. (38)

The Carter Oil Co. incorporated in West Virginia. (50)

The **Columbian Exposition** at Chicago gives great impetus to the use of fuel oil in America, all its boilers being oil-fueled. (35)

Thomas Alva Edison introduces motion pictures. (54)

First small experimental refinery erected in **India** by Assam Railways and Trading Company. In 1899 Assam Oil Company erected a refinery at Digboi. Other refineries were built by Stanvac in 1954, by Burmah Shell in 1955, by Caltex in 1957. Public Sector refinery at Nunmati was inaugurated on Jan. 1, 1962. (45)

Indiana—General assembly adopts a measure pertaining to unlawful flow of gas, well plugging, etc. (3)

Exports of oil begin from **Indonesia.** (Review)

In **Japan,** oil discovered at Higashiyama. (40)

Hiram Maxim, a Maine Yankee living in England, builds a giant three-**passenger plane** calculated to lift more than a ton—only to wreck it. (35)

A shipment of crude oil sent from **Peru** to California. It is less expensive to ship it there than from the East coast. There is no tariff against this crude, as Peru did not place a duty on American oil. (4)

S. MacEachen patents a **rotary rig on wheels** consisting of all the elements of such equipment—boiler, engine, hoist, pump, mast, crown pulley, swivel, rotary, and square kelly. (1)

At the World's Fair (Columbian Exposition), in Chicago, a new lemonade **straw dipped in paraffin** exhibited. (8A)

The **Panic of 1893** caused by agricultural depression, farm mortgages, reckless railway financing and unsound banking in the United States.

1894

Sept. 3—The **Big Moses, world's largest gas well,** comes in on Moses Spencer farm on Indian Creek, Tyler County, W. Va., at 1750 feet, flowing 100 million cubic feet per day through 8¼-inch casing under 575 pounds open pressure. (79)

In **Canada,** an eight-inch natural gas pipeline laid from Essex County, Ontario, to Windsor, then to a point near Detroit, in 1895, and Toledo, Ohio, in 1898. (40)

Kerosene introduced to **China** by the Standard Oil Company of New York. Kerosene would not burn properly in the native lamps so, Standard manufactured small tin lamps with glass chimneys, gave them away or sold them by the thousands and millions at a price which the humblest coolie could afford. The Chinese knew the Standard Oil Company of New York as "**MEI-FOO**" which, translated roughly, means "beautiful confidence."

Michael Cudahy, a meat packer of Omaha, Nebraska, drills two wells on town lots in the village of Muskogee, **Creek Nation.** Oil is found, but the quantity does not invite further investment. (21)

In Germany, **Rudolf Diesel** demonstrates an **internal-combustion engine** which ignites fuel by heat of compression instead of a spark. (Standard Oil Co. of New Jersey)

Slow-speed gas engines come into use, replacing the steam engine. (40)

Gas engine introduced as prime mover **for pumping wells.** (1)

E. B. Gray, of Tide Water Oil Company, cuts lube fractions with light naphtha before chilling. (40)

A portable cable driller invented by John Conner carries its own vertical steam engine on the front and boiler at the rear. One of his claims is for a "pivoted mast," perhaps a forerunner of some of today's modern **jackknife** derricks. (40)

Spang and Company founded as G. A. Spang in Butler, Pennsylvania, as manufacturers of cable system drilling and fishing tools. (50)

Gas mantles first used in **street lights.** (51)

Summerland field drilled by whipstocking holes under water of Pacific Ocean near Santa Barbara, California. (1)

70

Krebs, is credited with the invention of the **first petrol or gasoline automobile** incorporating many features of the modern car. He designs the car with a vertical engine and a modern-type chassis. (52)

Locomotive oil burner used successfully by Union Oil of California on Southern Pacific and Santa Fe steam engines. (Black Bonanza)

Midway-Sunset Oil Field, Kern and San Luis Obispo Counties, California, discovered by **Jewett and Blodgett** who drilled 16 wells which averaged a total production of 30 barrels daily of 8 to 16 degree gravity oil. Other areas of the field and dates of discovery include: Central, 1901; Global Anticline, 1912; Old Belgian Anticline, 1916; Republic, (Republic Petroleum Co.) March, 1928; Metson pool (Bankline Oil Co.) March, 1963; Shallow and Leutholtz pools (Western Mineral Co.) November, 1911, and Sunset area, prior to 1900. (74A)

1895

January 1—**Standard Oil Company of New York** establishes its first office in Hong Kong. (50)

January 23—**Posted field prices** for crude established by Standard Oil Company. (8A)

July 24—Standard Oil of Indiana's oil barge, S. O. Co. #75, leaves Whiting, Indiana, in tow by the tug Havana for Superior, Michigan. This is the beginning of transporting of oil in bulk on **Lake Michigan.** (13)

August 7—Geologist **John W. Otley** makes Trans-Mississippi Oil Line report to Savage Brothers, Beaumont, Texas, outlining oil producing potential from 100 miles East of Bismarck, N. D., through Kansas, Indian Territory, Northeast Texas, through Sour Lake, Batson, and Saratoga to a point just south of Beaumont. (53)

October 15—**John Galey** and Corsicana Oil Development Company complete discovery well of **Corsicana field** (following oil showing in water well for the city in 1894). Is first field of importance for Texas. (44)

While uninhibited acid has been used in lime wells in Ohio in 1894, it is not until 1895 that success is reported by **Herman Frasch** and J. W. Van Dyke and the Frasch patent is secured March 17, 1896. (**Acidizing**) (1)

The first **automobile road race** in the United States, sponsored by the Chicago Times-Herald. It is won by the Duryea "motor wagon." (54)

The first samples of hydrocarbons in **Bolivia** picked up on the shores of the Azero River, Department of Chuquisaca by explorer **Ignacio Prudencio.** (45)

George B. Selden, of Rochester, granted a patent covering "the principle of an **internal combustion engine** mounted upon a road vehicle." (16)

Albert Kingsberry conducts possibly the first experiments under scientifically controlled conditions on the characteristic now known as "oiliness." (35)

Wilhelm Roentgen, a German physicist, discovers **X-rays.** (Standard Oil Co. of New Jersey)

Steel pipe becomes available for pipe lines, instead of wrought iron. (19)

After the Japanese annex **Taiwan,** extensive exploration work made on this island, with only limited success. (45)

General Assembly of **Tennessee** passes act creating a procedure for closing wells, governing the placing and composition of the plug. (3)

Roland Eotvos developes the magnetic translatometer, essentially a **magnetic torsion balance.** Used to determine the magnetic polarity and preserved magnetism of clay objects, the **translatometer** is the forerunner of core orientation. (7)

L. Bertenson makes a special study of the workmen employed at the petroleum wells of Tartary and Persia, finds that, among 8465 workmen, 1216 have various skin eruptions and 1475 have respiratory diseases. (37)

Natural gas found at **Heathfield,** Sussex, England. (45)

1896

January 22—**Union Texas Natural Gas Corporation** founded as the Union Sulphur Company in New Jersey. (50)

May 30—**First automobile accident** in U.S. occurs in New York City when Henry Wells from Springfield, Mass., driving a Duryea Motor Wagon collides with bicycle rider Evylyn Thomas, breaking her leg. Wells goes to jail. (Houston Chronicle)

May—J. M. Guffey and John H. Galey touch off the first great Texas oil boom in **Corsicana,** with a 22-barrel producer following the 1894 discovery and several other two and three barrel wells. (10)

June—**Henry Ford** drives a car through the streets of Detroit and out to nearby Dearborn, Michigan. (16)

July 13—**H. W. A. Deterding** hired as Royal Dutch Company sales manager. On January 25, 1901 he became managing director. (50)

C. S. Wright, of Quaker City, Ohio, designs and builds **"A-mast" drilling rig.** It is not portable but is easily assembled, being built in sections. Patents sold later to **National Supply Co.** (1)

Acme Fishing Tool Company founded in Smithfield, West Virginia, as manufacturers of fishing tools and drilling tools (cable tools). (50)

Tom White, a prospector, finds oil and gas seepages at the head of Katalla Slough on the Gulf of **Alaska** in the Kenai Basin. (10)

Argentina—Oil produced at the Cacheuta field in Mendoza. (23)

Curtis bill terminates all **blanket leases** on Indian lands, providing for the cancellation of all non-producing leases and limiting leaseholds to

640 acres around a producing well. (H. T. Galey, Historical Outline of the Petroleum Industry in Oklahoma and Kansas, unpublished, 1930)

Weichert first concludes that the **earth's core** is composed of a rocky mantle surrounding iron. (7)

William Kane demonstrates the first boiler for generating steam using **gas as a fuel.** (38)

In **Java,** oil discovered at Ledok. (40)

The first **offshore drilling** in this country drilled directionally at Summerland, California, from piers. (15)

Edwin B. Foster leases the entire **Osage Indian Reservation** with the approval of the U. S. Department of the Interior. This was the only successful blanket lease of Indian land. (21)

The first recorded well, Toledo No. 1, drilled in Toledo, Cebu, Central **Philippines,** by Smith Bell and Co. (45)

Enamels for **coating pipe** introduced in the U. S. by the Wailes Hermiston Company of England. (38)

Dr. Samuel Pierpont Langley, secretary of the Smithsonian Institution in Washington, flies a steam-driven model **experimental plane,** somewhat larger than a condor, for 3000 feet. (35)

The **Pure Oil Company** begins operation. It was organized in 1895. (4)

Roland Eotvos, with D. Pekar and E. Fekete, proves experimentally the proportionality of inert and gravity masses. This is a basic assumption of Einstein's **Relativity theory,** and Eotvos' experiment was a geophysical contribution. (33)

George E. Whitney of Providence, R. I., patents a light steam car, and later sells it to the Stanley Brothers (then making dry plates for cameras in Newton, Mass.), and they in turn make the famous "**Stanley Steamer**" automobile. (35)

The **first Texas refinery** built at Sour Lake by the Trinity Lubricating Oil Company of Dallas. (44)

Roland Eotvos completes the development of the **torsion balance** that bears his name. (7)

Henri Becquerel observes that certain salts of **uranium** give off radiation which affects a photographic plate. (7)

Utah passes conservation statute that provides that "each lease shall contain covenants . . . that no waste shall be committed." No definition of waste is included. (3)

1897

April 15—**Michael Cudahy** drills to 1320 feet into what is now called the Bartlesville sand. A shot of nitroglycerine brings in the first commercial oil well in **Oklahoma.** It is the No. 1 Nellie Johnstone. (10)

June—**William C. Clark** granted a patent for an instantaneous **gas water heater.** (38)

October 18—**M. Samuel & Company** organizes the **"Shell" Transport and Trading Company, Ltd.,** to operate oil department of their business. (50)

The **Rothschilds,** joining forces with Frederick Lane of Lane & McAndrew, form the **Anglo-Caucasian Oil Company, Ltd.** Its purpose is to re-enter the British market from which the Rothschilds have been absent for some time. (4)

The first step in the utilization of refrigeration for cooling hot compressed gas to temperatures below those attainable with water, is the use of a **gas expansion cylinder,** driven by the same flywheel which powers the compression cylinder. It is not applied to natural-gasoline manufacturing until some 12 years later. (40)

The first Goodman **"gas stopper"** introduced to the gas industry. (38)

J. W. Mettler, Corapolis, Pa., first records account of **natural gasoline,** then called "drip" gasoline, which clogs up a small gas line running from Pennsylvania gas wells. (Natural Gas Processors Association)

Albert Kingsbury publishes his classical report on the air-lubricated journal bearing, confirming the findings of Reynolds on viscosity and the oil-wedge. He applies the principle of the oil-wedge to the design of thrust-bearings. (35)

W. Virginia—Amends Law of 1891 by prescribing more definitely a method of casing and plugging wells, defining and providing remedies with respect to waste. (3)

C. Engler prepares an illuminating oil, practically indistinguishable from commercial kerosene. (37)

Gas steam radiator invented by **Robert Calef,** of Massachusetts. His patents later purchased (1902) by James B. Clow and Sons. (38)

First inverted **incandescent burner produced.** (38)

Ruud Manufacturing Company incorporated. (38)

Buckeye develops **wheel-type trencher.** (38)

1898

January 11—**Michigan Consolidated Gas Company** (then named Detroit City Gas Company) incorporated under the laws of the State of Michigan. The gas business conducted by the Company in Detroit was started by predecessors in 1851. (50)

April 21—Spanish-American War starts.

April 23—**Ohio** passes H. R. 435, providing, among other things, for casing oil and gas wells drilled upon coal lands and their plugging in a specified manner. (3)

July 19—Patent to **Kenton Chickering**. First to show **worm gear drive**. (1)

Anglo-American Oil Co., the holding company for Standard Oil interests in Europe, buys control of **Imperial Oil,** Canada's leading oil company. (Standard Oil Co. of New Jersey)

The first complete, efficient refinery in Texas built at **Corsicana** by the **J. S. Cullinan Company** and stills fired December 25. (44)

The first commercial **Diesel engines** constructed in the U. S. built in St. Louis, Mo. (35)

East Ohio Gas Company founded by Standard Oil Company of New Jersey at Cleveland, Ohio. (50)

A German investigator, S. Kapff, concludes from his experiments that there is a property besides viscosity that is influential in reducing **friction.** (35)

Hope Natural Gas Company formed as subsidiary of Standard Oil Company of New Jersey in West Virginia. (50)

A Cotton Belt passenger **locomotive,** operating between Corsicana and Hillsboro, Texas, successfully uses oil as a fuel. (44)

Michigan—Michigan Development Company drills several wells on Goodrich farm, St. Clair County. By 1910 there were 21 wells in vicinity. (10)

Radium discovered by the Curies. (54)

Royal Dutch Petroleum Company employs Italian, Swiss and American **geologists** in **Sumatra.** (GeoTimes)

Wickwire Spencer Steel Division of The Colorado Fuel & Iron Corp., founded as Spencer Wire Company in Palmer, Mass., as manufacturers of wire rope. (50)

Ingersoll-Sergeant piston-inlet air compressor adapted to **compressing natural gas** near Fostoria, Ohio.   (38)

Russian production of oil exceeds, for a time, that of the United States. (Standard Oil Co. of New Jersey)

1899

March 26—Derrick's Handbook reports that South Penn Oil Company's No. 1 well on the Marrian Gallagher farm near the Marion and Wetzel County line in West Virginia is the **deepest producing oil well** in the country. It made 60 barrels daily from 3540 feet when it came in two months earlier. It is making 10 barrels per day in March. (43)

March 29—**Texas** Legislature passes first **conservation** act providing that water should be cased off, that abandoned wells should be plugged, that gas should not be burned in flambeau lights, and that gas from a gas well should not be permitted to escape. Subsequently, the Legislature in 1905, 1913 and 1917 added to the statutory law on the subject. (9)

June—**Kern River field,** California, discovered. (66)

June—Jersey Standard becomes the parent company of the **Standard Oil Trust.** (8A)

C. E. Hequenbourg patents his natural gas dehydration method, using **absorption** method, by passing gas over or through anhydrous materials that would absorb water vapors. (38)

First practically outlawed by the N. Y. Board of Underwriters, **acetylene gas** becomes a commercial product of importance for lighting and welding purposes. (8A)

The **air lift** used in the Baku region of Russia, according to A. Beeby Thompson. It was later used at Spindletop in 1901. (48)

The apparatus for **continuous distillation** of petroleum, patented by **Max Livingston,** of Philadelphia, Pa., perfected and in operation at the plant of **The Atlantic Refining Company** in Philadelphia. (37)

First national union in oil fields formed in Findlay and Bowling Green areas of Ohio under name of **International Brotherhood of Oil and Gas Workers.** (71)

November—**Edward Orton,** State Geologist of Ohio, emphasizes the importance of natural gas in oil production. He decries production practices that result in the **waste of gas.** (1)

Threllfall and Pollock devise the first **gravity meter.** (7)

Kansas—Act passed for inspection of petroleum and its products, including gasoline, used for both illuminating and heating purposes. (9)

Kansas—Act passed authorizing the owner of tracts in an unincorporated city to lay, maintain and operate natural gas pipe lines for the purpose of furnishing residents on such lands with natural gas for Light and Power. (9)

The Re Vollo Oil Refinery in **Norway** begins operations, obtaining its crude oil from Venezuela. (45)

Gothan invents the first kind of **orientating apparatus** in which a recording contrivance is directly fitted to a rotary core barrel during coring. (28)

A. F. Stahl and, independently, G. Kramer and A. Spilker, call attention to a possible **origin of petroleum** from diatoms which occur largely in peat. (37)

The Petroleum Times of London founded as The Petroleum Review. (Oilman, Inc.)

C. G. Knott first writes of **"Reflexion and Refraction** of Elastic Waves with Seismological Applications" in the Philosophical Magazine for that year. (7)

The **first seamless steel pipe** made experimentally in Philadelphia; it is 20 inches I.D. with ⅝-inch wall thickness and in six-foot lengths. (38)

U. S. Congress charges the War Department with the responsibility for determining whether the construction of jetties, oil rigs, and other structures in **navigable waters** interferes with navigation or commerce. (31)

C. S. Slichter and F. H. King of the U. S Geological Survey undertake detailed studies of the conditions and movements of **underground waters.** (1)

In **England,** natural gas used for lighting the railway station at Heathfield, Sussex. (38)

Robertshaw Thermostat Company founded. (38)

1900

April—The U. S. Supreme Court recognizes the right of a state to limit the waste of gas from an oil well and states the **doctrine of correlative rights** of landowners in a common source of supply. (Ohio Oil Co. vs. Indiana 177 U. S. 190)

May 24—Ground broken for New York City's first subway. (54)

July 2—First Zeppelin flight.

October 27—**Captain Anthony F. Lucas,** with financial backing from Guffey and Galey of Pittsburgh, spuds his second test at Spindletop, Texas. (44)

November 3-10—The first automobile show held in New York City. (54)

Acme Fishing Tool Co., founded by George L. McKain in Salem, West Virginia, as manufacturers of fishing tools. Later, in 1903, Acme moves to Parkersburg and is incorporated under the laws of West Virginia. (50)

Natural Gas discovered in artesian water bore at Roma, Queensland, **Australia.** (45)

Natural gas first found in **Austria.** (64)

The feasibility of **batching refined oils** under turbulent-flow conditions demonstrated. Three different grades of kerosene batched on a regular cycle without excessive mixing on a United States Pipe Line which operated until 1926. (40)

The **first billion barrels** of oil produced in the U. S. (40)

Yang Chun-Ching digs wells for oil and gas at the pool of Shih-You Kou, Szechuan Province, **China.** (45)

Coalinga, West field discovered in California. (11)

Peterson first patents an **electrical prospecting** method. (7)

Internal combustion engines begin to replace steam engines, and **iron sucker rods** are supplanting wooden sucker rods. (1)

L. Daft and A. Williams first propose the use of alternating current in **equipotential mapping.** (7)

First gasoline truck built in America. (6)

Both the McCormick and Deering factories place motor-driven **mowing machines** on exhibition. (13)

In **New Orleans,** a gas main laid under the Mississippi River, using the then-new technique of **"pulling" the pipe** across the river in sections. The crossing is 2100 feet long, and goes as deep as 120 feet. (38)

A shale oil plant erected at Orepuki, **New Zealand,** for the distillation of New Zealand shale and the manufacture of products therefrom. (37)

The **Powell field** discovered in Texas in the spring. (44)

Inserted or **rod pumps** first appear. (40)

O. Hecker records both longitudinal and transverse seismic pulses along a line of nine mechanical seismographs. This is the first modern **seismic profile.** (7)

Packard builds an auto with a **steering wheel** instead of a tiller. (Standard Oil Co. of New Jersey)

There are 8000 automobiles in the United States, and 4000 have been sold this year. (48)

The Ohio Oil Company (now Marathon) becomes first major producing organization to actually cooperate with manufacturers of gas engines to replace steam as an economical means of powering oil field equipment. **Gas for oil field power.** (50)

The **first wildcat well in Spain** drilled at Huidobro (province of Burgos). The well abandoned at 1600 feet. (64)

1901

January 1—**Parkersburg Machine Company** founded in Parkersburg, West Virginia, as a sales and repair shop. (50)

January 10—The **liquid fuel age** born when the famous **Lucas Gusher** comes in at **Spindletop,** south of Beaumont, Texas, flowing 100,000 barrels per day. Pattillo Higgins inspires the project, **Anthony F. Lucas** succeeds him and drills one dry hole (the fourth in the field) and **Guffey and Galey,** backed by Mellon finances, operate the well with the Hamill Brothers of Corsicana drilling it. Total depth is 1020 feet on a projected 1200 foot project. It is first discovery of oil on the prolific **salt dome structures** of the Gulf Coast. This discovery popularizes the use of **rotary drilling, drilling mud** and **air-lift** of oil. In addition to its great oil flow, Spindletop has the additional advantage of proximity to industrial markets and tidewater. (53)

Jan. 18—First oil field **"Christmas Tree"** employed by Hamill Brothers to cap famous Lucas Gusher. It is a well-head valve assembly of nipples, tees, gate valves, vertical and horizontal pipes designed for the purpose of controlling flow and pressure at the well-head. (53)

March 28—J. S. Cullinan, Dr. M. P. Cullinan and H. L. Scales obtain charter for **Texas Fuel Company** which, the following year, becomes The Texas Company. (5)

May 14—Mexico—**Doheny and Canfield's** first well comes in a gusher at **Cerro de la Paz**—Hill of Tar—thirty-five miles west of Tampico to open Mexico's oil boom. (10)

May 28—**William Knox D'Arcy** granted concession to explore for oil in Persia (**Iran**). (55)

May—**Andrew W. and Richard K. Mellon** organize **J. M. Guffey Petroleum Co.,** which acquires the assets of the Guffey interests. **Gulf Refining Co.,** of Texas, chartered in November and construction of a refinery starts at Port Arthur, Texas. (50)

June 25—Drs. J. W. C. Bland and Fred S. Clinton bring in a producer, near Red Fork, **Oklahoma,** the depth being 534 feet. Other activity is at Gotebo, Oklahoma, where a small refinery services eight to ten barrel wells. (5)

September 21—**Scott Heywood** hits a gusher at 1800 feet, on the Jules Clements farm six miles northeast of Jennings. The **Jennings field** is the first oil production in **Louisiana.** (10)

October 7—**Associated Oil Company** organized. (50)

December 12—Marconi sends the first trans-Atlantic radio message. (54)

The oil-**absorption** process used in connection with refrigeration to extract gasoline from natural gas. It was not until 1913 that the first commercial plant was built, however. (40)

Air lift used to produce oil wells in Spindletop, Texas, field. (53)

The **Chilkat Oil Company** discovers first commercial oil in **Alaska** in the Katalla-Yakataga area. (10)

Arkansas' first natural gas deposit of commercial importance discovered near Mansfield in Sebastian County. (American Gas Journal)

The **steamer type automobile** surpasses the **electric car** in favor. (Standard Oil Co. of New Jersey)

The **Ebano-Panuco area** of Mexico opened to prolific oil production. (70)

Helmert derives the first formula for gravity reduction based on the spheroid of the earth. **Gravity variation** with latitude is determined. (7)

The British Shell Trading & Transport Co. contracts with **J. M. Guffey Petroleum Co.** to buy 4½ million barrels of oil at 25 cents a barrel for export movement. (53)

The **H. & T. C. Railroad Company** becomes the first Texas railroad to adopt oil as a fuel for its **locomotives.** (44)

Kansas Legislature passes act providing for the control of natural gas and oil wells and for the prevention of waste of natural gas or the reservoir energy. (9)

Petroleum Law of **Mexico** authorizes **Weetman Pearson** to operate on vacant national lands. (14)

An oil **production crisis** confronts the oil industry when only 169 million barrels of oil are produced as compared with 463 million barrels in the year before, 1900. (1)

When Spindletop is discovered, the only **two refineries in the Southwest** are the Corsicana, Texas, refinery of the Corsicana Refining Company (later Magnolia Petroleum Company), and the Neodesha, Kansas, refinery of the Standard Oil Company. The combined output of the plants, built in 1897-98, is about 2000 barrels daily. (5)

Roland Eotvos makes the first full-fledged field survey by **torsion balance** on the ice of Lake Balaton, Hungary. (7)

First legislation classified as a basis for administration and conservation of oil in **Wyoming.** (3)

1901-1902—Exportation of oil from the southwestern part of the United States begins when Guffey Oil Company loads the SS **Cardium,** the first oil tanker to call at Port Arthur, in November 1901, and the Standard Oil Company tanker SS **Atlas** sails from Sabine Pass in March 1902 with a cargo of Texas crude. (53) (44)

John Henry Kirby, interested primarily in lumber and timber, is instrumental in the chartering in Texas of Kirby Lumber Company and **Houston Oil Company of Texas.** Assets of oil company sold to the Atlantic Refining Company and **Time, Inc.,** and company liquidated in 1956. (The Early History of The Houston Oil Company of Texas, by John O. King, published 1959 by Texas Gulf Coast Historical Association)

The **oxy-acetylene welding** process invented and used for the first time, in France. (38)

1902

January 2—The **Texas Fuel Company** goes into business. (Texaco, Inc.)

January 17—**Producers Oil Company** organized. (Texaco, Inc.)

February 17—**Lufkin Foundry and Machine Company** founded in Lufkin, Texas, as a repair shop for railroad and sawmill machinery; in 1920, oil field machinery; in 1939, truck trailers and truck bodies; and in 1939, commercial gears. (50)

March 7—**Sour Lake,** Texas, **field** opens when Great Western No. 2 encounters gusher production at 683 feet; area has long been known for surface seepage and its mud baths and has had minor production and a small refinery prior to 1900. (44)

April 7—**The Texas Company** incorporated in Texas. (50)

May 24—The **Oil and Gas Journal** founded as The Oil Investors' Journal. The present name adopted on April 20, 1910. (50)

June 17—The **National Petroleum Association** formally organized. (37)

November—**Lord John Rayleigh** first outlines the basic theory of **separation by distillation** in his now-famous paper: "On the Distillation of Binary Mixtures" in the Philosophical Magazine and Journal of Science, in Great Britain. This work paves the way to a thorough understanding of fractionation vapor-liquid equilibrium phenomena, which in turn lays the groundwork for the current widespread use of commercial **fractionation** installations. (40)

December 21—The word **"Texaco"** first used as a product name. (50)

The first portable **air compressor** introduced, a horizontal unit driven by an "oil engine." (38)

Henry Ford goes into the automobile business, and then builds a couple of racing cars, the "999" and the "Arrow," each having a four-cylinder engine developing 80 horsepower. (35)

The **Hamburg-American Line** adopts fuel oil. (8A)

Kern River Trading and Oil Company organized by Southern Pacific Railroad Company. (1)

Refinery plant built on the Texas Gulf Coast by George A. Burt, at Beaumont, Texas. The plant later becomes the property of the **Magnolia Petroleum Company.** (53)

Markets for fuel oil expanding. The Southern Pacific and the Santa Fe **railroads convert from coal to oil.** Sugar refineries and rice plantations in Louisiana install oil burners. Oiled surface for highways becomes popular. (53)

Rangeley field discovered in Colorado. (11)

In France, **E. A. Bashet** receives a patent for the continuous **rectification** of petroleum and volatile hydrocarbons. (37)

Royal Dutch-Shell formed. (50)

The **semidiesel engine,** with air injection, first tried on a pipeline in Pennsylvania; 11 years later the Prairie and Oklahoma pipelines place this hot-plate type of engine in service in Oklahoma and Kansas. (40)

McClure's Magazine begins publication of "The History of the Standard Oil Company," by **Ida M. Tarbell.** (50)

Roland **Eotvos** uses his **torsion balance** to indicate the subsurface extension of the Jura mountains in France. (7)

Roland **Eotvos** introduces the **double-beam balance.** (7)

Trinidad—The **General Petroleum Company** strikes oil at 1015 feet and gets 50 barrels a day from a well near the town of Guayaguayare. (10)

U. S. oil production lead assumed over Russia. (2)

California gets its first major trunk line from the San Joaquin Valley to San Francisco. (40)

American Stove Company founded. (38)

Aurora (Illinois) Gas Light Company lays the **first high pressure manufactured gas transmission main,** eight miles of four-inch steel pipe to serve Batavia. The line operates at 40 psi. (38)

The Kronininklijke Nederlandsche Petroleum Maatschappij (**Royal Dutch Petroleum Company**) starts its activities in Holland with the taking into service of the "Benzine Installatie" in Rotterdam. (45)

1903

May 23 to August 1—The first auto trip across the United States made from San Francisco to New York. (**Automobile, First Transcontinental trip**). (11)

May—The **First Exploitation Company** formed by William Knox D'Arcy and associates. (80)

July 7—H. R. Decker granted patent No. 732,925 for **blowout preventer.** (1)

September 7—Dr. **S. P. Langley,** with his assistant C. H. Manly as pilot, attempts the first heavier-than-air flight. Two attempts fail and Langley gives up. (35)

November 3—Operations begin at **The Texas Company's** Port Arthur, Texas, refinery. (50)

November 18—U. S. and Panama sign Panama Canal Treaty.

December 17—At **Kittyhawk, North Carolina,** the **Wright Brothers** make their **first heavier-than-air flight.** A 35 h.p. gasoline engine powers the flight, which reaches a height of 852 feet and lasts 59 seconds. (65)

Mark Mitchell of Franklin, Pennsylvania, takes out a patent on the process of injecting compressed air into oil sands to increase the flow. (**Air Injection**) (GeoTimes)

The **Asiatic Petroleum Company,** an agency company, organized to market petroleum products in the Far East. (50)

The **British Navy,** after a long series of experiments with fuel oil, fits some battleships to use it. In 1906, it installs oil-burning apparatus in more of its vessels, builds storage depots at various ports, order an oiler to service ships at sea, and places large contracts for fuel. (8A)

Standard of California completes **California's** first major pipeline, 280 miles in length, between Kern River and Richmond. Construction begun on the San Pablo, California, Tank Farm. (50)

The first waste act in **California** passed. (1)

Union Oil Calif.—Frank Hill uses **cement** in oil wells to shut off water, Lompoc, Calif. (1)

The **German Navy** launches its first **Diesel-engined submarine** and in 1904 Rudolf Diesel secretly develops a two-cycle engine for it. (35)

J. M. Guffey and **John Galey** bring the first natural gas to Tulsa, **Oklahoma,** to a brick plant there. (Oklahoma Natural Gas Company)

Gun perforating used for water-well completions in Texas. (5)

C. W. Hayes and **Wm. Kennedy** describe **salt domes.** (37)

Hayes and **Kennedy** present accurate hypothesis of the function of **hydrostatics** and gas expansion in oil production. (1)

Foreign markets become a major outlet for new fields and refineries, with Port Arthur, Texas, shipments totaling 8,989,027 bbls. (5)

Orcutt field discovered in California. (11)

Judge W. L. Douglas, William Weiss and S. W. Pipkin organize the **Paraffine Oil Company,** and land bought at Batson Prairie, Texas. (12)

Standard Oil Company of New Jersey establishes its first formal **pension plan.** (50)

I. L. Dunn forces gas under pressure into a well in the Macksburg, Ohio, field. After **repressuring** in this fashion, he releases the pressure and secures increased oil and better rates of flow. (48)

Impact of Texas crude disturbs foreign governments. France, Japan, and South Africa send military and industrial observers to report on the expanding fields. An English company begins operation in Saratoga field. (5)

Although not the first for **California,** nine gas wells are drilled in the Ventura field some 50 miles northwest of Los Angeles and natural gas is piped to Ventura. (38)

California provides the most important event connected with the output of U.S. petroleum, with the remarkable and sudden elevation to first position among oil producing states, superseding Ohio with 24.27 per cent of national production. In value, however, California oil is only 7.81 per cent of the total. (79)

Sun Oil Company researchers develop a process for the manufacture of high-quality **lubricants from naphthenic crude oils.** (50)

Ohio Gas Light Association meeting very productive—the group appoints a committee to study the possibility of "uniformity of gas meters" in an early effort to standardize meter sizes, and also appoints Henry L. Doherty head of another committee on "standard methods of testing fuel gas appliances." The latter group's undertaking is the beginning of recognition of the need for a **testing laboratory.** (38)

1904

January 31—**William Knox D'Arcy** strikes oil in Chiah Surkh, Persia (**Iran**) to open Middle East production. The well makes 122 barrels per day from around 1700 feet. Well suddenly goes dry in May. (55)

October 25—R. J. Hoffman and E. H. Hollingshead invent a vertically-acting **pneumatic sucker-rod cylinder.** (40)

The **Avant field** discovered in Oklahoma. (70)

In the **Dominican Republic** (Santo Domingo), seven wells drilled to depths ranging from 120 to 935 feet by Lancaster and Krieder in Azua Valley near oil seeps. All dry and abandoned. (G. H. S. Bulletin—Vol. 4 #9—May 1962)

First display of successful **inverted gas mantle.** (51)

Following oil discovery in Persia, First Sea Lord of the Admiralty in **Great Britain** appoints an Oil Committee. (55)

Illinois—The first commercial oil producer completed on the J. S. Philips farm, Clark County. (10)

Eastern gas men enter shallow eastern **Kansas** gas fields, construct three 16-inch transmission lines to serve local markets. (5)

Prairie Oil & Gas Co. constructs a six-inch line from Bartlesville field in Indian Territory to Caney, **Kansas.** Special Act of Congress is required to lay the pipe through Indian Territory. (5)

The **Kansas Natural Gas Co.,** the first important natural gas transportation company in the Mid-continent Area, organized. (47)

The first plant for extracting **natural gasoline** from natural gas by the **compression** and cooling method built by **Andrew Fasenmeyer** near the historic Drake well at Titusville, Pennsylvania. (47)

The new Robinson gravity method of **oil classification** by degrees Baume introduces at the end of this year. When the two categories are adopted in 1909, 32° Baume is set as the dividing line, although in practice 30° Baume is used. (8A)

Standard Oil Company of New Jersey organizes a company in Rumania, the **Romano-Americana,** its first affiliate engaged in oil production abroad. (50)

Sun Oil Company develops a process from which is obtained a high-quality asphalt, **Hydrolene.** This is the first commercial successful petroleum asphalt ever marketed. (50)

Experiments on **central house heating,** using gas as a fuel, begun in St. Louis by **Laclede Gas Light Company.** (38)

The United States Navy makes tests of **oil engines on torpedo boats.** (54)

A new-style **tin-case meter** developed that can measure up to 156 cubic feet per hour with only a one-half-inch pressure loss. (38)

1905

January 7—**Humble field** in Harris County, Texas, discovered by D. R. Beatty's No. 2 Fee well. In October of 1904, Higgins Oil and Fuel Company had brought in a large gas well. It is from this field, named for a small community nearby, that Humble Oil and Refining Company gets its name. (53)

April 1—**T. N. Barnsdall** and G. T. Braden organize the **Osage and Oklahoma Company.** This is the first time that the name "Oklahoma" is used in connection with the oil and gas industry. (Oklahoma Natural Gas Company)

October 10—**Pacific Gas and Electric Company** incorporated following merger of several predecessor companies including the San Francisco Gas Light Company which was incorporated in 1852 and first supplied gas to the public in San Francisco in 1854. First coal used by this company imported from Australia by ship. PG&E started to substitute natural gas for manufactured gas in 1929. (50)

Harry R. Decker's early oilfield innovation includes the first **derrick man's escape.** It is included on a derrick built for Higgins Oil and Fuel Company's No. 1 well in the Humble, Texas, field. (Houston Post)

December 14—AFL issues federal charter for the **Guffey Oil and Gas Well Workers.** This follows first strike of oilfield workers, which occurs in Batson, Sour Lake, Saratoga and Humble fields in the Texas Gulf Coast. (71)

December 19—**Glenn Pool,** Oklahoma, discovered by Galbreath & Chessley when their well on the Glenn farm comes in for 75 barrels per day at 1475 feet. (66)

Automobiles can be bought on the **installment plan.** (Standard Oil Co. of New Jersey)

An eight-inch pipe line built in Russia, from **Baku** to Batum—a distance of 550 miles. (19)

BJ Service, Incorporated, founded as The Independent Torpedo Company in Findlay, Ohio, to "shoot" wells with nitroglycerin. (50)

Caddo field in northwestern Louisiana discovered and marks the beginning of natural gas production for that state. (47)

E. H. Vavra of Cicero, Illinois, discovers and soon patents the **"cold waxing"** process for coating paper cartons now so widely used. (8A)

Clem Laessig and Harry Grenner, of the **Automobile Gasoline Company,** starts in St. Louis what is now generally acknowledged to have been the first **drive-in filling station** in America. (6)

Gulf Oil Corporation directs Geo. S. Davison (expert in water problems—no previous oil experience) to design and build pipeline from newly discovered Glenn Pool in Oklahoma, to Port Arthur, Texas. (1)

Kansas—Act passed to regulate mode of procuring, transporting and using natural gas and prohibiting use of any device for pumping or other artificial process, except "shooting" to increase flow of gas from well. (9)

Kansas declares that all pipe lines used for the conveyance of crude oil are common carriers. (9)

Kansas Legislature enacts law fixing the rates for carrying oil through pipe lines. (5)

Larkin Packer Company, Incorporated, founded as Larkin Brothers in Bartlesville, Oklahoma, as manufacturers of oil and gas well packers. (50)

Sectional **liner barrels,** including sleeve inserts which could be replaced when worn, brought out. (40)

National Commercial Gas Association organized. (Southern Gas Association)

The Territorial Legislature (**Oklahoma**) passes a law for what was then thought the proper manner of plugging wells and requiring wells to be plugged in this manner. (60)

Ransom E. Olds is the first to go in for **quantity automobile production;** he turns out 6,500 of the famous one-cylinder, curved-dash Oldsmobiles. (Standard Oil Co. of New Jersey)

Prairie Oil & Gas Company builds pipeline from Glenn Pool, Oklahoma, to its system in Kansas connecting to refinery at Neodesha, Kansas. (5)

L. P. Garrett first conceives idea of using **refraction seismic surveys** in prospecting for salt domes. (7)

The **"sweater"** comes into use. It further de-oils wax to produce a higher-melting-point product. These wax sweaters were common landmarks around some refineries until World War II. (40)

Tennessee—Act passed strengthening the law of 1895. Also prohibits gas waste. (3)

Texas imposes its first oil tax: 1% on crude oil, 2% on refined products, and 2% on pipeline flow. (5)

1906

February 20—The **Natural Gas Association of America** organized in Kansas City, Missouri. (38)

April 18-19—**San Francisco earthquake and fire** leaves 452 dead and losses totalling $350 million. Reconstruction of gas mains and plants begun immediately. Service restored in many areas within 30 days, almost completely in two months. (38)

April—First well ever drilled under **controlled pressure** is Sharp and Hughes No. 4 Herman in the Humble, Texas field. This is also the first well ever drilled with a **double deck derrick. Harry R. Decker** credited with the introduction of both developments. (Houston Post)

May 22—**Wright brothers** receive patent on a heavier-than-air, mechanically propelled aircraft. (Houston Post)

June 29—U. S. Congress passes the **Hepburn Act** providing for **federal regulation of pipelines as common carriers.** (5)

July 4—The **Louisiana** State Legislature passes an act making it a criminal offense to allow a gas well to remain out of control, or to burn or blow into the air wastefully the natural gas from any well, and authorizing the taking over of a neglected wild well by the state board of engineers at the order of the Governor. (47)

July—**American Gas Institute** organized. (47)

September 11—Columbia Corporation (predecessor of **Columbia Gas System**) incorporated in West Virginia. (38)

October 9—**Oklahoma Natural Gas Co.** formed to bring gas from Cleveland, Okla., to Oklahoma City; foundation laid for a major network of Oklahoma intra-state lines. (5)

October 17—The **British American Oil Company** Ltd., commences operations in a small office in the Canadian National Railways Building at the corner of King and Yonge Streets, in downtown Toronto, Canada. (50)

November 15—The Attorney General of the United States brings suit under provisions of Sherman Anti-Trust Act for the **dissolution** of the **Standard Oil Co.,** of New Jersey, and 33 subsidiaries, in the U. S. Court at St. Louis, Missouri. (37)

G. Koerner, an engineer of Nordhausen, Prussia, invents a spring pendulum apparatus for measuring deviation in boreholes. (28)

Bridgeport field discovered in Illinois. (11)

The **Canadian Oil and Gas Company** builds a thirteen-mile pipeline to Trois Rivieres and is marketing gas from thirteen wells by 1907. The company folded in 1908. (59)

Research toward adapting the oil-absorption process to natural-gasoline extraction started by the **Hope Natural Gas Co.,** under George Saybolt. He receives a patent in 1911, and in 1913, Hope builds a 40,000 gal. absorption plant at Hastings, W. Va. (40)

Louisiana passes a law declaring pipelines to be common carriers. (5)

Mechanical equipment for mixing drilling **mud** used in the Southwest. (5)

The **National Gas Association** (now the Natural Gas Department of the **American Gas Association**) holds its first meeting. (64)

Pacific Coast Oil renamed **Standard Oil Company (California).** Standard (California) acquires the business, plant and inventory of Standard (Iowa). The new company is the first fully integrated organization under Rockefeller management. (50)

Baron Rayleigh demonstrates that the outward heat flow and the internal temperatures of the earth depend mainly upon the distribution of **radioactive elements in the earth.** (7)

Regan Forge & Engineering Co., founded as Regan Oil Tool Company in Los Angeles, California as manufacturers of fish tail bits, standard cable tools and general forge and machine work. (50)

The **Robinson-Stoy field** discovered in Illinois. (70)

"**Squirrel cage**" **motors** first applied to pumping, the simplest of major oil field operations, in the Appalachian fields near Folson, W. Virginia. (35)

Anglo American Oil Company introduces for busses and other large vehicles, a cheaper, heavier gasoline—**Taxibus Spirit** (.760 degrees specific gravity) made from Sumatran oil. (8A)

Boston Consolidated Gas Company establishes an employee **profit-sharing** plan, first of its kind reported in the gas industry. Everyone but the company president is eligible to participate. (38)

James R. Sharp granted Patent No. 839,656 for **weight indicator** for drilling rig. (1)

Largest gasholder in the world (capacity of 15 million cubic feet) is under construction at Astoria, Long Island, for Consolidated Gas Company of New York. World's **largest gas mains** (72-inch diameter) are also underway from the Astoria plant. (38)

1907

January—**Gulf Oil Corporation** incorporated in New Jersey. It acquires the assets of the J. M. Guffey Petroleum Company and the Gulf Refining Company of Texas. (50)

April 8—**Western Oil and Gas Association** incorporated, under the name, Los Angeles Chamber of Mines. Present name adopted in 1945. (57)

April—Formation of the **Royal Dutch**—Shell Group. (6)

July 31—William Knox D'Arcy assigns all his shares in the First Exploitation Company to **Burma Oil Company.** (80)

August—**The Gulf Pipe Line Company** completes an eight-inch pipeline from the Glenn Pool in Oklahoma to Sour Lake, Texas. (44)

September—**The Gypsy Oil Company,** a subsidiary of Gulf Oil Corporation, formed in Oklahoma. (50)

October—**Texas** secures its **first** important **gas supply** when Navarro Refining Company completes a good gas well in the Petrolia field in the northern part of the state. (44)

December 13—**Argentina**—Jose Fuchs, drilling for the government, near Comodora Rivadavia, strikes oil at 530 meters. (10)

The **Anglo-Saxon Petroleum Company, Ltd.,** formed by the Royal Dutch and Shell companies. (50)

A Dutch company, the **Batavian Petroleum Company** (Bataafsche Petroleum Maatschappij) formed by the Royal Dutch and Shell companies to have charge of exploration, production, refining, and other technical matters. (50)

A German team hired for oil well drilling in Shensi Province, **China.** (45)

Andres J. Vigas sells a Venezuelan concession of two million hectares to **Colon Development Company,** a Royal Dutch-Shell subsidiary. (45)

Asbestos felt wrappers for pipe applied for the first time as a protective measure for coatings used to combat **corrosion.** (38)

Dr. L. Edeleanu, Rumanian chemist and petroleum technologist, evolves a radically different method of removing impurities from kerosene. (6)

Kern Trading & Oil locates **"resident geologists"** in oil fields. Studies subsurface conditions with cross sections. (1)

Amalgamated Oil—Fred B. Henderson, manager of Amalgamated, uses **graphic log strips.** (1)

H. P. Cady and McFarland discover natural gas to be a source of **helium.** This rare element found in the production near Dexter, Kansas. (47)

The Societa Petrolifera Italiana opens the Valezza field in the District of Emilia, Province of Parma, **Italy,** in the Appennine foothills. The first well drilled near a famous seepage at Monterotondo. It is a small producer of light oil at 449 feet. (10)

Lee C. Moore Corporation founded as Lee C. Moore Company, Inc., in Pittsburgh, Pennsylvania as manufacturers of tubular steel derricks, band wheels, bull wheels and rig fronts. (50)

The **Natural Gas Journal** begins publication. (47)

J. T. Atwood, of Wisconsin University, invents the first external **photographic device for boreholes.** (28)

The **rifled pipe line** invented by J. D. Isaacs and Buckner Speed. (37)

The **Santa Maria Gas Co.** of California becomes the first utility company in the state to provide natural gas domestic service. (47)

Wiechert and Zoepritz publish a paper on the theoretical treatment of **seismology** that puts the theory far ahead of actual experimental data. (40)

What is generally conceded to be the **first service station** dealing only in oil products (as contrasted with pumps in garages, grocery stores, etc.) established in Seattle, Washington by Standard Oil of California. Since this is a facility built at the company's bulk plant, it is not the first time that a building is devoted entirely to a service station (see 1911). The equipment includes a feed line from the main storage tanks to a 13-gallon tank, a glass gauge, a valve controlled hose, a display of oils and greases on two shelves, and other facilities designed to eliminate the slow and cumbersome filling of gasoline tanks from

cans. Gasoline is sold at tank wagon prices to retail customers. (8A)
(13) (50).

Texas begins to import natural gas from the **Caddo field** in Louisiana
to Texarkana. (47)

The Texas Company completes an 8-inch pipeline from Glenn Pool,
Indian Territory, to Port Arthur, Texas refinery. (5)

Tower still refining method introduced by Atlantic Refining Company—
Permits output of petroleum products in continuous process rather
than by batches. (50)

Trinidad—Commercial importance achieved when a well is drilled
near Point Lorin, near Guayaguayare. (10)

First recorded oil production in **Utah**—not in commercial quantities.
(54)

The United States Fleet makes its first round-the-world cruise. (54)

A permanent alliance made between the **Asiatic Petroleum Company,
Royal Dutch Petroleum Company** and The **"Shell" Transport Trading
Company Ltd.** (50)

The **Panic of 1907** begins with the downfall of an attempted combination of a chain of banks, copper interests and other enterprises, and is
followed by the collapse of Knickerbocker Trust Co., in New York, on
October 21, 1907.

Southern California Gas Company organized. (38)

Tide Water Oil Company, which has become the most important part
of the organization, trades places with the Tide Water Pipe Company,
Ltd., and thus becomes the parent company. (50)

1908

May 26—**William Knox D'Arcy** drills **Iran's** first discovery well in
the Bakhtiari hills, about 145 miles from the Persian Gulf, in an area
called Maidan-i-Naftun. (10)

May—The **Canadian Gas Association** holds its first annual meeting.
(38)

May—Forty men representing gas companies and appliance manufacturers meet at the Piedmont Hotel in Atlanta, Georgia to organize the
Southern Gas Association. (57)

June 8—**Goose Creek field** in Harris County, Texas opens with Goose
Creek Production Company's No. 2 Gaillard well making 800 BPD from
1600 ft. Production lags until after Producers Oil Company surrenders
its leases. Then on August 22, 1916, American Production Company
revives the field with a tremendous 10,000 BPD well on the Gaillard
lease from 2030 ft. This is the **first deep-seated salt dome** field, setting
off an intensive search resulting in some of the largest discoveries in the
country. (42)

June—Article suggests **gas to heat swimming pools.** (38)

September 17—First fatal air crash.

October 1—First **Model T Ford** built.

October 17—**Salt Creek field**, Wyoming, discovered by Petroleum Mattschappij of Wyoming at 1050 feet. (Salt Creek Wyoming, Harold D. Roberts, Midwest Oil Corp., Denver 1956). Minor production in Shannon sand had been discovered in 1889 and shale oil had been discovered in 1906. (70)

December 23—The Missouri Supreme Court finds **Standard Oil Company of Indiana** guilty of violating state antitrust laws. Its state franchise is revoked, a fine of $50,000 is levied and Standard is given until March 1, 1909, to conclude its business in Missouri. Standard appeals to the U. S. Supreme Court. On April 12, 1912, the U. S. Supreme Court upholds Standard Oil Company's conviction in Missouri ouster proceedings. Standard begins curtailing its Missouri activities. On June 28, 1913, the Missouri Supreme Court suspends a writ of ouster against Standard. The Court retains jurisdiction over Standard and may enforce the writ of ouster at any time. Standard has operated since that day in Missouri under a stay of the ouster order. (13)

December—The **Pennsylvania Gas Association** formed. (38)

Australia—Small quantities of gas and oil found in the Roma area of Queensland. (23)

Imperial Oil Ltd., opens **Canada's first service station** at Vancouver. The attendant uses a garden hose which he stoppers with his thumb. (Standard Oil Co. of New Jersey)

Cat Canyon field, California, discovered. (67)

Dr. F. C. Cottrell and **Buckner Speed** carry out successful experiments, in California, in the application of high potential electricity to effect the precipitation of water in a petroleum emulsion. (35)

Professor Goodman, of Leeds University, invents a **core orientation and borehole deflection apparatus.** (28)

Rudolph Conrader clearly discloses the principle of **gas displacement pump.** (1)

What is believed to have been the **first commercial natural gasoline plant** built at Sistersville, W. Va., by the **Reno Oil Company.** (40)

Associated Oil Company, in California, organizes **geological department** under **W. T. Hamilton**, Stanford University graduate. (1)

Howard R. Hughes designs the first **tri-cone bit** for drilling hard rock. (1)

C. G. Knott publishes the text, "The Physics of Earthquake Phenomena." (7)

Louisiana—Legislature creates Commission of Natural Resources, consisting of seven members. (9)

Lucey Products Corporation founded as J. F. Lucey Company in California as manufacturers of cable tool drilling units and the Lucey rotary drilling outfit. (50)

The Ohio Oil Company (now **Marathon**) becomes one of the first long-distance transporters of crude oil by pipe line, operating a crude oil trunk line from Mississippi River to New Jersey-Pennsylvania border. (50)

C. Engler is one of the first to propose that petroleum is formed from organic matter by a combination of bacterial decomposition and chemical reactions followed by high pressure distillation. (**Origin of Oil**) (22)

First use of the automobile by gas utilities was reported by the Los Angeles Gas and Electric Company and the Consolidated Gas Company of New York. (38)

Texaco becomes the first "gasoline" company when gasoline sales pass those of kerosene in volume. (50)

Brooklyn Union Gas Company establishes a **Home Service** Department. (38)

The first one-piece all-steel **sucker rod** developed by Oil Well Supply. Another very important advancement in sucker rods was the full heat-treatment, including liquid quenching of rods over their entire lengths, pioneered by Oil Well Supply in 1930. (50)

1909

February 6—British torpedo-boat destroyer Tartar breaks all speed records burning **Texas** oil. (18)

February—**National Petroleum** News starts publication. (50)

April 4—Anglo-Persian Oil Company (changed to Anglo-Iranian in 1935) formed and acquires all rights of the D'Arcy concession in Iran and all shares of the several companies which have been organized to operate in Iran. (10) (80)

April—**Coyote, West field,** California, discovered. (66)

April—**Naranjos-Cerro Azul field,** Mexico, discovered. (67)

June 4—The **Lone Star Gas Company** organizes and begins construction of a 16-inch line from Petrolia field to Ft. Worth and Dallas, a distance of 135 miles, the first long-distance natural gas line in the Southwest. (38)

July 17—Patent to **G. B. Selden. Hydrogen peroxide** is added to motor fuels to improve their performance. (29)

July 20—Standard Oil Co. announces the development of **petroleum butter,** a new dairy-product substitute. (18)

July 25—Louis Bleriot flies the English Channel from Calais to Dover. Time—37 miles in 37 minutes. (Houston Post)

September—President Taft withdraws public lands for use by Navy as future oil supplies, preparatory to the creation of **Naval Petroleum**

Reserves: Reserve No. 1, 38,969 acres, **Elk Hills,** Kern County, California; Reserve No. 2, 29,341 acres, **Buena Vista Hills,** Kern County, California; Reserve No. 3 (created in 1915), 9481 acres at **Teapot Dome,** Natrona County, Wyoming. (78)

November 27—The Chanslor-Canfield Midway Oil Co., No. 2-6 blows in as a discovery well in the **Midway,** California **field.** (18)

December 23—**Texas Gulf Sulphur Company** organized as Gulf Sulphur Company. The present corporate title was adopted in 1918. (50)

At the English Motor Show of this year, the Anglo-American Oil Company displays "**areo-naph**" to appeal to a new customer, the "**areoplane.**" (8A)

British Petroleum (then Anglo-Persian Oil Company) formed with Lord Strathcona as Chairman. (55)

Cincinnati receives natural gas through a 183-mile, 20-inch pipeline from fields in West Virginia. (46)

M. J. Munn is the first to suggest **compaction** as an agent in the migration of oil from source beds to reservoir rocks. (21)

David T. Day, termed by Who Was Who In America as the father of mineral resources studies in the Federal Government, deplores the rampant waste of gas; as remedial measures, he proposes **cooperative production** by the operators within a field and legislation to control production rates and to prohibit gas waste. (1)

History of taxation of incomes from depletive resources (**depletion**) established with 1 per cent federal excise tax levied on income of all corporations. (72)

The **Egyptian** Oil Trust, Limited, drills at **Gemsah** and finds oil. The discovery well produces 39 degrees gravity oil in Miocene sandstone at 1290 feet. (10)

Gas incinerator developed. (51)

D. W. Franchot, et al., builds first "**casing-head**" **gasoline plant** in Southwest at Kiefer, Oklahoma, in Glenn Pool, Oklahoma. Plant has output of few hundred gallons weekly. (5)

Hughes Tool Company founded as Sharp and Hughes in Houston, Texas, manufacturers of rotary rock bits, and introduces the first rotary rock bit equipped with two-cone cutters that roll on bottom. This bit revolutionizes rotary drilling by making it possible to drill rock formations. (50)

Maloney-Crawford Tank & Manufacturing Company founded as Maloney Tank Manufacturing Company in Tulsa, Oklahoma as manufacturers of wood tanks for storage of water, crude oil, and various petroleum products. (50)

Mexico Mining Law reaffirms exclusive ownership of deposits of mineral fuels by the owner of the surface. (14)

A 20-mile, eight-inch line from east of the Panuco River to Tampico is **Mexico's first pipeline.** (40)

A. Mohorovicic first discovers the discontinuity forming the bottom of the continental layers of the earth's crust. Gutenberg concluded in 1924 that the "continental" layers of the crust are missing only in the Pacific ocean. (**Moho**) (7)

New Mexico—"The Old Brown Well," in the Artesian Water Basin near Dayton, Eddy County, yields approximately 15 bbl. per day for a short time to start New Mexico oil search. (10)

New Mexico Territorial Legislature enacts a conservation law. (9)

Oklahoma—Legislature passes **Common Purchaser Act.**

Honolulu Oil Corporation's first geological engineer is Paul Paine, uses **peg models** for study of subsurface structure. (1)

J. Joly publishes the text, "**Radioactivity and Geology.**" (7)

Mrs. John R. Ramsay is the first woman to drive an automobile across the U. S. The trip takes over two months and sources of gasoline are few and far between. In Utah, she pays 62½ cents per gallon for gasoline which has to be carried 90 miles. (Oil Daily)

Standard of California—As contribution to efforts to exclude water from oil-producing strata, Standard posts **descriptions of formations** encountered in drilling each well. (1)

In the antitrust suit, the court rules against Standard Oil Company of New Jersey, enjoining it from exercising its rights of ownership in thirty-seven of the affiliates. **Standard Oil Company of New Jersey** appeals. (50)

U. S. Geological Survey recommends that surplus natural gas be stored in underground reserves, and forecasts early decline in supply. (**Underground gas storage**) (5)

The U. S. Supreme Court upholds for the second time the decisions of the Texas courts that the **Waters-Pierce Oil Company** has violated Texas antitrust laws; the company is fined and its permit to operate in Texas is revoked. (12)

Web Wilson Oil Tools, Inc., founded as Wilson & Willard Manufacturing Co., in Los Angeles, California as manufacturers of cable tool underreamers, tongs and elevators. (50)

The second billion barrels of oil produced in the U. S. (40)

Iron-case "A" **gas meter** introduced. (38)

Glenn Pool to Baton Rouge oil pipeline completed, to **Standard Oil Company of Louisiana** refinery. (5)

1910

January—The **Oil Age Weekly** begins publication, covering California affairs. (48)

February 10—**Buena Vista field** discovered in Kern County, California by Honolulu Oil Corporation. (74)

February 20—The British Admiralty announces its navy will replace coal with oil for fuel on all its ships. (18)

March 6—A **well** drilling a mile **offshore** in Lake Erie from Selkirk, west of Welland, Ontario, **Canada,** strikes gas in large volume. (18)

March 15—The **Lake View gusher,** near Maricopa in California's Midway Field, starts flowing at dawn and continues for 18 months, until September 9, 1911, when it caves in. The well produces 9,000,000 barrels. (54)

Spring—A large gas well, the first west of Osage Reservation in Oklahoma, brought in on land leased from the Miller Brothers 101 Ranch and the Ponca Indians by **E. W. Marland** and Col. E. R. Kenney. This is the beginning of the **Marland Oil Company.**

July 1—The **United States Bureau of Mines** established in the Department of the Interior. (48)

July 12—Rotary **Tool Joint** patented by M. H. Whittier. (1)

August 4—American oil men are expressing interest in a new method of lifting oil devised by an Austrian engineer and being adopted in the fields of Galicia. It consists of an endless band of ordinary flat hempen rope or cable faced with carpet shag or pile to increase its absorbent capacity. The absorbent band is lowered into the well over a rotating drum. (18)

August 11—The largest cargo of cased oil ever loaded from any port south of Baltimore moved out of **The Texas Co.'s** docks at Port Arthur, Texas, last week destined for Brazilian ports. It consisted of 100,000 cases of illuminating oil in hardwood boxes, prepared for handling for interior distribution. (18)

October 13—New 20,000 bbl. gusher drilled by **Producers Oil Co.** (The Texas Co.) extends Caddo field in Northwestern Louisiana 1½ miles and starts another drilling boom. (18)

October 25—First patent for in-the-hole **mechanical casing perforator** issued to J. C. Swan. (1)

November 24—**Louisiana Co.** (The Texas Co.) starts pumping oil from the Caddo field through the newly-completed Louisiana section of its new crude-oil pipeline from Ardis (Shreveport) tank farm to the Texas Co.'s refinery and terminal at Port Arthur, Texas.

December 1—The Busch-Everett Company, which recently announced plans for laying a pipeline from the big **Caddo field** of Louisiana to supply St. Louis with natural gas, abandons the project. Engineering reports indicate that transportation of natural gas a distance exceeding 200 miles would be impractical. (18)

December 22—Large shipment of petroleum unloaded from American ship at Chinampo opening direct trade between U. S. and **Korea.** (18)

December 27—Probably the **world's most productive single well,** the Mexican Eagle Oil Co. Ltd's No. 4 Potrero del Llano, whose location was staked by **E. DeGolyer** even before he returned to complete work for his geology degree, comes in flowing 110,000 barrels per day. The well eventually made more than 100 million barrels in eight years. It was located north of the Tuxpan river, near Veracruz, Mexico. Oil Trade Journal, Vol. 10, No. 1, January 1919, Page 3)

The Russian chemist, **Lehedev,** first converts **butadiene** into a rubber-like material. (25)

General Electric builds special multispeed double induction motor for **cable tool drilling.** (1)

First **"credit card"** system known to the oil industry initiated by DAPG, a Standard affiliate in Germany, in the form of coupon books issued to reliable motorist customers. (8A) (In the United States, major marketing companies started issuing credit cards in the early twenties.)

The first gas field discovered in **Germany,** south of Hamburg, when a well is drilled for water. (64)

Hughes Tool Company inaugurates the industry's first research program to study rock bit performance. (50)

Ideco Division of Dresser Equipment Company founded as S. H. Supply Company in Beaumont, Texas. (50)

The first **liquefied petroleum gas** produced at the Sisterville, W. Virginia, plant of the Riverside Oil Company. A. N. Kerr pioneered the development of the new industry. (38)

The Arkansas & Louisiana Railroad, operating between Bloomberg and Atlanta, uses gas as a fuel in one of its **locomotives.** The project is later abandoned when it is decided that the risk is too great. (44)

Louisiana creates Conservation Commission and a Department of Mining and Minerals. (9)

Louisiana—Act passed for providing for plugging of wells. (10)

Gulf Oil Corporation obtains a lease on 8,000 acres of lake bottom in **Ferry Lake, Louisiana.** Preparations made for the first **over-water drilling** for oil. (**Offshore drilling**) (50)

L. Mrazee suggests that diastrophic movements are probably the most important causes of the **migration of oil.** (22)

F. G. Clapp proposes the first detailed **classification of oil and gas pools.** (22)

Oildom Publishing Company founded. (50)

Oklahoma, fearing an untimely depletion of its resources, tries without success to adopt legal measures to prevent the exportation of natural gas. (47)

The **Oklahoma Natural Gas Company** builds the first **compressor station in the Southwest.** (40)

G. Leimbach and H. Lowy first propose use of **radio frequency** methods for prospecting. (7)

The theory of **refraction profiling** recognized. (40)

Republic Supply Company founded in Houston, Texas as a supplier of oil field equipment. (50)

The advent of **thermal cracking** helps to solve the cold-test problem by providing blending stocks of lower cold test along with other properties which have a bearing on viscosity. (40)

University of Pittsburgh offers three courses in oil and gas, and three courses in oil and gas law. (1)

The **New York and Bermudez Company** begins to exploit the world's largest asphalt lake, the Guanoco Pitch Lake, in **Venezuela.** (45)

Vinton field discovered in Louisiana. (5)

The first effective way of converting petroleum and alcohol into rubber discovered by Matthews and Strange, in England. (25)

Refineries begin using **continuous distillation** method of refining crude oil. Previously, batch method in common use. (5)

There are 468,500 motor vehicle registrations in the United States. (11)

Lone Star Gas Company completes the first long-distance natural gas transmission line in the Southwest, from **Petrolia field** to **Fort Worth** and **Dallas, Texas**—a distance of 126 miles. (50)

Standard Oil Company creates a central office to advise the marketers on advertising. Its chief is **H. K. McCann,** who later founded the **McCann-Erickson Advertising Agency.** (Standard Oil Co. of New Jersey)

Standard Oil Of Louisiana enters the producing business. (Standard Oil Co. of New Jersey)

1911

January 5—The steamship Honolulan, the first exclusively **fuel-oil-burning vessel** to round Cape Horn completes a notable 14,000-mile voyage from Baltimore to Seattle carrying a competitive cargo of 7000 tons of coal. It consumes 14,000 bbl. of oil. This represents one barrel of oil moving 7000 tons of coal per mile. (18)

January 17—**Electra,** Texas, **field** discovered by Producers Oil Company No. 5 Waggoner for 50 barrels per day at 1,825 feet. (44)

January—**Admiral George Dewey,** hero of Manila Bay, in his capacity as president of the General Board of the U. S. Navy, declares for **naval fuel oil stations.** (2)

February 2—**Midwest Oil Company** chartered in Arizona. In 1951

Midwest merged with Saltmount and Mountain Producers to form **Midwest Oil Corporation.** (University of Wyoming Archives)

February 2—Twenty steamers chartered to load a record-breaking oil export shipment of more than 1,000,000 cases of refined petroleum at Philadelphia destined for ports in China, Japan, New Zealand and Australia. (18)

February—Humble Oil Co., predecessor of the present **Humble Oil & Refining Co.,** which became largest domestic crude producer, chartered in Texas. (5)

March 23—The Belgium Colonial Government authorizes the laying of a 200-mile, four-inch pipeline across the **Congo** from a bulk tank-steamer terminal at Matadi, on the coast, to a bulk-distributing station at Stanley Pool, 1000 feet above sea level. (18)

March 30—The five-year rampage of the **Caddo Gas and Oil Company's** notorious wild, cratered gas well in the **Caddo field** ends. Relief wells drain pressure and kill the burning cratered blowout. (18)

April—Rear Admiral Cone, Chief of Bureau of Steam Engineers, **U. S. Navy,** announces specifications of two new battleships calling for exclusive use of oil as fuel, also stating that all future specifications would be for oil. (2)

May 1—The **first gasoline service station** ever located in a building constructed for that express purpose opened by R. L. Francis of the **Central Oil Company,** a small jobbing concern, in Detroit, Michigan, at the corner of West Fort and First streets on a lot 100 by 150 feet with a 20 by 25 foot shelter in the center of the lot. The station is designed and built by F. A. Bean, a consulting engineer. Tank capacity is 1000 gallons and gasoline is dispensed by a one-gallon stroke pump, blind hand type with two outlets. Free air is not dispensed until 1913 when an air compressor is added. The building, driveways, pump and other equipment cost approximately $1200. First sales are less than 100 gallons a day. In six weeks, sales are up to 200 gallons daily and by the end of the first six months they are up to 2000 gallons. First sales are at tank wagon prices. After two weeks the garage price is put into effect, making this the **first service station market.** The company becomes the **first chain of service stations** by adding a second station in the fall. It is also the **first service station ever robbed.** (TOTC —Houston Post)

May 15—United States Supreme Court orders **dissolution** of the Standard Oil Company. (8B)

August—The stimulating of production from oil wells by **forcing air through oil sand** started on the Wood farm of the Cumberland Oil Company near Chesterhill, Ohio, by **I. L. Dunn.** (1)

September 17 to November 5—First transcontinental airplane flight, New York to Pasadena, California, by C. P. Rodgers. (AP)

November 9—Power lines of the Beaumont Ice, Light & Refrigerating

Co., are extended to Spindletop oil field, southeast of Beaumont, Texas, where the use of **electric power for pumping oil wells** will be tried out for the first time. The first motor installation, in operation only a few days, seems to be giving satisfaction. (18)

December 1—**John D. Rockefeller ends his career** as president of Standard Oil Company of New Jersey, following dissolution of the "Oil Trust." He is retiring from all active official participation in the oil business, and is joined by William and William G. Rockefeller, **C. M. Pratt, H. M. Flagler, E. T. Bedford,** and others long active in the company. **John D. Archbold,** one of the few remaining members of the "Old Guard," replaces Rockefeller as president of the reorganized **Standard Oil Co., of New Jersey.** (18)

December 9—The Ohio Oil Company (now Marathon) again becomes a separate and independent oil company following **dissolution of Standard Oil Company** under Sherman Act. (50)

December 21—**Midwest Oil Company** starts oil runs through its newly completed 55-mile pipeline from the Salt Creek fields to storage at Casper, Wyoming, where it is building an entirely new refinery.

Abegg & Reinhold Company founded in Los Angeles, California, as manufacturers of forged hand tools and heat treating. (50)

Patents issued for oil **absorption process** to E. W. Saybolt of Hope Natural Gas Company, New York. (Natural Gas Processors Association)

Alabama enacts its first oil and gas conservation law. (Alabama General Acts, 1911, Act 409.)

The **American Gasol Company** founded in Pittsburgh, Pennsylvania. This is the first American company organized to produce and market **liquefied petroleum gas** extracted from natural gas and natural gasoline. (50)

Bradford Motor Works founded in Bradford, Pennsylvania, as manufacturers of subsurface pumps and parts. (50)

California Legislature grants to the City of **Los Angeles** submerged lands fronting on Los Angeles out to the three-mile limit. (31)

V. T. Day is the first to demonstrate the importance of **capillarity in the migration and accumulation of oil and gas** in his experiments with fuller's earth. (22)

The two-plug process for control in placing **cement** patented by A. A. Perkins and Edward Double. (40)

Internal upset **drill pipe** developed in California. (1)

The first **Edeleanu** commercial **plant** operates in France. (48)

The use of frothy mixtures for petroleum **fire fighting** investigated at Wilhelmsburg, near Hamburg, Germany. (37)

For the first time in petroleum history in the United States, **demand for gasoline exceeds that for kerosene.** (TOTC—Houston Post)

Illinois—Act of 1905 amended by adding sections relative to drilling of wells near mine openings and through coal seams. (3)

The first practical **orifice meter** design developed by J. G. Pew and H. C. Cooper, and first used to measure large volumes of natural gas on an installation in West Virginia. The device evolved from the **Pitot tube.** (38)

The Bureau of Mines starts the annual statistical section on Natural Gasoline in the Survey's **"Mineral Resources,"** continuing this service through 1931. (48)

North Dakota enacts law pertaining to gas waste and its conservation for use as light, fuel and power purposes. (3)

Miri Field, Sarawak, discovered, the first oil field found in British Borneo. (70)

The Texas Company completes its eight-inch pipeline from Caddo, La., to Port Arthur, Texas.

Water flooding starts in Pennsylvania. (40)

Welding of pipe joints by oxy-acetylene introduced by the gas industry, the first practical application being made on an 11-mile line of the Philadelphia & Suburban Gas Co. (47)

The **Weymouth flow formula** introduced to the gas industry as the first formula to permit accurate calculation of gas flow in high pressure natural gas lines. (38)

Interest in the possibility of indigenous petroleum resources stimulated by the discovery of crude oil in a borehole sunk in the course of coal mining operations near Newark, Nottinghamshire, **England.** (45)

Kern Trading & Oil—**J. A. Taff** becomes **"geologist in charge."** (1)

Oil seepages reported near Vailala River in Papua, **New Guinea.** (45)

Southern Counties Gas Company organized. (38)

1912

January 12—**Continental-Emsco Company** is organized under name of Continental Supply Company in St. Louis, Mo. In January, 1957, Continental Supply Company and Emsco Manufacturing Company of California merged to become Continental-Emsco Company, a division of Youngstown Sheet and Tube Company. (50)

February 22—The first ocean liner ever to be driven by **diesel power,** Denmark's "Selandia", of 4,950 gross tons, makes her maiden voyage from Copenhagen to Bangkok. (Petroleum Press Service)

March 25—**Cushing field** in Oklahoma discovered by Chas. B. Shaffer and T. B. Slick when well on the Wheeler farm comes in for 60 barrels per day from the Wheeler horizon at 2194-2208 feet. (Mid-Continent Oil Scouts and Landmen's Association) (Geotimes).

April—The Bureau of Standards publishes the first edition of its famous

"Circular 32"—which helps establish standards for gas, manufactured and natural, replacing the old "candlepower" standards. (38)

May 2—A new **drilling-time record** has been set in the large Blue Creek field of Kanawha County, West Virginia, with the completion by W. S. Edwards Oil Co., of its 5-B Jones to a depth of 1640 feet in only 17 days. Previous fastest time for any well to comparable depth has been 20½ days. (18)

May 2—The Hungarian Government monopolizes the tremendous natural gas sources recently discovered at Kissarmas, in Transylvania. The field is proclaimed as the most important source of gas in the world. Daily yield of 25 MMCF of gas. Government engineers estimate that there will be sufficient gas to light all communities in **Transylvania** and to justify laying a gas line to Budapest. (18)

May 17—First installation of cylinders of **liquefied petroleum gas** for domestic cooking and heating made at the farm of John W. Gahring, Waterford, Penn. This is the birthplace of the LP-Gas industry. (Natural Gas Processors Association)

June 13—I. C. C. declares interstate **pipelines common carriers.** (8B)

July 8—**Burkburnett field** brought in by Corsicana Petroleum Company's No. 1 Schmaker at 1837 feet. It is a small (85 barrels per day) well. (75) (44)

July—**Freeport Sulphur Company** chartered. Starts production at Bryan Mound, Texas, in November, 1912. Obtained first oil production at Section 28 Dome in St. Martin Parish, Louisiana, in 1948. (50)

August 22—The United States Department of the Interior opens lands of **Osage Indians** for leasing and oil and gas development. Long controversy over rules and regulations ends. First three applications for leases are filed. (18)

September 3—The **American Gasoline Company** organized for the purpose of marketing imported gasoline in the Pacific Northwest and the San Francisco Bay areas. (Shell Oil Company)

October 1—**Roxana Petroleum Company** organized. (50)

October 4—The first cargo of **Sumatra gasoline** arrives at Richmond Beach, on Puget Sound, just outside of Seattle, Washington. (Shell Oil Company)

November—John Johnston and L. H. Adams take temperature surveys in a bore hole near Findlay, Ohio, going to 3000 feet and measuring regular **geothermal gradients.** Operate with maximum thermometers. (1)

In Iran, the **Abadan refinery** put into operation. (45)

R. C. Baker, an independent oil operator and later founder of **Baker Oil Tools, Inc.,** invents the **cement retainer** to pack off between the casing and tubing when pumping cement through tubing. (1)

Combination rig developed on the Gulf Coast. (1)

Ancon No. 1, drilled by Anglo-Ecuadorian Oilfields Ltd., yields small production from 1500 feet, the first for **Ecuador,** other than oil recovered from hand-dug pits as early as 1700. (10)

C. Schlumberger introduces a **two-electrode equipotential** device to explore from the surface of the ground. (7)

V. I. Vernadskii makes the first fully complete **classification** of **natural gases.** (27)

Socony—General Petroleum Corporation begins using "**resident geologists**" in California oil fields. (1)

Geologists start **mapping outcrops** to locate favorable places to drill. (32)

Mexican Gulf Oil Company organized as Gulf Oil Corporation's first foreign production venture. (50)

A. G. Heggem and J. A. Pollard of the Bureau of Mines recommend use of **mud-laden fluid** in drilling cable-tool holes after studies in Oklahoma. (1)

Australian Government drills at Upoia with oil shows reported in some. Oil seepages reported near Vailala River in Papua-**New Guinea** in 1911. (45)

New Mexico—Legislature of 1912 (New Mexico had just come into statehood then) passes an act designed to prevent waste. (9)

R. H. Johnson regards the presence of gas as a factor in the **migration of oil** in conjunction with moving water, capillarity, and differential specific gravity. (21)

Oregon Basin field, Wyoming, discovered. (67)

The first major improvement in pipe-laying techniques comes with the development of the **pipe-screwing machine.** (19)

The **Royal Dutch-Shell** group enters the United States. (50)

Dr. Duisberg of the Badische Company in Germany attends the International Congress of Applied Chemistry, in New York, and exhibits a set of automobile tires made of **synthetic rubber.** (25)

Conrad Schlumberger begins systematic studies of electrical surveying along the surface of the earth (French patent 450,784). (73)

O. W. Maloney invents and patents a **bolted steel tank** for storage of petroleum products, water and other fluids. (50)

The **Trumble pipe still operation** first introduced in California. (40)

In Iraq, British and German capital form the **Turkish Petroleum Company,** claiming oil rights conflicting with the unconfirmed U. S. Chester concession. (40)

Oil and Gas Geology given as a new course at **University of Pittsburgh,** by Roswell H. Johnson. (1)

Thomas R. Weymouth's 1911 **formula** for computing the flow of natural gas through pipe lines made public in a paper before the **A.S.M.E.** (47)

1913

January 7—**Dr. William Merian Burton** of Standard Oil Company of Indiana granted patent on petroleum cracking process for which he had made application on July 3, 1912. He had introduced the process in 1912. In 1918 he is awarded the William Gibbs Medal and in 1921 the Perkins Medal in recognition of his work in petroleum chemistry. This is a significant breakthrough in the distillation of gasoline. The U. S. Board of Tax Appeals places a value of $70 million on the process. (13) (65)

February 25—The 16th Amendment to the United States Constitution authorizes a federal **income tax.** (Standard Oil Co. of New Jersey)

February—**Granville A. Humason** of Shreveport, La., files application for patent on the first practically designed **cross-roller rock bit,** the forerunner of the Reed cross-roller bit. (1)

March 1—Revenue Act of 1913 sets **depletion** deduction at five per cent of the gross value of oil and gas to be taken every year until the recovery of the original cost or its market value as of this date. **Depletion for oil properties first became effective.** (8B) (72)

March 1—Standard Oil Company of Indiana announces a new **"motor spirit."** It is to cost the consumer three cents a gallon. (8B)

March 3—The **British Royal Commission** of which Admiral Sir John Arbuthnot Fisher is chairman, reports in its final memorandum that the navy should, in the interests of speed and efficiency, fuel with oil, which has to come from abroad, instead of with coal. (2)

April 28—The first natural gas delivered to **Los Angeles** where it is mixed with manufactured gas. The natural gas is conveyed through a 120-mile pipe line from Buena Vista Hills. (47)

May 14—Rockefeller Foundation formed.

July 13—British House of Commons approves a suggested agreement by which the British Government would acquire shares valued at £2,000,000 out of a total capital of £4,000,000 in **Anglo-Persian Oil Co.** (now **Anglo-Iranian Oil Co.**) and would have an absolute veto on company policy. (2)

July 17—**Winston Churchill,** First Lord of the Admiralty, announces the **British oil policy** to acquire its own supply from sources under British control or influence. (2)

August—The **American Gasoline Company** purchases **California Oil-Company** when its Apple-Franklin well comes in making 25 B/D from 920 feet. (75)

August 4—**Healdton field** in Oklahoma discovered by Red River Oil

fields, Ltd., at Coalinga, California. Purchase price is $13 million. (Shell Oil Company)

September 5—**Guanoco field** discovered in Venezuela, by a New York and Bermudez Co. well completed at 615 feet. (77)

September 9—The first recorded **dual completion** is on a well in Wicey Pool, Oklahoma. In the Panhandle field in Texas in 1926, N. O. Miller devised a cable tool method of dual completion to prevent waste and fire hazard, and to eliminate recementation. (1)

September—The Panama Canal completed. (54)

November 1—**New York State Natural Gas Corporation** incorporated in New York. (50)

The Oil & Gas Committee of the A.I.M.M.E. created with Captain **Anthony F. Lucas** as first chairman. Distinguished members are Ralph Arnold, David T. Day, Frederick G. Clapp, Edwin T. Dumble, John R. Edwards, R. S. Haseltine, Phillip W. Henry, Walter O. Snelling, William L. Watts, H. A. Wheeler and W. A. Williams. (1)

The oil **absorption method** for natural gasoline recovery initiated by **John G. Pew,** of Hope Natural Gas Co., Hastings, West Virginia. (47)

Baker Oil Tools, Inc., founded as the Baker Casing Shoe Company in Coalinga, California, as manufacturers of casing shoes, cement retainers, packers, fishing tools and bailers. (50)

Engineers of the newly-organized petroleum division of U. S. **Bureau of Mines** assigned to **Cushing,** Okla., field to study drilling problems. (5)

A discovery in southern Alberta is the **first oil found in western Canada.** (Standard Oil Co. of New Jersey)

Surface chokes for controlling flowing wells used in the **West Coyote field** of California; possibly a first use. (1)

Friedrich Bergius succeeds in converting about 50 per cent of heavy oil into gasoline without the formation of coke, by supplying hydrogen under high pressure during the oil **cracking process;** he also investigates effect of high pressure on chemical actions, develops processes for production of motor fuels by hydrogenation of coal under pressure and for production of sugar from wood; was awarded (with Karl Bosch) 1931 Nobel Prize for chemistry. (25) (65)

Exner-Dodge, Inc., founded as the Exner-Dodge Packer Company in Coffeyville, Kansas as manufacturers of packers, nipples, bull plugs, and other oil field nipples and couplings. (50)

The first oil company to organize its **subsurface geologists** and field engineers into a working group which reports to operating officials is the Shell Company of California. (1)

United States Commerce Court overrules Interstate Commerce Commission and declares **Hepburn Act** unconstitutional, since it deprives gas companies of the use of their own property without just compensation. (See also 1914) (8B)

Prince B. Galitzin is the first to stress the importance of the exact form of the **hodograph,** a travel time curve, in refraction computations. (7)

Exports of oil begin from **Iran.** (Review)

In **Kuwait,** Sheik Mabarak gives the British Political Resident a letter promising "to show the place of bitumen (oil seepages) at **Burgan** and elsewhere," and promising "we shall never give a concession in this matter to anyone except a person appointed by the British government." (AP)

Missouri School of **Mines** offers elective courses in petroleum geology. (1)

Natural gas discovered in **Montana,** in Dawson county. (47)

"Oil Production Methods" written by **Paul Paine** and **Ben Stroud.** (1)

Oklahoma—Legislature passes an act which provides for ratable production from the common reservoirs of natural gas, this being, it is believed, the first one of its type, relating either to oil or gas, to have been enacted by any state. Because of its penalty provisions, it was sometimes called **"The Larceny Act."** (9)

Oklahoma—Act purports to make **common purchasers** of every corporation, partnership, or person claiming or exercising the right to carry or transport natural gas by pipeline for hire, compensation or otherwise, within the limits of the state. (3)

The **Oklahoma Independent Oil & Gas Association** organized. (15)

"Parol," a fuel for use in internal combustion engines introduced. It is reported that it is made from paraffin by a chemical process and without the use of heat. (37)

Gulf Oil Corporation claims the world's **first drive-in service station,** at Baum Boulevard and St. Clair Street in Pittsburgh. (50)

Standard Oil Company of New Jersey creates a general **engineering department.** (50)

Subsurface geologic methods introduced into prospecting for oil. (5)

First **bolted steel lease tanks** for the petroleum industry. Gantz Tank Co. produces lease tank of a flanged bottom and flanged deck type. (1)

E. B. Durham gives a course in petroleum technology at **University of California.** First courses given in new four-year curriculum in petroleum engineering in 1915, by **L. C. Uren.** (1)

A one-million hectare concession in Venezuela sold to **Venezuelan Oil Concessions,** which eventually becomes a Shell subsidiary. (45)

R. Ambronn uses a two-electrode method (that of Brown) as a **well-logging** device. He uses a fixed and a moving electrode in a comparatively homogeneous **drilling fluid** to measure variations in resistivity of formations traversed. (7)

W. Virginia—Public Service Commission created. (3)

Boverton Redwood states that in Russia and India the relation between petroleum and mud volcanoes is very noticeable. (37)

Oil production reaches cumulative total of 3 billion barrels in the U. S. (40)

Heggem and **Pollard** advocate the "**mud-laden fluid method**" of drilling to conserve oil and gas. Mud had been used as a drilling fluid as early as 1900 by the **Hamill brothers** at Spindletop, when **Curtis G. Hamill** dug shallow holes, drove mules through after watering down, and used mud to aid in first salt dome drilling. (53) (64)

<h2 style="text-align:center">1914</h2>

April 2—**Reginald Fessenden** files his original **Sonic Sounder** application for patent for determining ocean depths. This is the first use of a reflection seismic method. According to DeGolyer, Fessenden clearly was the discoverer of the **reflection seismic** method. (7)

April 9—**Columbus Production Company** chartered in Columbus, Ohio. Twelve days later, name changed to **Ohio Cities Gas Company**. In 1917, Pure Oil Company (New Jersey) acquired by Oil Cities Gas. On July 1, 1920, name of Oil Cities was changed to **Pure Oil Company.** (50)

April 18—At **Mene Grande** (Big Seep), **Venezuela,** the **Caribbean Petroleum Company,** a Shell subsidiary, drills the first commercial well. It is the Zumaque No. 1. (10)

April—First **Montana** oil in commercial quantities discovered at the **Cedar Creek Field,** Fallon and Wilbaux Counties. (54)

May 7—The **first proration order** issued by a state regulatory body is Order No. 813, by the Oklahoma Corporation Commission. It relates to the Cushing field and, unlike later orders, it deals with oil to be taken by pipe line companies. (9) Voluntary proration had been established previously.

May 14—Herron and his associates in **Calgary Petroleum** strike oil in **Turner Valley,** Alberta, **Canada.** (63)

May 20—The British government signs a contract to acquire a controlling-share interest in **Anglo-Persian Oil Company** with the specific understanding that the government will not ever interfere in purely commercial and operating matters of the company. (80)

June 22—U. S. Supreme Court reverses decision of U. S. Commerce Court and declares pipelines to be common carriers under **Hepburn Act.** (8B)

June 28—The **Turkish Petroleum Company** (now Iraq Petroleum Company) granted a concession for the exploitation of the oil fields in the vilayets of Mosul and Baghdad, **Iraq.** (80)

June—**Grass Creek field,** Wyoming, discovered. (68)

July 1—The Petroleum and Natural Gas Division of the **Bureau of Mines** officially recognized as a unit, with **W. A. Williams** as Chief Petroleum Technologist. (1)

July 14—An oil tank embodying an automatic chemical **fire extinguisher** demonstrated at Bayonne, New Jersey. (54)

July 24—The name of **American Gasoline Company** changed to **Shell Company of California,** Inc. (50)

July 28—Austria declares war on Serbia.

July 28—U. S. oil interests actually are producing oil in only two foreign countries, Mexico and Rumania; although they have refining investments in Argentina and Austria, and hold shares, leases or concessions in Russia, Colombia, Poland and Argentina. (2)

August 1—Germany declares war on Russia.

August 3—Germany declares war on France.

August 14—The Atlantic Refining Company completes the **first modern service station** in the East. (50)

September 6-9—General Joseph Gallieni, the military governor of Paris, musters all available men in uniform and rushes them to the front in a motley commandeered fleet of taxis, lorries and private automobiles, known as the **"taxicab" army.** This occurs during the First Battle of the Marne. (Standard Oil Co. of New Jersey)

October—**Dr. O. E. Bransky,** at the Standard of Indiana Whiting laboratories, treats viscous oils and introduces the world's first medicinal white oil refined from American crude oil. It is put on the market under the name **"Stanolax."** (13)

October—Construction starts on the transcontinental Lincoln Highway. (54)

November 28—The Ohio Oil Company organizes The **Illinois Pipe Line Company,** which was subsequently dissolved in 1942. (50)

First compressor in **Canada** to be used for the extraction of gasoline from natural gas. It is installed by W. Dingman. (40)

Dr. G. O. Curme prepares ethylene by pyrolysis of ethane from natural gas. In 1920, **Carbide and Carbon Chemical Corp.** was chartered and immediately began to set the basis for its wide and deep entry into aliphatic chemicals by sponsoring a program at Mellon Institute under Dr. Curme. This resulted in a large oil-cracking installation at South Charleston, W. Va. (**Petrochemicals**) (40)

Clayton Act passed. It bans mergers which may tend to lessen competition or create a monopoly, also exclusive-dealing contracts and other forms of "tying arrangements." (NPN)

In **Czechoslovakia,** oil discovered at Gbely. (40)

E. DeGolyer becomes a petroleum consultant. In 1936 L. W. MacNaughton joined DeGolyer and on January 1, 1939 they organized a formal partnership of **DeGoyler and MacNaughton.** The firm of DeGoyler and MacNaughton incorporated on October 17, 1949. (50)

Federal Trade Commission Act passes creating FTC and giving it broad authority to define unfair methods of competition and declare them unlawful. (NPN)

The first rational formula developed for computing the **flow of fluids through pipe** under varying conditions makes a major contribution toward precision engineering of pipelines. (1961 Rockwell Adv.— Gas Age)

International Petroleum Company, a Standard Oil Company of New Jersey affiliate, is established to operate newly acquired properties in **Peru.** (50)

Missouri School of Mines adds course in petroleum production methods. (1)

W. W. Orcutt, a California operator, mentions oil **loss from storage** in open reservoirs that is 50 per cent of the most valuable fractions in five months. (64)

Pakistan—The Attock Oil Company, Limited, brings in what is considered the first commercial well. During the next year, **Khaur field** extended and oil discovered in the nearby Dhulian field. When Pakistan was formed in 1947, it obtained West Punjab and the Rawalpindi district wherein lie the oilfields. (10)

"High-pressure" gas lighting burners featured at the **San Francisco Exposition,** and an important feature of the piping system installed is that all joints on the gas main are welded, using oxy-acetylene method. (38)

Screen and preperforated pipe used in completing oil wells. (5)

V. R. Garfias lectures on courses in petroleum engineering at **Stanford University.** (1)

The work of **Stanton and Pannell** gives engineers a rational formula for designing pipelines for a wide range of fluids. Before this time they were dependent on the empirical formulas that were not always reliable. (40)

Value of **foraminifera** in oil geology, first recognized by **J. A. Udden.** (Geotimes)

The **Totumo field,** west of Lake Maracaibo, **Venezuela,** discovered. (45)

Well spacing recognized as a problem of production in the **Illinois** fields. (1)

The first ship traverses the Panama Canal. (Standard Oil Co. of New Jersey)

G. Bergstrom first successfully finds new ore deposits in **Sweden,** using alternating-current **equipotential mapping.** (7)

The Bureau of Mines starts studies of **fuels for aircraft** engines with a special study for the War Department. (48)

1915

January 15—A patent for the **Dubbs cracking process**—distillation under self-generated pressure—issued. (54)

February 11—**Oklahoma**—Legislature passes act embodying, among others, these three essential features: (a) a definition of waste, (b) the limitation of production from any common source of supply of oil, and (c) a standard for the proration of the over-all pool limitation among all the wells in the pool. The Corporation Commission empowered to enforce the act. (9)

February 21—**Thrall field,** Texas, discovered by Fritz Fuchs in his No. 1 Fee, making approximately 250 barrels per day from 808-899 feet gives the United States its first field producing from an altered igneous rock. (44)

March 30—**Oklahoma**—A comprehensive gas conservation act passed. It is the first elaborate gas conservation measure to be enacted by any state. It replaces the defective 1913 gas act. (9)

May 7—Lusitania sinking.

June 5—The first **proration order** issued by a state regulatory body and applying directly and indirectly "to the production of oil and not to the marketing of the same" is Order No. 920 of the Corporation Commission of Oklahoma. (9)

June 30—United States **Bureau of Mines** Director mentions in his annual report that A. G. Heggem, **a petroleum engineer,** is beginning a study of precautions to be taken to prevent and methods to extinguish **fires at wells** and tanks in Oklahoma, Texas and Louisiana. (1)

July—**Ventura Avenue field** discovered by State Consolidated Oil Company (now Tidewater) No. 1 Lloyd which blows out at 2558 feet. (68)

September 27—A tank car of **"casinghead"** gasoline explodes at Ardmore, Oklahoma, killing 43 and injuring 500. The product being shipped is a "wild" natural gasoline, then called "casinghead", derived from oil well casingheads. This disaster leads to many changes in the industry. (Natural Gas Producers Association)

September 29—**West Virginia Oil and Natural Gas Association** holds its first annual meeting at Parkersburg, West Virginia, having been formed earlier in the year. (57)

October—El Dorado field in Kansas discovered by Cities Service in small 600-foot well. H. L. Doherty had put faith in geology and leased 30,000 acres on such recommendations, the first wide-scale geological survey for oil in history. The find becomes the basis for the organization of Empire Gas and Fuel Company, one of the nation's pioneer successful experimenters in scientific exploration and large scale employers of petroleum geologists and engineers. (50)

October—**Elk Basin field** discovered in Wyoming by Jim Hurst et al. (68)

Oklahoma—**Air-repressuring** in Oklahoma first attempted in an old stripper well area in Rogers County, Oklahoma. (9)

The "Red Wheel Lorain **Oven Regulator**," developed in 1913 by an engineer of the **American Stove Company,** introduces the "time and temperature" cooking method to the gas industry and consumers. (38)

At Port Arthur, Texas, **Dr. A. M. McAfee** of Gulf Oil Corporation begins the long and costly experiments which lead to the commercial manufacture of aluminum chloride **Alchlor.** (50)

Dr. Hermann Aushiitz Kalmpfe, of Kiel, invents a device which provides an audible warning in the initial stages of deflection. (28)

The clock and timing pendulum, invented and patented by Taussig of U.G.I., is combined with hydraulic control of valves introducing "**automatic control**" gas making plants. (38)

The Petroleum and Natural Gas Division of the U. S. **Bureau of Mines** receives a separate appropriation of $25,000.00. (64)

The **Bureau of Mines** begins annual surveys of the quality of motor fuels sold in the United States. (48)

California Legislature creates a department of petroleum and gas in the State Mining Bureau, and a state oil and gas supervisor. (9)

The Legislature of the State of **California** acts to make it obligatory upon all operators of petroleum properties to comply with the rule established for setting casing to shut off upper water from oil and gas reservoirs. (1)

David White re-discovers and re-announces the principles of the "**carbon-ratio**" **theory** in accordance with the law of C. Hilt. (22)

Colorado—Act passed creating the office of the State Inspector of Oil, charged with inspecting fluid substances produced wholly or in part from petroleum. Law makes it unlawful for persons to permit flow of gas or oil from any well and provides for plugging, etc. (3)

The first natural gasoline plant in Texas built at **Electra** in north Texas by the Corsicana Petroleum Company. (44)

Sale of **gasoline** becomes largest single source of revenue for the Southwest petroleum industry. (5)

The State of **Louisiana** passes its first mineral leasing act, a statute superseded by another act in 1936. (31)

The **Oklahoma** Legislature passes a law that requires **ratable take** by purchasers of oil and gas, and includes a **market demand** provision for the production of oil. (60)

When the Russian supply is cut off, the manufacture of liquid **petroleum,** or "white medicinal oil," starts on a large scale in the United States. (37)

110

First University of Pittsburgh students to accept degrees as **petroleum engineers** are F. A. Johnson, C. Y. Chan and Baerin Y. Long. Degrees granted June 16. (1)

U. S. dominates **world oil production,** accounting for 65 per cent of the total, producing 777,000 bbl. of the 1,186,000 bbl. average daily world yield. (2)

Standard Oil Company of New Jersey reduces the work week of all employees from six 9-hour to six **8-hour days.** (50)

Fekette and Pekar make first practical gravity survey, that of the one-well Egbell pool in Czechoslovakia, using an Eotvos **torsion balance** on behalf of the D'Arcy Exploration Company. This survey is a striking success. (7)

The first successful **underground storage** of natural gas made at Welland, Ontario, Canada. (38)

University of California offers four-year complete undergraduate course in petroleum engineering. (1)

Discovery of new oil fields results in construction of 17 refineries in the Southwest. (5)

The Bureau of Mines makes a survey of all facets of the petroleum industry in **California.** (48)

The Carter Oil Company of West Virginia establishes a new division with headquarters at Tulsa, Oklahoma. (Standard Oil Co. of New Jersey)

"Standard" specifications for gas ranges prepared by the National Commercial Gas Association. (38)

Burrell, Seibert and Robertson first apply the distillation of **liquefied natural gas** to the determination of its constituents. (34)

German army uses **sound ranging** for big guns in World War I. (7)

1915-1920—The **Bureau of Mines** draws up operating regulations for the drilling and producing of oil and gas wells on all Government-leased land to insure protection from waste and from damage by infiltrating water and other causes. (48)

1916

April 15—**Service Pipe Line Company** incorporated in the State of Maine. Harry Sinclair is the organizer. Originally it was named Sinclair-Cudahy Pipe Line Company. (50)

April—The **British government** announces that it will take complete control of the output, exports, imports and distribution of motor spirits or gasoline throughout Great Britain and its possessions. (2)

May 10—**Texas Iron Works** incorporated in Goose Creek (now Baytown), Texas, for manufacture of oilfield supplies. (50)

June 6—Patent to **J. N. Wingett.** "Motor fuel" is produced by distilling a mixture of kerosene, toluene and nitric acid. (29)

111

June—First intensive **repressuring** project, where an entire field is included in the operation, started in Hamilton Corners Field, near Oil City, Venango County, Pennsylvania. (1)

September 2—One of the nation's important gas fields, the **Monroe field** in Northern Louisiana discovered by Progressive Oil and Gas Company in its Fisher No. 1. The well is started on June 28, 1916 and completed for two million cubic feet per day at 2300 feet and then deepened for oil in 1917 and abandoned at 2902 feet. (United Gas Corp.) (66)

September 15—First military tank used.

September—The Ohio Oil Company acquires **Mid-Kansas Oil and Gas Company.** (50)

November 18—Sinclair opens the **Garber field** in Oklahoma as the first important pool to be discovered far in advance of production purely on the basis of **geology.** (H. T. Galey, Historical Outline of the Petroleum Industry in Oklahoma and Kansas, 1930)

December 15—The first **casinghead gasoline association** organized. (40)

The **Bureau of Mines'** first nationwide survey of the quality of gasoline marketed in the United States published, covering the gasoline sold in the preceding year. (48)

The first **California** gasoline plant built by **Standard Oil Company of California** at Newhall. By the middle of 1917, California has a total of 31 plants. (40)

An improved process for breaking down heavy products to produce gasoline of superior quality developed, in which a **catalyst** is used for the first time. (39)

The first experimental **Cross cracking plant**—a 200 barrel unit—operated in Kansas. (48)

Revenue Act of 1916 removes percentage deduction and substitutes a provision granting oil and gas producers a "reasonable allowance" for **depletion** not to exceed actual cost of discovery, except on properties discovered before March 1913 which could be depleted at fair market value. (72)

Montana—Production is 45,000 bbl. of oil per day from the **Elk Basin.** Wells produce a greenish oil of 39 degrees gravity from upper Frontier sandstone at 1200 feet, and from the lower Frontier sandstone at 1400 feet. Many of these first wells flow as much as 1000 bbls per day. (10)

Carleton Ellis discovers a practical way of making alcohol from light petroleum distillates. (8B)

Shell Company of California establishes its production geologists as a separate group called **"exploitation engineers."** (1)

J. S. Cullinan, who is known as the dean of Texas oilmen, proposes **federal control** in the interest of conserving petroleum resources. (12)

First organized meeting of **petroleum geologists** is held in Norman, Oklahoma. (5)

H. P. Gott Manufacturing Company founded in Winfield, Kansas as manufacturers of double wall, thermo type water containers. (50)

Inhibitive-type **grease coatings** for pipe developed; the first application to gas lines made in 1918. (38)

The United States Congress enacts the first law authorizing federal **highway grants-in-aid** to the states. (62)

Roswell H. Johnson reports that he believes oil is carried as thin films around gas bubbles as the gas is forced from the fine to the coarse pores in the rock. (22)

The **U. S. S. Maumee**, a tanker, is the first large U. S. Naval vessel to be driven by Diesel engines. Fleet Admiral **Chester W. Nimitz**, USN, then a full lieutenant, is her executive officer and chief engineer when she is commissioned. (Petroleum Today)

The first pipeline in The **Middle East** completed as a 133-mile, 10-inch line in Iran. (40)

Sven Nordsen's valve patented. First lubricated plug valve. (50)

The use of porcelain enamel on gas appliances adds greatly to their appearance. (38)

"Principles of Gas & Oil Production" written by Roswell H. Johnson and L. G. Huntley. (1)

The **"Radiant-fire" gas heater** introduced by General Gas Light Company. (38)

Reed Roller Bit Company founded in Houston, Texas as manufacturers of Disc-type Roller Rock Bits. (50)

F. Wenner introduces apparent **resistivity measurements**, passing electrical current into the ground between two electrodes and measuring the potential difference between two other electrodes. (7)

Magnolia Petroleum Co. starts operating one of the first large **thermal cracking** installations consisting of two batteries of 10 stills each of the Burton process. (5)

Underground storage of natural **gas** in depleted gas fields first tried at Concord, N. Y., to serve peak demands of the City of Buffalo. (40)

Unitization first advocated—"to get the best results the operators should act in unison for the protection of their common sources of supply and for their mutual benefit." (U.S.B.M. TP 130)

University of West Virginia offers a course in oil and gas engineering, the **Colorado School of Mines** offers a course in petroleum geology, **Oklahoma A. & M. College** offers a course in petroleum technology, with C. K. Francis as instructor, and a short course of lectures dealing with petroleum geology and oil production; refining and marketing is announced by **Kendall College** (predecessor to University of Tulsa);

and in 1918 a course in petroleum chemistry is added at **Colorado School of Mines.** (1)

Wm. F. McMurray and James O. Lewis write a technical paper on the **prevention of waste.** (64)

The first **wheel-type ditcher** in the Mid-Continent region used. (40)

Consolidated Gas of Baltimore undertakes on a large scale the development of gas heating on its lines, and introduces a special secondary step rate of 35 cents per Mcf for large volume gas users. (38)

Sun Oil Company introduces the first all-petroleum emulsifying **cutting oil—SECO.** (50)

Secretary of the Navy Josephus Daniels establishes **Naval Fuel Board** with Cmdr. H. A. Stuart assigned to administer **Naval Petroleum Reserves.** (78)

In England, a single distillation plant comes into operation at **Shell Haven,** Essex, on the Thames Estuary. (Shell Refining Co., Ltd.) (45)

Howard Smith Company founded in Houston, Texas, as manufacturers of well screen and fittings. (50)

1917

February 10—The **American Association of Petroleum Geologists** organized as the Southwestern Association of Petroleum Geologists at Tulsa, Oklahoma. Its present name adopted in 1918. The objects of this Association are to advance the science of geology, especially as it relates to petroleum and natural gas; to promote the development of the technology of petroleum and natural gas and to encourage improvements in the methods of exploring for and exploiting these substances; to foster the spirit of scientific research throughout its membership; and to disseminate facts relating to the geology and technology of petroleum and natural gas. (57)

February 20—The **Texas** Legislature enacts Senate Bill No. 68 which declares pipe lines to be common carriers and places them under the supervision of the **Texas Railroad Commission.** The bill also provides that the Commission should promulgate and enforce regulations for the prevention of waste of oil or of dangerous practices. (44)

February—Texas legislature passes the **"Texas Company Bill"** that authorizes a company organized for the operation of oil pipelines to engage in the oil and gas producing business, but conditions its right to do so upon separately incorporating and operating oil pipelines. The oil company, however, is permitted to own all the stock of the pipeline company. (12)

March 21—**Ohio**—Provisions amended so as to provide the method of plugging abandoned oil and gas wells, whether or not drilled on coal lands. (3)

April 6—The United States enters World War I.

April 25—A committee of oil men with **A. C. Bedford,** president of

Standard Oil of N. J., chairman, appointed by **Council of National Defense.** Meeting in Washington with Rear Adm. Samuel McGowan, Chief of Bureau of Supplies and Accounts. Subject of conference is furnishing of gasoline supplies to meet naval coastal patrol needs. (2)

May 1—**Mexico**—The Constitution of this date, under Article 27 affirms that the direct ownership of subsoil deposits belong to the nation and that this right is "inalienable and imprescriptible." It provides that only Mexicans and Mexican corporations may acquire land or concessions to exploit minerals. Similar rights may be extended to foreigners who agree to consider themselves nationals in the exercise of their right and not to invoke the protection of their governments. (14)

June 13—**Phillips Petroleum Company** issued a Delaware charter. It is incorporated by two Phillips brothers who have been active independent operators for several years. (50)

June 21—**Humble Oil & Refining Company** formed by small group of independent oil producers to insure a steady supply for potential markets. (50)

June 26—The **Texas Pipe Line Company,** a wholly-owned subsidiary of The Texas Company, incorporated in Texas. (50)

July—The **Schulz Gasoline Company** incorporates and it is one of the earliest gasoline compression plants in Texas. (12)

August 10—**H. A. Garfield** named Fuel Administrator for the United States during World War I.

August 24—**Senate Public Lands Committee** favorably reports the bill to open for leasing all government lands withdrawn for oil, gas, coal and phosphate, and recommends its passage. (2)

September 7—Tyndall-Wyoming Oil Company completes its No. 1 Hogg as a small producer at a depth of 2802 feet and follows it on January 14, 1918, with No. 2 Hogg, which makes approximately 25 barrels per hour. This discovery of commercial production in the **West Columbia field** follows years of exploratory drilling dating back to 1901-1902 when Equitable Mining Company secured some minor production at shallow depths. (44)

October 4—**Montebello field** in the Baldwin Hills of Southern California discovered when Standard of California's Baldwin No. 3 comes in with a flow of 7500 B/D from a sand at 3755 feet. (50)

October 13—The **Mid-Continent Oil & Gas Association** formed in Tulsa, Oklahoma. (57)

November 13—The Texas Company absorbs **Producers Oil Company.** (50)

Hope Natural Gas Co. files patent suit against Oklahoma Natural Gas Co. involving use of absorption method in natural-gasoline plants. **Absorption method** in operation at a few Southwestern plants despite suit and when Saybolt patents invalidated, building of oil absorption plants stimulated. (5) (Natural Gas Processors Association)

Albania—Oil discovered at Drasciovitza near Valona. (23)

Sidney Powers is one of the first to suggest gravitative settling of the sediments overlying buried hills as a contributing factor in the **origin of anticlines.** (22)

Arkansas General Assembly passes its first conservation act, "An Act to Conserve the Natural Gas Resources of the State of Arkansas and to Appoint a Gas Inspector and for Other Purposes." (9)

The real beginning of **automatic heat** in homes takes place when two Americans, M. J. Hammers and C. L. Lewis produce an electrically-ignited, fully-automatic oil burner. (35)

New York City boasts of the first **gas heated battleship**—the first and only warship to be heated by gas. Consolidated Gas installs 43 pressed steel gas radiators to do the job, and as finishing touch cooks Thanksgiving Day dinner on gas range for 500 Navy recruits. (38)

Shell completes the discovery well in the **Bolivar Coastal Fields** in Venezuela. (45)

Union Oil Company of California successfully uses the **reverse method of circulation** in drilling in the Coalinga, Midway and other fields. (1)

Shell, in Eastern **Coalinga,** with permission of California State Oil and Gas Supervisor R. P. McLaughlin, drills a rotary well to the oil sand with no intermediate casing, the water sands being sealed off with mud. (1)

A drillable cast-iron plug screwed into the steel casing shoe used as a "float plug." (40)

J. H. Gardner is one of the first to explain the origin of some of the structures in the Mid-Continent area by vertical movements. (22)

"Touch a Button" **gas lighter** perfected. (51)

Schweydar makes the first **gravity survey** of a **salt dome,** the Hanigsen dome near Hanover in North Germany, using an Eotvos torsion balance. (7)

Dr. W. P. Haseman, head of the department of physics at the University of Oklahoma meets with **J. C. Karcher,** his former pupil, at the National Bureau of Standards at Washington. They discuss the possible use of reflection sound waves **(seismic waves)** to determine the location of oil field structures. (7)

The U. S. Bureau of Mines interests the Military in the idea of producing **helium** for aeronautical purposes. (64)

Montana—First legislation aimed at conservation of oil and gas enacted. (37)

Natural-gasoline plants in operation in Oklahoma number 234; 11 in Texas, 20 in Louisiana, and six in Kansas. (5)

Oklahoma—Act passed creating an oil and gas department under the jurisdiction and supervision of the Corporation Commission. (3)

E. W. Shaw proposes that **pendulum surveys** be used in search of salt domes in coastal Louisiana and Texas. (7)

Hughes Tool Company introduces a **reaming cone bit,** equipped with regular cones and a reamer built into the body of the bit. (50)

All private oil properties in **Russia** confiscated and the Russian fields held by the **Royal Dutch-Shell** group lost by expropriation. (50)

Secondary recovery operations inaugurated in the Southwest with gas repressuring in Nowata County, Oklahoma. (5)

Standard Oil Company of California adopts an **eight-hour day** for oil field workers. (50)

J. A. Gardner publishes results of tests on heat-reflecting properties of colors applied to oil and gas **storage tanks.** (1)

The United States Congress imposes the first **federal taxes** on motor vehicle owners—a three per cent levy on automobiles, motorcycles, trucks and buses. (62)

Hugo V. Boeckh, geologist, first calls attention to the fact that the **torsion balance** can locate domes or anticlines with light or heavy cores. (7)

Famous "**Trap-Shooter**" **well** completed in El Dorado Field, Kansas. Well flows 20,000 bbl. per day. (9)

In **Venezuela,** a 10-mile, eight-inch pipeline built on the Lake Maracaibo shore. (40)

Production and exports begin in **Venezuela.** (Review)

The fourth billion barrels of oil produced in the U. S. (40)

American Gas Light Journal changes name to **American Gas Engineering Journal.** (38)

Reed Roller Bit Company begins the manufacture of cross roller rock bits. (50)

The Bureau of Mines completes arrangements for the monthly compilation and publication of **refinery statistics.** (48)

In Massachusetts, the **Webster & Southbridge Gas and Electric Company** reports it installed 11 miles of three-inch pipe by "modern methods," using a small gasoline-engine-powered **trench digger,** a modern-type **pipe layer,** a trench **back-filler, tampers** to compress the backfill, and an **electric welder** to weld together the miles of pipe required. (38)

1918

January 1—The first **gasoline pipeline** placed in operation, a 40-mile, three-inch line from Salt Creek to Casper, Wyoming. (54)

January 3—**Texas Gulf Coast and Louisiana Oil and Producers Association** meet to consider first serious oil field strike. (44)

February 19—**Mexico,** by decree, declares oil an inalienable national resource and a tax is levied on oil lands and contracts made before May 1917. Titles to oil lands made into concessions. (Encyclo. W. Hist.)

March 1—**Wallace E. Pratt** appointed geologist for the Humble Oil & Refining Company. (12)

March 4—On the Martha Goff farm, Harrison County, West Virginia, the Hope Natural Gas Company's well No. 4190 drills to 7386 and brings the **"world's deepest well"** record to the U. S. Previously, the deepest well drilled had been drilled at Czuehon, Upper Silesia, Germany, total depth 7345 feet. (40)

March 12—The first pipeline between Drumright, Oklahoma and Chicago built by **Service Pipe Line Company.** (50)

April 20—**Infantas,** Colombia **field** discovered by Tropical Oil Company (Benedum and Trees) well flowing 5000 barrels per day from 2260 feet. (10) (70)

June 21—AFL grants charter to **International Association of Oil Field, Gas Well & Refinery Workers** which had been created on June 8 by 14 oil workers in St. Paul, Minn. (71)

June—The **American Gas Association** organized through consolidation of the American Gas Institute and the National Commercial Gas Association. (47)

July 16—The **New York State Oil Producers Association** formed at a meeting held in Bolivar, New York. (57)

July 22—Republic Production Company and Houston Oil Company of Texas discover the **Hull field** in Liberty County, Texas when their No. 3 Fee comes in for an initial production of 1000 barrels per day from a depth of 2352 feet. In 1922 they discover the overhang of this piercement type salt dome with their No. 55 Dolbear Fee. (44) (42)

July 29—"Fowlers Folly" completed for an initial production of 2200 barrels per day from a depth of 1739 feet by Fowler Farm Oil Company to touch off the **Burkburnett townsite** boom. (44)

August 27—Mark L. Requa, Director General of the Oil Division, U. S. Fuel Administration, issues his famous **"gasless Sunday"** request. It is not an order and is aimed only East of the Mississippi. Raises tumult as to why people West of Mississippi are not asked to join. (2)

August—Gladstone Oil & Refining Company well completed for 60 barrels daily at 2272-84 feet as the discovery of the **Cement** oil **field** in Oklahoma. (Mid-Continent Oil Scouts & Landmen's Association)

August—Oil Trade Journal reports stabilization of **crude oil prices** for balance of World War I. (2)

September 8—Total savings from seven **"gasless Sundays"** estimated at 60,000,000 gallons. (2)

September 9—The U. S. Senate adopts a resolution offered by Senator Lodge calling upon the Fuel Administration for data as to production, consumption, exploration and reserve supply of gasoline. Resolution offered to get at the reason for the **"gasless Sundays."** (2)

September 14—**Barbers Hill field** in Chambers County, Texas proven for good production by United Petroleum Company's No. 1 Fisher well making 70 barrels per day from a depth of 2142 feet. **Humble** and Gulf had found the first oil in April 1916 when their No. 4 Chambers County Agricultural had come in for 40 barrels at 1571 feet. Humphreys Corporation No. 2 Ilfrey completed February 26, 1930 for 1062 barrels from a depth of 5087, after drilling through 878 feet of salt overhang. **Pattillo Higgins,** of Spindletop fame, selected this dome as his second prospect and drilled there in 1902 without success. (44) (42)

September 23—Roxana Petroleum Company's (**Shell Oil Co.**) Wood River, Illinois refinery goes on stream.

Nov. 4—H. F. Wilcox Oil and Gas Company organized in Tulsa. Company name changed to **Wilcox Oil Company** Aug. 16, 1944, when its founder disposed of his holdings and retired. (50)

November 11—World War I Armistice signed and need for oil for the military ceases. (2)

December 9—**Lord Curzon,** in London at a banquet for members of the Inter-Allied Petroleum Council says: "American oil, and hardly any other, made up that 'wave of petroleum' on which the war was won." (2)

December 9—Natural gas discovered in the northern part of Potter County, Texas, more than one hundred miles in advance of production, in what later became the renowned **Panhandle field. Amarillo Oil Company,** organized by local capital, had employed **Charles N. Gould** in 1916 to map and report on the **Amarillo fold** which he had first observed in 1903; his map, when completed, showed a large dome several miles in diameter and with considerable uplift and, on the basis of it, leases were taken and the No. 1 Masterson well drilled which was completed for 10 million cubic feet per day at 2246 feet. (44) (Covered Wagon Geologist, by Charles N. Gould, University of Oklahoma Press, 1959)

Following authorization by Congress, the first **air mail** route is established between New York and Washington by way of Philadelphia. (35)

Gallacher, in Johannesburg, invents a **borehole surveying** device designed to survey both the deviation from the vertical and from the azimuth, to be read direct from the instrument on withdrawal, without surface calculations. (28)

Charcoal absorption process developed by George Oberfell (former vice-president Phillips Petroleum Co.) and Dr. George Burrell (former president, Burrell Inc.) as a result of gas mask work in World War I. (Natural Gas Processors Association)

Colombia—Mike Benedum and Joe Trees, owners of the Tropical Oil Company, drill in the midst of a primeval jungle, and at 80 feet a 50-barrel-a-day flow starts. On April 20, 1918, the well comes in flowing 5000 barrels a day from 2260 feet. Before the year was over they have two more wells—both better than the first. Benedum and Trees then deal with Jersey leaders, and a Jersey affiliate takes over Tropical stock valued at $33 million. (10)

Core drill brought to Southwest for evaluation of surface structures. (5)

Revenue Act of 1918 authorizes producers to base the "reasonable allowance" either on the discovery cost or the fair market value of the property in figuring depletion. In 1921 it was provided deduction to depletion could not exceed 100 per cent of the producers profit from each property, and in 1924 this limit was reduced further to 50 per cent, a provision which remains in effect. (72)

Standard Oil Company of New Jersey installs the plan of employee representation conceived by Clarence J. Hicks, consultant on labor relations. It also installs a program of annuities and benefits. (50)

Commercial production of helium starts at Fort Worth, Texas under the direction of George A. Burrell and Richard B. Moore. (47)

Hopper Machine Works, Inc., founded as Hopper Machine Works in Oil Center, California as manufacturers of self-propelled oil well servicing hoists. (50)

The International Petroleum Register first published. (50)

"The Lamp," a magazine for Standard Oil Company of New Jersey employees, publishes its first issue. (50)

Louisiana—Act passed authorizing limitations on allowables for natural gas wells. (9)

Solidified nitroglycerine being molded into torpedoes of different sizes to cope with different well conditions. (1)

Geologists in Texas recommend drilling offshore, when there are indications of oil structures. (5)

A. R. Segelhorst designs and operates a long-stroke, hydraulic pump on a lease of the Standard Oil Company of California in the Montebello oil field. (1)

Standard Oil Company of New York acquires a 45 per cent non-voting stock interest in Magnolia Petroleum Company, a Texas joint stock association and adds 25 per cent stock interest in next two years. (50)

American Tank Company produces a steel tank with staves or sheets approximately 60 inches wide and eight feet high, which design is the forerunner of our present A.P.I. bolted tanks and another type of bolted steel lease tank with countersunk bolthead introduced by a Mr. Walsh, of the Superior Tank Company. (1)

120

Mid-Continent and Gulf refiners ordered by the War Department to produce **toluene, benzene,** and other products needed for explosives. First commercial output of toluene produced in April. (5)

Young Engine Company starts adapting higher speed, multi-cylinder engines to cable-tool drilling. (1)

In **Yugoslavia,** the first natural gas field discovered. (64)

The Bureau of Mines prepares a map and report showing gasoline storage facilities in the United States for the Signal Corps. (48)

The Atlantic Refining Company develops the first **combat aviation gasoline.** (50)

Bell Oil & Gas Co. founded in Tulsa, Okla., by Samuel I. Lubell. (50)

Pittsburgh Pipe and Coupling Company starts business. (50)

The Gilliam Well Tool and Supply Company, Inc., founded by Robert Newton Poindexter. This company is now known as the **Superior Iron Works** and **Supply Company,** Inc. (50)

1918-1919—Introduction of **diamond core-drill** by Shell's Van der Gracht. (6)

1919

January 10—**Elk Hills field** in Kern County, California, discovered by Standard of California's No. 1 "Hay" well at 2500 feet on faulted anticlines "en echelon." (74)

February 25—The first **state tax on gasoline** goes into effect in Oregon, a one-cent tax for use in road construction and maintenance. (54)

February—The United States Congress increases **excise taxes** on automobiles, motorcycles and buses to five per cent and imposes new five per cent tax on parts and accessories and tires and tubes. (62)

March 14—The **American Petroleum Institute** organized with headquarters in New York City, and incorporates in the District of Columbia. (62)

March 26—The **American Petroleum Institute** becomes a tangible organization at a session of its directors, former members of the **National Petroleum War Service Committee,** at the Blackstone Hotel in Chicago. T. A. O'Donnell, of Los Angeles, elected president. (2)

March 31—**Texas** Legislature enacts Statute requiring the conservation of oil and gas, forbidding waste, and giving the Railroad Commission jurisdiction. Acts 36th Leg., Reg. Sess., 1919, C.155 (58)

May 15—All **World War I rules,** regulations and orders governing licensed units in the oil and natural gas industries have been vacated and set aside by Fuel Administrator Garfield. (2)

May 24—The first organizational meeting of the **Texas Mid-Continent Oil and Gas Association** held in the Chamber of Commerce Building,

Fort Worth, Texas, and on May 30th, it becomes known as **Texas-Louisiana Division** of Mid-Continent Oil and Gas Association. (57)

May 31—**Crescent Petroleum Corporation** incorporated as Shaffer Oil and Refining Company. Name changed to Crescent Petroleum Corporation on April 16, 1958. (50)

June 5—**Hewitt,** Oklahoma **field** discovered by The Texas Company No. 1 A. E. Denny producing 410 barrels per day at 2100-34 feet. (66)

June 18—The first well to bring definite indications of natural gas in **Costa Rica,** drilled on the eastern flank of the Talamanca mountain range by Costa Rica Oil Co. (45)

July 1—The **Mid-Continent Oil and Gas Association, Kansas-Oklahoma Division** formed. (57)

September 23—**Sinclair Oil Company** organized. (50)

October 2—**Skelly Oil Company** incorporated at Tulsa, Okla., with W. G. Skelly, founder, as president. (50)

October—**Murphy Oil Company of Pennsylvania** organized to incorporate oil-producing properties of estate of Michael Murphy, former Pure Oil Company president. (50)

October—Union Oil Company discovers the **Santa Fe Springs,** California **field** with its No. 3 Meyer making 3000 barrels per day at 4595 feet. Water breaks in and after recompletion well makes only 150 barrels per day. (66)

Fall—**Richfield,** California **field** discovered by 2000 barrel well at 2900 feet. (66)

November 19—Standard Oil Company (Indiana) purchases controlling interest in **Dixie Oil Company,** producing subsidiary. (50)

December 19—First **Colombian** law on petroleum enacted as Law No. 120. (45)

December 31—**Service Pipe Line Company** acquires the properties of Sinclair Gulf Pipe Line Company and War Pipe Lines Company. (50)

Gulf Coast Machine Shop founded in Beaumont, for manufacture of wellhead equipment. (50)

Baash Ross Tool Company formed by L. F. Baash, H. C. Ross and A. F. Brown in Brea, California. (50)

The Asphalt Institute organized as The Asphalt Association. (57)

Karl Kegel, a mining engineer of Freiberg in Saxony, invents an ingenious floating plunger plumb-bob device for **borehole surveying.** (28)

In Pittsburgh, the **Bureau of Mines** opens its new $1 million laboratories, designed to conduct fuel investigations. (38)

U. S. **Bureau of Mines** establishes petroleum experimental station at Bartlesville, Oklahoma. (5)

The first planned geological survey of Western **Canada** started under the direction of an English geologist, Dr. T. O. Bosworth. On his recommendation, Imperial Oil Company Ltd., drilled near Fort Norman, just below the Arctic circle. (63)

The Bureau of Mines begins publication of statistics on **carbon black.** (48)

Bureau of Mines studies in the Cushing, Oklahoma, field lead to the use of **cementing** to exclude water and production increases directly by several thousand barrels daily. (48)

Erle Halliburton introduces **cementing** with the two-plug method into the Mid-Continent area in the Burkburnett field of North Texas. There is no appreciable demand until after a 1920 blowout of a **W. G. Skelly** well in Hewitt field of southern Oklahoma. The well is successfully killed with 250 sacks of cement. (40)

The first plant for recovering natural gasoline by the **charcoal absorption process** built at Lewis Run, Pa., on the property of the United Natural Gas Company. (47)

First application of Jan Koster's (Holland Geological Survey) **double barrel core drill** for use in loosely consolidated formations, in Santa Fe Springs by Shell Oil Company of California. (1)

A diamond coring rig used at Sayre, Oklahoma. (5)

Gulf Oil Corporation makes the first attempt at **metering crude** at its old Crosby Station in Harris County, Texas. The meter is a six-inch turbine that was built in Gulf's shops at Beaumont, Texas. Gulf's next attempt is in 1924 in the Smackover Field of Union County, Arkansas, when two eight-inch venturi meters are installed. (50)

Humble is one of the first companies to use **electricity for pumping and treating** when they introduce it in the **Goose Creek field.** They also introduce it to West Columbia in 1921. (12)

Evaporation of gasoline from crude oil on leases amounts to 3 million barrels in the Midcontinent area alone. (48)

The first large-scale **underground gas storage** field developed in Kentucky, the Menifee field, by Central Kentucky Natural Gas Company. (38)

The first practical oil burner for modern, **central home heating** developed. (54)

Standard Oil Company of New Jersey buys a 50 per cent interest in **Humble Oil & Refining Company.** (50)

Indiana creates a Department of Conservation. (3)

Esther Richards, under **E. T. Dumble** of the Rio Bravo Oil Company, starts work in **micro-paleontology.** Humble Oil & Refining Company initiates the use of **micro-paleontology** as an aid in finding oil, at its Ft. Worth headquarters under **Alva C. Ellisor.** (12)

M. R. Daly regards fissures caused by faulting and jointing of the

123

rocks as of considerable importance in the **migration and accumulation of oil and gas.** (22)

Mintrop, a prominent European scientist, applies for a patent in Germany covering the use of **refraction profiling** for locating the depth and type of subsurface formations. (40)

Possibly the earliest of reliable U. S. **natural gas reserves estimate** made by geologist E. W. Shaw who places them at 15 trillion cubic feet. (47)

The first West Texas refinery built in El Paso, Texas by the **Rio Grande Oil Company.** (44)

The Russian petroleum industry brought under complete Soviet government control and **Russia's** share of foreign production reaches a low of 9.6 per cent in 1921, rising slightly to 11.7 per cent in 1922. (2)

Practical **seismic exploration** for the determination of geologic structures starts in a small way in Europe. (33)

Dr. Ralph Arnold, of the U. S. Treasury Department, calls oil men together in Washington, D. C., to assist in formulation of methods for establishing an **oil and gas tax structure.** (40)

C. E. Van Orstrand makes his first attempt to correlate **temperature** with structure in Oklahoma, working in cooperation with Dr. Goerge C. Matson, Chief Geologist of the **Gypsy Oil Company.** (1)

Hughes Tool Company introduces the first heat-treated alloy steel **tool joint.** (50)

United States companies receive their first **Venezuelan concessions** in Zulia State. (45)

The **Texas Railroad Commission** begins organization work on the Oil and Gas Division June 18th; issues its first **Shut Down Order** July 11th (Burkburnett area) and its first **Proration Order** July 18th (Northwest extension to Burkburnett); issues first rules relative to field development July 26th and additional rules, including famous **Rule 37** (dealing with spacing of wells) adopted November 26th; permit No. 1 as an exception to Rule 37 granted December 9th. The Commission had previously been given jurisdiction over pipe lines when they were declared Common Carriers in 1917, and later (in 1920) given jurisdiction over gas pipe lines and utilities. (44) One of the two main purposes for the spacing rule is to reduce fire hazards; the other is to prevent danger of water percolation into oil stratum from nearby wells. (58)

The Legislatue of the State of **New York** passes appropriate measures to permit legal **injection of water** into oil reservoirs; revised 1879 law. (water flooding) (1)

W-K-M Manufacturing Company, Inc., founded as W-K-M Company, Inc., in Houston, Texas as manufacturers of rotary slips, and pipeline valves of which the company has the original patents. (50)

Wyoming—First and only statute which specifically defines waste enacted in Wyoming. (3)

Dr. E. T. Dumble, pioneer petroleum scientist, hires **John R. Suman,** probably the first petroleum geological engineer, as assistant to the general manager of **Rio Bravo Oil Company,** a Southern Pacific Railroad subsidiary. (1)

England's first producing oil well completed at Hardstoft, Derbyshire. (45)

The **Esso Research and Engineering Company** organized. (Standard Oil Co. of New Jersey)

"Largest gas well in the world" (at this time) reported brought in 25 miles north of Amarillo in Potter County, Texas. Expert test reports flow of **71 million cubic feet** per day. (38)

Consolidated Gas Company of New York reports a **record sendout for any gas company** in the world—160,327,000 cubic feet in one day— during zero weather. (38)

The first **roller cutter rotary reamer** built by Reed Roller Bit Company. (50)

The Bureau of Mines begins semi-annual surveys of the quality of motor fuels sold in the United States in order that **seasonal variations** can be determined. (48)

The **"simplex" prepared joint** for cast iron pipe developed by American Cast Iron Pipe Company. (38)

The five billionth barrel of oil produced in the U. S. (40)

1920

January 1—The first report on United States **refineries and their capacities** made by the Bureau of Mines. (48)

January 27—The name of Service Pipe Line Company changed to **Sinclair Pipe Line Company.** (50)

February 8—The first **Holmes-Manley thermal cracking** units go into operation at The Texas Company's Port Arthur, Texas refinery. (50)

February 25—The **Oil Land Leasing Bill** enacted. It gives the Secretary of the Interior the right to make leases with private companies and individuals on lands previously withdrawn from oil development. However, the Naval Oil Reserves remain under the aegis of the Secretary of the Navy. (2)

February 28—The first concession in **Bolivia** granted in favor of Richmond, Levering and Company of New York. (45)

February—**Sunray Mid-Continent Oil Company** formed as Sunray Oil Company. Mergers: Superior of Oklahoma, 1943; Darby Petroleum Co., 1944; Transwestern Oil Co., 1946; Barnsdall Oil Co., 1950; Mid-

Continent Petroleum Corporation, 1955. Wholly owned subsidiaries, Mid-Continent Pipeline Co., and Suntide Pipeline Co. (50)

April 9—Adoption of the **Dyer resolution** directing the Federal Trade Commission to start another investigation of the oil industry. (2)

May 7—**Halliburton Company** organized as Halliburton Oil Well Cementing Company at Wilson, Oklahoma, by Erle Halliburton and Eddie Steen, succeeding the New Method Oil Cementing Company formed earlier during the Burkburnett boom in Texas. (50)

May 12—The American ambassador to London, John W. Davis, presents a note to Lord Curzon, British Foreign Secretary, protesting against a **policy of exclusion** in Mesopotamia, specifically the San Remo Agreement. (2)

May 13—**Burbank field** discovered in Oklahoma by Marland Oil Company and Roxana Petroleum Company; well made 700 barrels at 2949-2967 feet. (Mid-Continent Oil Scouts and Landmen's Association)

June 4—Act of Congress grants Secretary of Navy broad powers to use his own discretion in developing, operating, or leasing parts of **Naval Petroleum Reserves** or selling oil or gas products from them in exchange for petroleum products needed by the navy. (78)

June 12—**Texas** Legislature declares the production and sale of natural gas to be a public utility and gives the Railroad Commission jurisdiction. ("**Cox Gas Law**") Acts 36th Leg., 3. C.S., 1920, C.14. (58)

June 18—First **Permian Basin** oil discovered when Underwriters Producing Company's No. 1 Abrams well comes in as a small producer at Westbrook in Mitchell County, Texas on a lease presently owned by Standard Oil Company of Texas. (Colorado City (Texas) Record)

July 20—The W. H. Abrams Well No. 1, one of the most prolific wells in petroleum history, brought in at **West Columbia,** Texas by The Texas Company. (50)

August 3—**Huntington Beach,** California field discovered by Standard Oil Company's "A" 1 Huntington which shows for a producer in May but sands up and later completes for 1800 barrels at 2700 feet. (66) (28th Annual Rept. State Oil & Gas Supervisor)

August 20—**Cameron Iron Works, Inc.,** founded in Houston, Texas as manufacturers of fishing tools, mud pump repair parts, fishtail bits and drill collars, and blowout preventers. (50)

October 29—The American Petroleum Institute publishes the first issue of what is now the **Statistical Bulletin.** (62)

November 5—**Asiatic Petroleum Corporation** incorporated in Delaware. It is a subsidiary of the Royal Dutch Shell Group. (50)

November 25—Col. A. E. Humphreys No. 1 Rogers well completed for 150 barrels per day at 3060 feet as the discovery well of Woodbine production at **Mexia,** Texas and results in the Mexia Fault Line play. (44)

November—Speaking at the first annual meeting of the API, M. L. Requa, V. P. of the Sinclair Consolidated Oil Corporation and formerly director general, Oil Division, U. S. Fuel Administration cites the need for a **voluntary oil conservation policy.** (2)

November—Speaking at the first annual meeting of the API, Admiral W. S. Benson, Chairman, U. S. Shipping Board, cites that 75% of the **U. S. Navy** is oil-burning. (2)

December 17—A plea for **nationalization** of oil for future protection of American interests on the sea made by Secretary **Josephus Daniels,** speaking in Washington, at an annual dinner for the American Society of Naval Engineers. (2)

The Dallas, Texas, office of the U. S. **Bureau of Mines** opens. (64)

Associated Oil—Practice introduced of **cementing shoe** of surface conductor strings. (1)

Occidental Petroleum Corporation formed in Los Angeles, Calif. (50)

Creole Petroleum Corporation organized. Standard Oil Company (New Jersey) obtains a major interest in Creole Petroleum in 1928. (50)

International Petroleum Company buys Tropical Oil Company and its producing rights in the **De Mares Concession** in **Colombia.** (Standard Oil Co. New Jersey)

The **Democratic platform** is very positive in its urgings to American citizens to acquire and develop oil properties in foreign lands. (32)

Dresser-Ideco Company founded as International Derrick and Equipment Company in Columbus, Ohio, as manufacturers of Galvanized steel derricks, drilling and production equipment, crown blocks, traveling blocks, safety platforms and sheaves. (50)

The first use of the term **"petroleum engineer"** by a large company made when **E. G. Wagy** appointed petroleum engineer of Standard Oil Co. of California. (1)

According to R. Van A. Mills, the Smith-Dunn Company, near Marietta, Ohio, first successfully maintains fire in a well in October. The fire burns for 24 hours, and the rate of production from the well doubles. (**Fireflood**) (1)

City of Omaha, Nebraska, takes over the city's gas company; the plant makes **gas from corncobs,** said to be good after purification. (38)

Gulf Oil Corporation makes the first attempt at **automatic tank gauges** with the installation of four sets of pneumercators at its Sour Lake Station, Texas. These are remote reading. These devices are air operated and are usually used for water depth sounding on ships. (50)

Geochemical prospecting introduced in the Gulf Coast area. (5)

Kansas—Gas "shooting" act of 1905 amended to permit "acidizing." (60)

In **Kuwait, Major Frank Holmes** opens negotiations for concessions,

127

and simultaneously opens negotiations with the sheiks of Bahrein and King of Saudi Arabia. In the early 20's he opens vigorous campaigns to dispose of these concessions. He was turned down by Anglo-Persian, Royal Dutch-Shell, and Standard of New Jersey. In 1927, he succeeded in selling Gulf a concession covering Kuwait and Bahrein (but tenuous title was never validated for Saudi Arabia). Gulf assigned half its interest in the concession on Bahrein to Standard of California for obligation to drill. (55)

Louisiana—Act passed providing for **proportionate marketing** of petroleum during period of overproduction. (9)

Combination **meter-regulator** introduced. (38)

J. Ray McDermott & Co., Inc., founded as a partnership, J. Ray McDermott & Co. In 1932 it was incorporated in Texas as J. Ray McDermott & Co., Inc., and was succeeded by a Delaware corporation of the same name on April 15, 1946. (50)

President **Carranza,** of **Mexico,** consents to the issuance of provisional drilling permits, pending the introduction of an organic petroleum law, as the production crisis (invasion of salt water) forces his action. (2)

The Natural Gasoline Association of America formed. (40)

The **Norman Wells field** in the Northwest Territories discovered by Imperial Oil Company. (66)

Walter O'Bannon Company founded in Tulsa, Oklahoma as manufacturers of sucker rod pumps. (50)

"Make and Break" **rotary tables** developed to promote safety and save time in making trips. (Oil Well Supply Company)

The **chain-driven sand reel** introduced by Parkersburg Rig & Reel Company. (1)

San Remo Oil Agreement signed between Britain and France on April 24 and 25. Britain assigned protective mandate over Palestine and Mesopotamia, and France granted mandate over Syria and Lebanon. France awarded 25 per cent interest in Mesopotamia petroleum, and French are to permit construction of two pipelines from Mesopotamia through French-mandated territories to the Mediterranean. (8B)

Sargent Engineering Corporation organized at Huntington Park, California to manufacture various oilfield supplies. (50)

Refiners freed of gravity in speeding their dewaxing operations. Through the cooperation of **Max B. Miller** and **P. T. Sharples** the **centrifugal separator** comes out of the nation's creameries to aid in removing wax from oil more efficiently. (40)

Venezuela enacts its first Hydrocarbon Law. (45)

First **acetylene welding** on pipelines performed by Noah E. Wagner, Prairie Pipe Line Co., on 15-mile, eight-inch line from Bartlesville to Ramona, Okla. (5)

Proposal made by Senator Phelan of California to organize a government-supported **nationalized oil company,** by introduction of bill in Congress to form "United States Corporation." Proposal thwarted when President Wilson's Secretary of State, Bainbridge Colby, points out serious objections to such a measure. (2)

Natural gas for drilling successfully used near Three Rivers, Texas. (38)

Odorless Incinerator Company, Philadelphia, demonstrates new "garbage disposer"; device, lined with firebrick, has positive draft up flue, uses temperatures of 1800 F. Positively odorless. (38)

Conrad Schlumberger makes public for the first time his studies of **electrical exploration** in his doctoral thesis, "Etude sur la Prospection Electrique du Sous-Sol," presented at the University of Paris. He utilizes it for tectonic studies whereas others are using it only in the search for metals. (50)

Eastern and General Syndicate, Ltd., formed with Major Frank Holmes as a free lance agent. (80)

Spain, through the Geological Institute, investigates and carries out prospecting and drilling for oil. (64)

Ute Oil Company erects plant at Debeque, Colorado, for **shale oil extraction.** Process developed by **G. W. Wallace,** superintendent of St. Clair County Gas & Electric Company of Illinois. (38)

Vertical casting process for cast iron pipe announced by **Cast Iron Pipe Bureau.** (38)

There are 9,239,161 motor vehicle registrations in the United States. (11)

1921

January 1—**Wilson Supply Company** founded in Houston, Texas, as wholesale and retail distributor of oil well drilling and production equipment and supplies. (50)

January 10—**Busey-Mitchell No. 1 Armstrong** completed for 3000 barrels, or more, per day from about 2000 feet to open up **El Dorado,** the first **oil field** for **Arkansas.** (10)

January 17—Oil supplies from U. S. to any country discriminating against American oil interests could be cut off at the discretion of the President under a bill introduced by Senator Phelan (Dem., California). Persons or firms violating a prohibitory order would be subject to fines of $10,000. (2)

January—**Royalite Oil Co. Ltd.** formed. (63)

February 9—Standard Oil Company of Indiana acquires a half interest in the Sinclair Pipe Line Company (**Service Pipe Line Company**) (50)

April 4—**Kirby Petroleum Company,** a Delaware corporation, organized to succeed Bass Petroleum Corp. Most assets sold to Continental Oil Company in 1954, and the Delaware corporation liquidated in 1955, after non-producing assets had been spun off onto a new Delaware corporation, Kirby Oil and Gas Company, which operated under that name until 1957. Present Kirby Petroleum Co., a Nevada corporation, formed under name of Kirby VenSyn Petroleum Company. In 1957 VenSyn part of name dropped. Merger of Feb. 7 formed present company with assets of Kirby Oil and Gas Company, Venezuela Syndicate, Inc., Murchison Trusts, George J. Greer Trustee, and Montex Exploration Company being combined. In December, 1957, the company acquired all assets of Toklan Oil Corporation. On Dec. 20, 1962, the company acquired assets of Hanlon-Boyle, Inc.   (50)

April 21—A "white paper" on oil situation in form of a note which **Lord Curzon** sends to British Ambassador in Washington, contains memorandum compiled by British Petroleum Department giving statistics on oil resources in all British Empire and showing extremely small oil production and absence of any general policy for exclusion of foreigners from oil-producing areas. (2)

April 22—Association of Natural Gasoline Manufacturers organized in Tulsa, Oklahoma. The name subsequently changed to Natural Gasoline Association of American on November 1, 1927 and to **Natural Gas Processors Association** on July 1, 1961. (57)

April 23—National Supply Co. acquires the Chatillon dynamometer and adapts it to well weighing—which represents probably the first application of the **dynamometer** for determining well loads. (1)

April—**Haynesville field** discovered in Louisiana. (67)

May 5—First **oil field** in **Panhandle** area of Texas discovered with flow of 190 barrels per day at 3052 feet, by Gulf Oil Corp.'s No. 2 S. B. Burnett. (44)

May 31—By executive order, President Harding turns over administration of **Naval Petroleum Reserves** to Secretary of Interior (Albert B. Fall). This was later considered one prelude to **Teapot Dome oil scandal.** (78)

May—First **Alchlor batch** still placed in operation by Gulf at Port Arthur refinery. It is a pioneer catalytic cracking process. (50)

June 23—**Long Beach field** discovered in California by Shell Oil Company in its Alamitos Land Company No. 1 on **Signal Hill** at a depth of 3114 feet. The field has produced more oil per acre than any field in the world. (50) (68)

June 29—**Tonkawa field,** Oklahoma, discovered by Marland Refining Company and Cosden Oil & Gas Company well No. 1 completed for 1000 barrels at 2660 feet. (66)

July 1—**John R. Suman's** book, **Petroleum Production Methods,** published by Gulf Publishing Company, Houston, Texas, to bring together in a single volume important information of value to practical oilmen, now found only in the various transactions of the technical societies. (50)

July 12—**President Harding** writes to Chairman Fordney of the House Ways and Means Committee expressing his absolute disapproval of taxes on oil and crude petroleum imposed under general tariff bill. (2)

July—**Standard Oil Company** (Indiana) purchases controlling interest in Midwest Refining Co., giving Standard additional large crude reserves and refineries in Wyoming and Utah. (50)

August—In **Colombia,** the first refinery put on stream at Barrancabermeja with daily capacity of 37,500 barrels. (45)

September—**T. E. Swigart** and **C. R. Bopp** begin experiments to ascertain the **effect of back pressure** on the production of oil and gas from pumping wells in Osage, Oklahoma. (1)

Nov. 1—The Electra Welding Co. organized in Bartlesville, Oklahoma. Firm name subsequently changed to Welding Engineering Company and still later to **H. C. Price Co.** (50)

December 9—Antiknock properties of **tetraethyl lead** discovered by **Charles F. Kettering** and **Thomas Midgely, Jr.,** after five years of extensive research. (Ethyl Corporation)

December—The API, working with U. S. Bureau of Mines and U. S. Bureau of Standards, recommend that only the scale based on the modulus 141.5 be used in the petroleum industry, and that it be known as the **"API Scale."** From this date on, official and standard designation has been in degrees. (1)

Standard of Jersey's chemical engineering consultant, **W. K. Lewis,** sets up the first of his so-called **bubble towers** at Bayway. (8B)

The **California** Legislature practically duplicates the Federal Mineral Leasing Act of 1920. (31)

The U. S. Government begins long series of protests against British-French policy; urges American oil companies to get **Middle East concessions.** (40)

"Deep Well Drilling" written by Walter Jeffery. (1)

Socony-General applies term **"petroleum engineer"** to head-office men who supervise **"resident geologists."** (1)

Lubrikup Company, Inc., founded as Williamsport Development Company in Williamsport, Pennsylvania as manufacturers of composition valve cups. (50)

Iowa District Gas Association, in conjunction with the engineering department of the Iowa State College, conducts the first short course for **gas metermen.** (38)

Michigan creates a Department of Conservation, consisting of seven members. (9)

Montana passes law requiring that location and manner of plugging an oil or gas well be filed. (3)

131

New Mexico—Attention focused on the northwest section of the state by the discovery of gas on the McElms structure across the line in Colorado. (10)

Homer Craig, while employed by the Huasteca Petroleum Company in Mexico, develops a **high-pressure oil saver** which is used to complete the larger oil producers in the Tampico area of Mexico. (1)

Ben K. Stroud makes up a mud for a Louisiana well using **iron oxide.** He gets the **added mud weight** he needs and iron oxide is one of the materials used to weight mud for the next 15 years. (40)

The U. S. Geological Survey and the American Association of Petroleum Geologists classify **reserves** in the United States for the first time as proved and possible. (64)

The **Rocky Mountain Oil and Gas Association** organized. It became dormant during the war but was reactivated in 1945. (57)

The first commercial production of steel pipe having **electrically welded seams.** (38)

Dr. J. C. Karcher and **Dr. W. P. Haseman** conduct first successful **seismic reflections** in Oklahoma. (5)

Standard Oil Company of New Jersey organizes **Standard Oil Company of Venezuela.** (50)

Stanford University organizes Petroleum Engineering department. (1)

Southwestern producers demand a **tariff on oil** to curtail the flood of crude from Mexico. (5)

President Gomez of **Venezuela** calls on the cooperation of U. S. companies to help draw a Petroleum Law acceptable to all. (45)

The Legislature of the state of Pennsylvania passes appropriate measures to permit legal **injection of water** into oil reservoirs. (1)

Principal **Wyoming** conservation statute, under which industry now operates, enacted. (3)

Richard Ambronn carries out **radioactivity measurements** on a series of samples from an oil well at Celle, Hanover, Germany. (1)

American Gas Engineering Journal changes name to **American Gas Journal.** (38)

Atlantic Refining Company and its subsidiary, Atlantic Oil Producing Company, first hire **petroleum engineers** at Smackover field in Arkansas to work on oil field problems, such as separation of water from crude oil. (1)

Development of first specifications and test methods by NGPA leads to considerably greater safety in producing and shipping products of desired quality. Also leads to dropping the old name "casinghead" and adoption of the name **"natural gasoline."** (Natural Gas Processors Association)

Nevada enacts law to protect oil-bearing and fresh water strata and to insure plugging wells upon abandonment. **(Conservation legislation)** (60)

1922

February 8—**Shell Union Oil Corporation** organized under Delaware law as a holding company to own former Union of Delaware properties, Shell Company of California, Roxana Petroleum Corporation, and Ozark Pipe Line Corporation. (50)

March 15— **W. K. Warren** organizes **Warren Petroleum Company** in Tulsa, pioneer company in the field of **LPG.** (50)

March—Although numerous non-commercial wells and attempts have been made, **Ventura Field** in California comes in with Shell's Gosnell No. 3 well. In 1916 a Shell well had produced 120 barrels of oil and 500 barrels of water for some days before being abandoned as non-commercial. (50)

April 13—First **salt dome flank production** hit by **Yount-Lee Oil Company** on Stengler lease in Hull field, Liberty County, Texas. (53)

April 14—**Smackover field** in Arkansas discovered by Oil Operators' Trust No. 1 T. J. Murphy well which comes in making 30 million cubic feet of gas. Shortly thereafter V. F. K.'s No. 1 Richardson well comes in as first oil producer. (75)

April 18—Contracts leasing part of naval oil reserves known at **Teapot Dome Reserve,** Wyoming to private interests for development signed by representatives of government and private development expected to begin immediately. (2)

April 21—All facts about leasing of **naval reserve oil fields** to private persons or corporations asked by resolution introduced into Senate by Senator **La Follette of Wisconsin.** (2)

April—**Sligo field** discovered in Bossier Parish, Louisiana. (67)

May 15—**Hillman-Kelley** founded as Hillman-Cooney, Incorporated in Los Angeles, California as manufacturers of air powered tongs. (50)

June 7—**Torrance, California field** discovered by C. C. M. O. No. 1 Del Amo at a depth of 3500 feet; called **Redondo field** at first, it starts a townlot boom which reaches a peak in May 1924. (6) (66)

June—Standard Oil of Indiana goes on the radio when the Standard Oil Band of Whiting gives a "**radiophone**" concert over station KYW in Chicago. (13)

July 10—Superior Oil Company founded. In November, Keck Investment Company formed and in November 1933, Limited Oil Company merged with and succeeded Keck Investment Company. On Oct. 31, 1936, The Superior Oil Company formed from consolidation of Superior Oil Co. and Limited Oil Company in California. (50)

July 31—The final curtain is ringing down on the **Golden Lane.** This is the interpretation oil men place on appearance of salt water in Toteco-Cerro Azul field in **Mexico.** (2)

July—**Fuel Oil and Oil Heat** first published. (50)

August 8—**Luling-Branyon field,** Texas, discovered by United North and South Oil Company. No. 1 Rios opens up the **Edwards Lime trend** when completed making 150 barrels per day at 2175 feet. (44)

August 8—Investigations into **gasoline prices** open before special sub-committee of five senators, to seek to ascertain if price advances of past few months were warranted in face of government figures showing record-breaking oil reserves. (2)

August 25—Midwest Refining Company spuds in its first well on the Hogback Dome on the Western edge of the Navajo reservation in San Juan County. It is completed within a month, producing 375 bbls. per day at 796 feet in the Dakota sandstone. The **Hogback field** makes **New Mexico** a commercially productive oil state. (10)

September—First use of **electric welding** to repair large oil field tank bottom. Welding done for Empire Pipeline Company, El Dorado, Kansas by Welding Engineering Company (now H. C. Price Co.). (50)

November 23—Senator Walsh, of Montana, introduces resolution in Senate for **investigations by Committee on Public Lands,** of all leases entered into under Mineral Land Leasing Act, to ascertain to whom these leases were made and to whom they were transferred, together with business relation between lessees and large oil-producing corporations. The inquiry also calls for copies of contracts for disposition of oil and names of parties through whose hands oil would pass before reaching consumer. (2)

November—The **first natural gasoline plant** in the Texas Panhandle built by the Cannon Gasoline Company. (44)

December 2—The **Neutral Zone of Kuwait** in which the Kingdom of Ibn Saud and the Shaikhdom of Kuwait have undivided equal rights established. The neutral zone of Iraq also established in which the Kingdom of Ibn Saud and the government of Iraq have undivided equal rights. (80)

December 14—Barroso No. 2, near **Lake Maracaibo, Venezuela,** blows in at 1500 feet. Its flow begins at 2000 barrels a day, increases rapidly until it blows wildly at 100,000 barrels, destroys the derrick and blows a column of oil 200 feet into the air. The well blows one million barrels of oil in nine days before it is plugged. (45)

December 21—The Board of Directors of the American Petroleum Institute creates a General Committee to investigate, develop, and approve **API Standards** for the manufacture of oil field and refinery equipment. (54)

December—Venezuelan Oil Concessions Ltd. completes Las Flores No. 1 as the discovery well of the **La Paz field** in Venezuela. (77)

December—The first well to encounter gas in what is now the **Hugoton** gas area completed in Seward County, Kansas. (66)

The **AIME** committee on Oil and Gas expanded into a professional division of the Institute—Petroleum Division AIME. (57)

The **jet-cement mixer** patented by Halliburton. (40)

First notable success of **diamond core-drill** is discovery of the northern extension (the most prolific part) of the Tonkawa, Oklahoma, field. (6)

A **forged steel coupling** produced and placed on the market by Pittsburgh Pipe and Coupling Company. Prior to this time, wrought iron couplings were in use. (50)

A workable **float shoe** designed, and in 1924 the float collar comes on the market. (40)

The **rotary displacement meter** introduced to the gas industry. (38)

A manual defining efficient utilization and **conservation of natural gas** prepared by the U. S. Bureau of Mines and distributed by the Natural Gas Association of America to natural gas consumers. (47)

New Mexico becomes a gas producing state with the completion of its first gas well. The 2428-foot well opens up the UTE Dome gas field in San Juan County. (38)

A floating foam known as **"Sealite,"** for decreasing evaporation, developed by Frank A. Howard, Clarence I. Robertson, and James M. Jennings of Standard Oil Company, of New Jersey. (1)

Signal Oil and Gas Company organized. Dates of mergers: December 31, 1958, merged with Hancock Oil Co.; July 10, 1959, merged with Bankline Oil Co.; September 23, 1959, merged with Eastern States Petroleum & Chemical Corporation. (50)

John R. Suman, a Humble Oil & Refining Company engineer, granted a patent on a pumping unit which has a double pitman with an equalizing yoke bolted to the beam. The pitman has bearings on either end. (40)

Oil is discovered at Talang Akar, **Sumatra,** by **NKPM,** Far Eastern affiliate of Standard Oil Company of New Jersey. (50)

Amerada brings first **torsion balance** to U. S. A. Hires C. V. Millikan as a geologist.

Two **torsion balances,** previously ordered by DeGolyer, are shipped to America, one for the **Mexican Eagle** in Mexico and one for use in the United States. These instruments have been used in Egypt by the Royal Dutch-Shell prior to that time. (AAPG IX) A survey of the Spindletop dome by DeGolyer in December is probably the **first geophysical survey of an oil field** in the United States. (66)

First use of **electric welding** on field pipelines. Job done for Empire Gas and Fuel Company at Caney, Kansas by Electra Welding Co. (now H. C. Price Co.). (50)

Colorado School of Mines Petroleum Engineering department founded. (1)

Missouri School of Mines organizes Petroleum Engineering department. (1)

United States Bureau of Standards begins study of **soil corrosion.** (38)

1923

January 4—The **Mid-Continent Oil & Gas Association, Texas Division** and the **Mid-Continent Oil & Gas Association, Louisiana-Arkansas Division** formed. (57)

February 2—"**Ethyl**" gasoline first placed on public sale by a service station in Dayton, Ohio, operated by the Refiners Oil Co. (8B)

February 22—Texas grants first permit for **carbon-black** plant to J. W. Hassel & Associates in Stephens County. (5)

February 22—Chapter 185, a combination waste prevention and plugging statute passed by **Oregon.** (3)

February 23—The **Texas Railroad Commission** adopts its first field rules for an individual producing area—the Laredo district in Southwest Texas. (44)

February 27—Grip tubing spider, grip casing spider and grip casing elevator introduced to the industry by **Bovaird Supply Company.** (50)

February—American Petroleum Institute directors appoint a **Unitization** Committee to study methods of conservation, at its annual meeting. Judge A. L. Beaty, president of The Texas Company is president. (2)

March—**Emsco Manufacturing Company** founded as Emsco Derrick & Equipment Company in Los Angeles, California, to design, engineer and manufacture steel derricks and allied equipment. (50)

April—The first Mid-Continent well to be drilled with **electrically powered rotary equipment** is said to be a Humble Oil Company well in Wichita County, Texas. (12)

May 6—Eastern and General Syndicate, Ltd., granted a concession of **Hasa** (the Eastern province of Arabia). (80)

May 28—**Big Lake field** in Texas discovered when the famous **Santa Rita well** by **Texon Oil and Land Company** blows in. This is the first successful well drilled on the now extensive oil and gas lands of the University of Texas. (Santa Rita by Martin Schwettmann, Texas State Historical Association, 1943)

June 6—A. G. A. creates an Industrial Gas Section. At the **Massachusetts Institute of Technology,** an industrial gas course established with the first classes conducted by the New England Association of Gas Engineers. (38)

August 31—The **Pennsylvania Grade Crude Oil Association** organized. (57)

September 7—**Dominguez field,** then Dominguez Hills field, in California discovered by Union Oil Company, No. 1-A Callendar at a depth of 4068 feet. (50) (66)

October 8-14—The **International Petroleum Exposition** (originally called Petroleum Exposition and Congress) first held in Tulsa, Oklahoma. (The Tulsa Tribune)

October 15—Chairman Smoot, of Senate Public Lands Committee, calls the committee together to consider the report of two geologists, who, by direction of the Senate, investigated conditions at **Teapot Dome,** naval oil reserve. The session is behind closed doors, preliminary to public hearings. (2)

Oct. 23—U. S. Senate Committee on Public Lands and Surveys starts **Teapot Dome investigation.** Final result is conviction of **Harry Sinclair** and Secretary of Interior **Albert B. Fall,** and cancellation of leases to private firms by Fall, of **Naval Petroleum Reserve** lands at **Elk Hills** and **Teapot Dome.** (78)

October 27—**Lion Oil Company** founded as Lion Oil Refining Company. (50)

November 11—A patent for **in-situ combustion** granted to **F. A. Howard;** the first known application of this method in the United States was in Oklahoma in 1952. (1)

General Assembly of **Arkansas** passes an act for the taxation of natural resources severed from the soil. "Severance Tax." (9)

Oil and gas regulatory powers conferred upon the **Arkansas Railroad Commission.** (9)

H. L. Doherty employs **C. E. Beecher** to undertake laboratory experiments on the relations between **reservoir gas and oil.** It includes the measurement of viscosity and surface tension of gas-saturated, or bubble-point, crude oils. The conclusion is that dissolved gas lowers viscosity and surface tension, and, therefore, increases the efficiency of oil recovery. (1)

Safety engineers join the Petroleum Division of the Bureau of Mines to study accidents in the industry, to train oil field and refinery workers in safety, and to teach the use of **safe practices and safe equipment** in the oil fields and in the refineries. (48)

Stanco, an affiliate of Standard Oil Company of New Jersey, markets a new insecticide called **Flit.** (50)

The refining industry is startled when **General Motors Corporation** introduces **tetraethyl lead,** offering it on a royalty basis. (5)

Amerada makes studies at Brock field, Oklahoma, on effects of back pressure on **gas-oil ratio.** (1)

Executive board of American Gas Association approves plan to raise a fund to start an **appliance testing laboratory.** East Ohio Gas Company sets up temporary testing laboratory facilities in Cleveland, Ohio. (38)

First use of **electric welding** to repair large oil field tank shell and to electric-weld new steel roofs on large oil field tanks for Marlin Refining Company, Texas City, Texas by Welding Engineering Company (now H. C. Price Co.). (50)

Oklahoma displaces West Virginia as the **leading state in natural gas production** (and in 1928 lost the lead to Texas). (38)

L. Mintrop organizes the **Seismos Gesellschaft** in Germany. (GeoTimes)

Public Service Company of Colorado formed by consolidation of Denver Gas and Electric Light Company and the Western Light and Power Company of Boulder. The new firm is a subsidiary of Cities Service Company. (38)

Rochester Gas and Electric Corporation establishes "radiophone" station 8XQ—as a new form of advertising and to help create "good will." (38)

First trillion-cubic-foot year marked in natural gas industry as quantity of gas produced and marketed in one year reaches that figure. (47)

The presence of oil in **Holland** first established. Slight traces of oil discovered while drilling in search of coal and salt near Winterswijk in the province of Gelderland. The quantities are too small, however, for commercial exploitation. (45)

Western **Kansas** gets first development in **Fairport field,** 125 miles from nearest drilling. (5)

Kobe, Inc., founded in Vernon, California, to perform the service of slotting well liners with a newly perfected oxy-acetylene torch cutting machine. (50)

The Atlantic Refining Company becomes interested in seismograph and sets up a project called "**the McCollum Experiment.**" This is made in Mexico under the auspices of the Cortez Oil Corporation, then Atlantic's Mexican subsidiary. In 1924, work begins in Mexico in a wildcat area close to Tampico. Both reflection and refraction methods are used, with greater emphasis given to the latter. Though the first well is dry, the well log confirms the seismograph finding. This well, the La Gatero No. 4, is probably the **first ever drilled on a seismograph location.** (40)

The University of Texas announces course in **micro-paleontology** under Dr. F. L. Whitney and Columbia University offers a similar course under J. J. Galloway. (1)

Pacific Pumps, Inc., founded as the Pacific Pump Works in Huntington Park, Calif., as manufacturers of deep well turbine pumps. (50)

Pure Oil Company, after studies and tests by its engineers, concludes that **aluminum paint** is the most efficient type for reducing evaporation losses and the company adopts this type of paint as a standard for its crude oil, refined products, and even its bulk station storage. (1)

R. Van A. Mills reports on paraffin problem in oil wells. Points out causes of **"paraffining,"** methods of prevention and methods of removal. Briefly describes shooting, electric heaters, mechanical scrapers, solvents, other chemicals including acids, and burning. (1)

The introduction of electric drives to **pipelines** starts a trend toward **electric centrifugal packages** which are to dominate the industry. Four-stage, 1800 RPM pumps directly connected to 200 hp induction motors are installed on a California line. (40)

Reid Vapor Pressure method adopted by NGAA replacing old "Vapor Tension Method" for determining the volatility of natural gasoline. (Natural Gas Processors Association)

Standard Oil Company of New Jersey begins to give out **road maps.** (50)

Dean E. Winchester publishes his report on **"Oil Shale of the Rocky Mountain Region"**—and in 1928 publishes one on the whole U. S. (32)

Activity begins in **San Juan basin** of New Mexico, with development of a natural-gas well near Artesia. (5)

Conrad Schlumberger begins to apply surface technique to oil prospecting as well as in mining. (50)

A German **seismograph** crew sent to Mexico in early summer for use by Mexican Eagle, and later in the year, Marland Oil Company is persuaded to try seismic investigations in the **Mexia** fault area. (66)

South Dakota passes an act which provides for the regulation and inspection of oil and gas wells, and the prevention of waste of natural gas. (3)

To reduce **sucker-rod** breaks, the practice of heat-treating rod ends starts. (40)

The first **spherical storage tanks** built. (40)

A 10- and 12-inch line laid from the well-known **Teapot Dome** field of Wyoming to Mid-Continent carriers. (40)

Henry L. Doherty, head of Cities Service Companies, proposes federal **compulsory unit-operation law.** (40)

Wyoming gets its first major line to the Chicago area. (19)

The first export cargoes of unblended gasoline leaves Texas Gulf Coast ports. (44)

R. Van A. Mills shows that the escape of gas with associated oil and water through fissures has been an important factor in the migration and accumulation of **oil and gas in faulted areas.** (22)

1924

February 2—Ashland Refining Company formed. In 1936, Ashland Refining Company merged with its affiliate, Swiss Oil Company, to form **Ashland Oil and Refining Company.** (50)

February 5—**Turbodrill Principle** patent granted to **Charles C. Sharp-**

enberg, Bakersfield, California. Patent called "Fluid-operated Well Drilling Apparatus." Fluid supplied by drill pipe from surface. Lowering and hoisting of machine in and out of hole done by drill pipe. (Patent No. 1,482,702)

February 13—The Forest Oil Company, Inc., chartered in Pennsylvania November 12, 1916, is consolidated with the January Oil Company, the Brown Seal Oil Corporation, the Andrews Petroleum Corporation and the Boyd Oil Corporation to form the **Forest Oil Corporation.** (50)

February—The **first important discovery by geophysics** in the United States is the **Nash dome** in Texas discovered by Rycade Oil Company using a torsion balance. (66)

March—Commonwealth Oil Refineries Ltd. goes on stream at Leverton Victoria, **Australia.** Closed 1955. (45)

March—The first long-distance crude pipeline to serve the **Rocky Mountain area** constructed by Sinclair Pipe Line Company (Service Pipe Line Company).

April 22—Venezuela—**The British Equatorial Oil Company** brings in first well in **Lake Maracaibo** waters, flowing 2359 barrels per day. (10)

May 17—Eastern and General Syndicate, Ltd., granted a concession on Saudi Arabia's undivided half of the so-called **Kuwait Neutral Zone.** (80)

May—A second location made in the **Golden Lane** area of Mexico, as the No. 7, Lot 199, Amatlan. This well, when drilled, proves to be the **first producer drilled** on a seismograph location, and came in as a 400 bbl/day producer. (40)

June—The Ohio Oil Company (now Marathon) purchases **Lincoln Oil and Refining Company** and for first time enters petroleum refining and retail marketing, under trade name "Linco." (50)

July 28—**International Oil Scouts Association** chartered in Texas as the National Oil Scouts Association of America. (57)

August 19—**Ethyl Corporation** formed as successor to General Motors Chemical Company, which had marketed "Ethyl" antiknock compound originally. (50)

October 10—**Inglewood** field, California, discovered by Standard Oil Company No. 1-1 L. A. Investment Co., at 2134 feet. (66)

December 19—**President Coolidge** appoints a **Federal Oil Conservation Board.** It is composed of the Secretaries of War, Navy, Commerce and Interior. Hubert Work, Interior Secretary is chairman. Its purpose is to study supply of fuel oil for the use of Navy in time of emergency. (2)

Compressed air is introduced and used extensively in the Bartlesville field to stimulate production. (1)

First natural-gasoline plant in West Texas built at **Big Lake.** (5)

The **British American Oil Company, Ltd.,** enters the United States as a producing company, the Toronto Pipe Line Company organized, and in 1925, the British American Oil Producing Company organized. (50)

Fanny Carter Edson, at the Roxana Petroleum Corporation (now Shell Oil Company), undertakes the assignment of defining the sedimentary formations and unconformities of the Mid-Continent region. (1)

The reports of **D. B. Dow** and **C. E. Reistle, Jr.,** on laboratory determinations of gas solubilities in oil at various pressures indicate an early appreciation of the importance of **properties of reservoir fluids.** (1)

The **dry seal gas holder** introduced in the U. S., and is built in sizes up to 20 million cubic foot capacity. (38)

Ohio Oil Company (now Marathon) commences **gas injection** in old fields of Illinois under supervision of J. C. Askam. (1)

Cranfill and Reynolds incorporated in Texas. In December 1933, the corporate name changed to **General Crude Oil Company.** (50)

L. C. Uren granted a patent covering **gravel packing** oil and gas wells; also a patent covering the equipment for such a process. (1)

In an attempt to speed the rate of water advance, the Forest Oil Corporation pioneers what is now known as the **line-drive type of water injection** in Bradford field. (40)

First roller-type **Kelly Bushing** introduced by Baash-Ross Division of Joy Manufacturing Company. (50)

Louisiana—Act passed to protect the natural waterways of the state against pollution by salt water, oil, and other substances. (9)

Louisiana—Act passed relating generally to the subject of the conservation of natural gas and providing detailed drilling and production regulations. (9)

Magnetometer introduced in the Southwest for mapping structures. (5)

The Natural Gas Association of America directs its technical and research committee to undertake a study of gas measurements by **orifice meters.** Much of this work is done in cooperation with the American Society of Mechanical Engineers and the U. S. Bureau of Standards. (47)

The **Natural Gas Act** largely comes about as a result of the decision by the U. S. Supreme Court in **Missouri** v. **Kansas Natural Gas Company** 265 U. S. 298, which holds generally that the State of Missouri can not prevent an increase in the price of gas sold to local distributors by Kansas Natural Gas Company which has transported it in interstate commerce. (59)

"**Petroleum Production Engineering**" written by **L. C. Uren.** (1)

Photogeology employed in prospecting principally as an auxiliary aid to surface geology. (5)

The first long-distance, all-welded natural gas pipe line completed by the Magnolia Gas Co. of Dallas. The line consists of 14-, 16-, and 18-inch telescoped pipe, acetylene welded, and runs 214 miles from the Webster Parish field in Louisiana to Beaumont, Texas. (47)

T. E. Swigart and R. R. Bopp report an exhaustive field study that indicates back-pressure can be used to control gas-oil ratios of producing wells. (1)

Recycling of natural gas is an innovation in Osage field, Oklahoma. (5)

The API rejects both federal and state regulations; asks only state laws permitting voluntary agreements for proration and unit operations. (40)

Thomas Reinhold, Chief Geologist of the Geological Survey Department of Holland, invents a photographic apparatus which gives a record of the strata pierced so as to obtain the nature of the same, detect the presence of fissures and get the dip of the beds. (28)

Gulf Oil Corporation discovers Orchard, Texas, salt dome with refraction seismograph; technique principally for reconnaissance. (5)

H. C. Miller and R. V. Higgins bring Cutler's rules of well spacing up to date to put them in line with advances in production methods. (64) Professor Charles A. Kraus devises a practical manufacturing process of tetraethyl lead. (Standard Oil Co. of New Jersey)

Turner Valley, Canada field proven for important production from limestone pay at about 9150 feet, after having produced from shallow pay since 1914. (66) (67)

Topping and cracking in one operation introduced in processing crude from Healdton field. (5)

Torsion-balance method proves successful in locating shallow salt domes in Gulf Coast province. (5)

The Laramie, Wyoming, office of the U. S. Bureau of Mines opens. (64)

Lone Star Gas Company engineers succeed in developing a method of modifying and controlling the heat content of residue gas through the development of a new technologic process that permits its satisfactory use. (50)

Humble Oil & Refining Company establishes a geophysical department. New tools of underground exploration—the seismograph, the torsion balance and the magnetometer—are being developed. (Standard Oil Co. of New Jersey)

Prof. Charles A. Kraus, of Clark University, discovers a manufacturing process which makes possible a reduction in the selling price of tetraethyl lead from one cent per cubic centimeter to less than one-fifth cent. (8A)

Lago Petroleum Corporation (a precursor of Creole) is first United States company to export oil from Venezuela. (45)

Stanford University offers a course in **micropaleontology** under Dr. Hubert Schench. (1)

University of Oklahoma organizes department of Petroleum Engineering. (1)

Waterless gas holder introduced in U.S. by Bartlett-Hayward. (38)

A study by the U. S. Bureau of Mines indicates that it will be possible to mine oil sands at a cost that is probably cheaper than the cost of making synthetics from shales and coal. (64)

1925

March 14—The Iraq Government awards seventy-five-year concession to Turkish Petroleum Company, Limited (name changed to **Iraq Petroleum Company Limited** on June 8, 1929). (45)

March 31—Patent to A. Arutunoff. Pioneer of the commercial electric submersible oil well pump. Started with the development of an oil-filled and oil-cooled motor. Other motor patents relating to squirrel cage induction motors (Dec. 9, 1924) issued to him. His first **submersible pump** patent issued Dec. 14, 1926. (1)

May 28—Federal court decision cancels government lease of **Elk Hills** and contract for storage tanks at Pearl Harbor, on basis that E. L. Doheny has given Secretary of Interior Fall $100,000. Doheny's **Pan American Petroleum and Transport Company** ordered to make restitution of $24,237,341 to government. (78)

May—**Gas Magazine** begins publication as Western Gas. (50)

June 1—**A. G. A. Testing Laboratory** established at Cleveland. It is founded to promote and insure safe and satisfactory gas service to consumers, through research, formulation of standards, and testing of appliances. (38)

July 1—By Executive Order of President Coolidge, the Bureau of Mines transferred from the Department of Interior to the **Department of Commerce.** (48)

September 30—**McCamey field** (Upton and Crane Counties, Texas) discovered by McCamey, Johnson and Marland's Baker 1 well making 70 barrels at 2240 feet. (42) (44)

October 20—The first **Diesel electric locomotive** bought by an American railroad begins switching service in New York. (54)

November 13—**Spindletop** second boom starts as **Yount-Lee Oil Company** hits 5000-barrel well south of the old Lucas Gusher in its McFaddin No. 2 well to bring in flank production. As the first discovery had led to a parade of salt domes, this one points the way to a new boom in **salt dome flanks.** (53)

November 15—**Howard Glasscock field,** Texas, discovered by Fred Heyer et al, No. 1 Clay completed for 25 barrels per day at 1542-1566 feet. (44)

November 21—**Magnolia Petroleum Company** incorporated in Texas and the assets of the former joint stock association transferred to it. (50)

December 2—Eastern and General Syndicate, Ltd., granted a two year option to acquire an exclusive oil **exploration license over Bahrein Island.** (80)

December 9—**Mission Manufacturing Company** founded in Houston, Texas as Mission Sales Company. Present name adopted in 1932.

Commercial production of **petrochemical alcohols** begins. (48)

Arkansas—Office of Commissioner of Conservation and Inspection created. (9)

Bolivia—In the area near the Argentina frontier, **Standard of Bolivia's** Bermejo No. 2 comes in, capable of producing a little more than 1000 bbl. per day. In 1926, the Sanandita field opens, Sanandita No. 1 producing 183 bbl. per day. In 1935 the Bolivian government took over the oil industry and **Yacimientos Petroliferos Fiscales Bolivianes** assumed development. (10)

Commercial size units for retorting **Colorado shale** constructed. (64)

Hughes Tool Company develops **self-cleaning cones** that more than double the footage and penetration rate of rock bits. (50)

First units of the **Jenkins cracking process** in Southwest installed in El Dorado, Kansas, by Skelly Oil Co. (5)

Houston Pipe Line Company, now wholly owned by **Houston Natural Gas Corporation,** organized and pioneered gas pipe lining in the Gulf Coast area. (50)

Martin-Decker Corporation founded as Loomis Oil Well Control Company in Long Beach, California, as manufacturers of weight indicators. (50)

Mexico—The government sets up the National Petroleum Administration, a government agency which engages in production and refining in competition with private capital and also regulates the domestic prices of petroleum products. (14)

Mexico requires oil companies to exchange their titles to oil lands for fifty-year concessions. (14)

Michigan—The first important production comes in with the Saginaw field. Production is from the Berea sandstone at 1800 feet and the oil is 46 gravity. One well drilled within six feet of the Bancroft Hotel, the stock tanks buried beneath the parking lot. (10)

Montana—Legislation provides that the Board of Railroad Commissioners prescribe and enforce rules and regulations covering drilling, casing and abandonment of oil and gas wells and the waste of oil and gas, except on certain public lands. (3)

The Bureau of Mines begins annual reports on **natural gas production and consumption.** (48)

New Mexico—Legislature enacts a law having to do with conservation. Remains in effect until 1935. Creates the office of State Geologist. (9)

Seamless pipe developed and becomes available to the natural gas industry. An important advance in technology, it paves the way toward construction of large diameter pipe lines capable of carrying higher pressures. The use of this pipe with welded joints also effects a reduction of internal friction. (47)

One of the earliest attempts to determine a fluid level and compute the corresponding **"bottom-hole" pressure** accurately in a pumping well in Kansas. (1)

The **API opposes regulation** but sets up study groups on production practices and reservoir control. (40)

Geophysical Research Corporation surveys Earlsboro, Oklahoma, structure, which is the first Southwest oil field to be discovered by **reflection seismograph** technique. (5)

South Dakota—Act passed, replacing act of 1923, assigning the state geologist charge of the conservation of natural resources in the state and the prevention of waste therein. (3)

Standard Oil Company de Mexico organized. Capitalization at close of year approximately $250,000,000. (50)

The **spherical storage tank** adapted to storage of gas under pressure by Chicago Bridge and Iron Works. Known as "Hortonsphere," it is the outgrowth of tanks used earlier for gasoline storage. First tank of this type erected at Phoenix, Arizona, had diameter of 57½ feet. (38)

The **Moody-Seagraves** group of Galveston, Texas, constructs pipelines from Corpus Christi to Houston, from Shreveport to Houston and Beaumont, from the Jennings, Texas, field to **Monterrey,** Mexico, and from the Jennings field to San Antonio and Austin. Moody-Seagraves became a subsidiary of **United Gas Corporation** in 1930 along with several other companies. (50)

Pat Elliott invents a tool ("**water witch**") for the purpose of finding the source of water entering wells. First run in a well near Taft, Calif., this year. (1)

A. O. Smith Corporation develops the first **all-welded pressure vessel** for an oil refinery (The Texas Company). (50)

Crown Central Petroleum Corporation, a Delaware corporation, comes into existence, changing its name from United Central Oil Co. Later incorporated in Baltimore, Md., September 23, 1937. (50)

Rights to the Platen-Munters electric refrigerating system acquired by **Servel, Inc.,** from Swedish Electrolux Company. Ultimately, a mechanical refrigerator without use of electricity or any moving parts was developed by Servel and the utilization department of Consolidated

Gas Company. In March 1927, the first Servel **gas refrigerator** was installed on lines of Consolidated Gas Company in New York. By June, over 1000 units had been installed. In 1948, Servel introduced and marketed the first "all-year" **gas-fired air conditioner.** In 1952, Servel introduced the automatic ice maker. In 1957, **Arkansas Louisiana Gas Company** acquired Servel's air conditioning division and Evansville, Indiana plant, and formed Arkla Air Conditioning Corporation as a subsidiary. In 1958, Whirlpool Corporation, St. Joseph, Michigan, acquired Servel's gas refrigeration division and other major facilities. (38)

1925-26—In **Colombia,** the Andean National, a 10-inch and 12-inch line from the **De Mares concession,** laid. (40)

1925-26—The first successful **profiling** of salt domes completed at High Island and Fannett Domes with the **refraction technique.** The method is successful for profiling the top of domes and a short distance over the shoulder, but leaves the flanks undefined. This limitation is overcome by putting detectors in wells previously drilled off the flanks of the dome and shooting through the dome. This method has proved to be invaluable in salt dome profiling. (40)

1926

January 12—Patent No. 1,569,247 for Cameron Iron Works' first ram type **blowout preventer** issued. Application had been made for patent April 14, 1922, by J. S. Abercrombie and Harry S. Cameron. The first preventer (Type MO) had been made by Cameron Iron Works in 1921 and used successfully by Abercrombie in the Hull, Texas, field. (50)

January 13—**St. Louis field** discovered in Oklahoma by Independent Oil and Darby Petroleum's No. 1 Davis well. (66)

January 18—The **Bowlegs field** of the Greater Seminole area of Oklahoma discovered by Indian Territory Illuminating Oil Co. No. 1 Goforth. (66)

January 27—**Standard Oil Company of California** incorporated under laws of Delaware. March 29, 1926, Standard Oil Company (Calif.) and Pacific Oil Company properties conveyed to Standard Oil Company of California. (50)

February 1—**National Tank Company** founded with headquarters and manufacturing plant in Tulsa, Okla. (50)

February 19—First broad scale **gas repressuring** project instituted. Cook Ranch field, Shackelford County, Texas. (1)

March 1—The **Earlsboro field** discovered in Oklahoma by Morgan & Flynn No. 1 Ingram. (66)

March 6—**Ben K. Stroud** granted patent No. 1,575,945 on his principle of **weighted drilling mud.** Stroud granted exclusive sales rights under this patent to National Lead Company. (1)

March 7—**Seminole City field** (not to be confused with Greater Semi-

146

nole) discovered by **Indian Territory Illuminating Oil Company No. 1** Jones well which comes in making 1100 barrels daily from the Hunton limestone between 3975 and 4012 feet. (75)

March 16—**Robert Hutchins Goddard** fires the first liquid fuel **rocket** in history. It remains aloft for two and one half minutes. (NBC)

March—The **Tide Water Associated Oil Company,** a holding company, organized. It acquires control of Tide Water Oil Company and Associated Oil Company. (50)

April 18—**McElroy field,** Texas, discovered by Church and Fields No. 1 University. Completed for 190 barrels per day at 3040 feet. (44)

April 25—Basic **gun-perforating** patent issued to **S. W. Mims** (Lane-Wells).

May 14—**Lagunillas field,** Venezuela, discovered by Venezuela Gulf Oil Company. (77)

June 1—Humble Oil & Refining Company makes its first **geophysical discovery,** when a refraction crew, under Edgar S. Sherar, finds the Moss Bluff salt dome in Liberty County, Texas. (12)

June 15—The Ohio Oil Company pioneers **machine accounting** in oil industry with the installation of Hollerith mechanical bookkeeping machines for royalty and general accounting. Machines are forerunners of modern IBM data processing and computer equipment. (50)

June—The first **centrifugal pumps** on an oil pipe line in Texas installed by the Magnolia Pipe Line Company at its station near Beaumont. (44)

July—**Mount Poso field** discovered in Kern County, California, in Shell's Vedder No. 1 well. (74)

August 3—**Hendricks field,** Texas, discovered by Westbrook & Co. well on Hendricks ranch which made 57 barrels per day at 2529 feet and completed March 28, 1927, for 400 barrels per day at 3049 feet. (44)

August 4—**Seal Beach field** discovered by Marland Oil Company No. 2 Bixby on acreage which had been dropped by Shell three months earlier after four years of unsuccessful and highly expensive exploration; initial production 1256 barrels at 4427 feet. (6) (66) (70)

August 26—**The Texas Corporation,** a holding company, organized. (50)

October 28—**Yates field** in Pecos County, Texas, discovered when Mid-Kansas Oil and Gas Company (Ohio) brings in the No. 1 Ira G. Yates "A" well with an initial flow of 100 B/D from 990-997 feet. By 1927 the field makes 5 million barrels. In 1929 it produces 41 million barrels. (42)

October—The **Columbia Gas System, Inc.,** organized. (50)

November 20—**Houston Natural Gas Corporation** granted a charter and immediately begins to pipe the area that encircles Houston, Texas. (50)

December—The **McCallum field,** Colorado, discovered. The discovery well is sometimes referred to as the "Lemon Sherbet Well" as a result of minor oil production with large quantities of frozen CO_2. (66)

December—The president of the API appoints a **Committee of Seven** to "devise and suggest" measures for petroleum including gas conservation. (12)

December—A 170-mile, 22-inch line completed from the **Monroe field** to Baton Rouge, Louisiana, representing a pioneer effort in construction of large **gas lines through low, swampy terrain.** (38)

National Pigments & Chemical Company, a subsidiary of National Lead Company, begins to sell its barite under the trade name of **"Baroid."** (50)

Ken Sclater of Marland Oil Company builds a **bottom hole pressure bomb** which runs in casing. (50)

Cardwell Manufacturing Company founded as H. W. Cardwell Company in Wichita, Kansas, as manufacturers of portable hoists, various servicing hoists, rotary drives, rotary workovers and cable tool spudders. (50)

Cities Service Company organized as a holding company. (38)

First pipeline laid in **Colombia,** with 78,000-barrel per day capacity, linking El Centro and Mamonal. It is laid by the Andia Company. (45)

U. S. Bureau of Standards, working with A.G.A., API and ASME, initiates technical meetings to study **corrosion problems,** cathodic protection, and pipe coatings. (38)

Percentage **depletion** provision of 27.5 per cent enacted by Congress and signed by the President. House votes for 32 per cent, Senate Finance Committee recommends 25 per cent, but Senate passes a bill calling for 30 per cent depletion. A joint conference committee of both houses compromises on 27.5 per cent. (W. H. Geis, in paper delivered to 37th Annual Meeting of the API, 1957 in Chicago)

The **Edeleanu process** first applied to lubricating oils. (39)

The first all roller-bearing piston valve fully enclosed **twin-cylinder engine** built by Flory Hoist Co. of Bangor, Pennsylvania, for the Atlantic Refining Co. (1)

The **"Esso"** name registered and placed in use on a broad scale. (Standard Oil Co. of New Jersey)

The development of seismic **"fan shooting"** begins. (33)

W. G. Heltzel of Sinclair Pipe Line Company (later Stanolind and Service) experiments with the **flow of fluids** through eight- and 12-inch pipelines. His experiments enable him to conclude that the results of Stanton and Pannell's work with small brass tubes applied also to large operating pipelines. (40)

The first use of the word **"gal"** in German geophysical literature. (33)

The Bureau of Mines changes refinery statistics from a **gallon basis** to the present **42-gallon barrel** basis, the same unit used in crude oil production statistics. (48)

The German process called **hydrogenation** brought to the attention of Standard Oil Company of New Jersey. (50)

Federal Board recommends an **interstate oil compact.** (40)

Johnston Testers, Inc., founded as Johnston Formation Testing Company in El Dorado, Arkansas, as manufacturers of oil well drill stem testing equipment. (50)

The **La Cira field** discovered in Colombia. (70)

Development of mass-marketing methods and utilization of equipment for **liquefied petroleum gases** started by Phillips Petroleum Corp. (50)

Rotary well log developed as a correlation aid. (5)

McCullough Tool Company founded in Los Angeles, California, as manufacturers of oil well fishing tools, rotary jars, releasing sockets, rotary spears, casing cutters, drill pipe cutters, and mechanical long-knife perforators. (50)

E. L. Rawlins reports some methods for **testing natural gas lines** for leakage losses that proves valuable in subsequent practice. (64)

Pressure maintenance, in flush production of oil, first practiced in certain California, Kansas and Texas oil fields as an important conservation measure. (47)

First recorded use of a **"rolling rig"** for revolving pipe during application of coating; device used on the 22-inch line from Monroe to Baton Rouge, Louisiana. (38)

The **Society of Economic Paleontologists and Mineralogists** formed and becomes a technical division of the American Association of Petroleum Geologists. (57)

Standard Oil Company (New Jersey) completes a refinery at Palambang, **Sumatra.** (Standard Oil Company of New Jersey)

Patent issued to **H. A. W. Howcott** of New Orleans; a patent on a hydraulic well drill (probably **turbodrill**). Sometime in 1950's Russians were using a turbodrill with success. In 1956 Dresser Industries received shipment of 40 turbodrills from Russia. (U. S. Patent Office and Oil Weekly)

Shell Oil Company of California installs the first complete oil-field **vapor-recovery systems** of which there is record in some of its newly discovered fields in California. (1)

Erle P. Halliburton invents a **"well-sounding device"** which uses a round plow-steel wire around a measuring wheel with a counter and run through a stuffing box. (1)

149

Invalidation of patents held by Carbide and Carbon Chemicals Corporation, New York, covering fractionation and stabilization at plants, by Phillips Petroleum Company. This opens up processes and equipment improvements permitting separation of individual hydrocarbons at plants and stimulates production of butanes and propanes. The **LP-Gas industry** begins to grow at this point. (Natural Gas Processors Association)

Lone Star Gas Company builds pioneer **pipeline suspension bridge** at Granbury, Texas, over the Brazos River. (50)

Hughes Tool Company develops first **roller core bit** for use in hard rock formations. (50)

University of West Virginia organizes Petroleum Engineering option. (1)

The pipe line network connecting West Texas with Gulf points and the Great Lakes begins. (19)

1927

February 28—U. S. Supreme Court upholds **Elk Hills oil scandal** decision of lower court, of May 28, 1925. (78)

March 8—The **first drill stem test** conducted in the East Field, El Dorado, Arkansas, by Johnston Testers. (50)

May 12—Representatives of the oil companies operating in the Seminole area of Oklahoma, meet in New York. On May 25 approve of a resolution for restricting the drilling and completion of **unnecessary wells** in the Seminole Pool and vicinity. (2)

May 20-21—**Charles A. Lindbergh** flies nonstop New York to Paris. (65)

June 8—**Colorado Interstate Gas Company** incorporated. In 1951 a merger consummated between the Canadian River Gas Company and Colorado Interstate Gas Company. (50)

July 1—The **Little River field,** Oklahoma, discovered by Indian Territory Illuminating Oil Co. No. 1 House. (66)

August 1—The Natural Gas Association of America merges with the **American Gas Association.** (47)

August 28—**Oil Center Tool Company** formed in Houston, Texas, by Arthur J. and Kirby T. Penick. FMC Corporation acquired Oil Center Tool Company on January 1, 1957. (50)

August—**American Gas Journal** changes to monthly publication; buys and absorbs Gas Industry magazine. (38)

Summer—Marathon Oil Company (then Ohio) pioneers the use of **electric power for pipeline pump stations** at Coulter, Ohio on the 1908 steam power line from Lima to Negley, Ohio. In 1928, the company builds a trunk line from Iraan, Texas, to the Mexican border at Del Rio, with 16 pumping stations equipped with electric power. (50)

September 5—**Conrad and Marcel Schlumberger** record the **first experimental electric log at Pechelbronn,** France. A single lateral-resistivity curve recorded at fixed points and later plotted as a graph against depth. Probably the most important date in **well-logging** history. (73)

October 1—Operators in the Yates field, Texas, pioneer **Maximum Efficient Rate of Production (MER)** for conservation of crude oil by submitting plan to Texas Railroad Commission for allocation of field's production which would result in greater ultimate recovery; this is a beginning step in proration of oil production in Texas and an important marker in the history of conservation. (Ohio Oil Company)

October 11—U.S. Supreme Court hands down unanimous decision invalidating **Teapot Dome lease** on grounds of fraud, ending civil suits in oil scandals. **Mammoth Oil Company** ordered to repay government $9,560,000. (78)

October 15—Iraq's first oil discovery, the Baba Gurga No. 1, roars in making an estimated 100,000 barrels of oil per day. Located on the **Kirkuk anticline,** it is operated by British, American, French and Dutch interests who later form the **Iraq Petroleum Corporation.** The well is spudded on June 30. It comes in at 1521 feet. (10)

October 25—Ozark Pipe Line Corporation changes its name to **Shell Pipe Line Corporation.** (Shell Oil Company)

November 30—**Eastern Gulf Oil Company,** wholly-owned subsidiary of Gulf Oil Corporation, enters into two contracts with Eastern and General Syndicate, Ltd., to acquire concessions in Bahrein and al-Hasa, the Neutral Zone and Kuwait. (80)

December—**API** Board of Directors authorizes the establishment of a **Division of Development and Production Engineering.** (1)

December—The API Committee on the Prevention of Waste of Gas goes on record as favoring state legislation that will prevent the **waste of gas** in the production of petroleum. (2)

December—**Blanco Mesaverde field** discovered in New Mexico. (67)

The Indian Refining Company refinery, at Lawrenceville, Illinois, first uses **acetone and benzol** in removing wax. Others follow shortly, employing propane, trichlor-ethylene, and combinations of solvents. (40)

A Committee on Conservation of Mineral Resources set up by the Section of Mineral Law of the **American Bar Association.** (12)

Arizona legislature passes S. B. No. 100, "Providing for the conserving of the natural resources of the state, by regulating the drilling and operation of oil and gas wells." (3)

Arkansas—General Assembly enacts law creating honorary Board of Conservation to Administer and Enforce Laws Pertaining to Conservation of Oil and Gas, and By-Products, and for Other Purposes. (9)

Standard Oil of New Jersey, at this time holder of large concessions, drills successfully the first commercial oil well in Camiri, **Bolivia.** (45)

151

Cities Service Co. constructs 250-mile gas pipeline from Panhandle field to Wichita. (5)

Colorado—Another act passed requiring persons drilling for oil and gas to keep accurate and complete well logs. (3)

Law creates **Colorado Gas Conservation Committee.** (3)

The API appoints a **Committee of Five** to study legal questions. Three prominent authorities on oil law appointed by the American Bar Association to the **Committee of Nine,** which is established under the Federal Oil Conservation Board to represent the public, the bar, and the oil industry in the study of the industry's problems. (12)

The first high-tensile-strength, large-diameter, natural-gas-transmission pipeline constructed in the Southwest for **Dixie Gulf Gas Co.,** in Louisiana. (5)

Esso Standard Oil Company formed. (50)

First **five-spot flood** to increase oil production rate launched as a 190-foot development by Arthur E. Yahn in northeast Bradford field. (40)

The first privately-owned **helium** plant is constructed in Dexter, Texas. (5)

A drilling crew at **Huntington Beach,** California, drills a **slanted hole seaward.** (15)

The Standard Oil Company of New Jersey opens the first **tourist information bureau.** (50)

Time-depth measurements successfully performed by seismic crews of the Amerada Petroleum Corp. (1)

Minneapolis-Honeywell Regulator Company formed by merger of Minneapolis Heat Regulator Company and Honeywell Heating Specialties Company. (38)

The first natural gas field in Michigan discovered two miles from **Muskegon** and that city becomes the first in the state to use the fuel. (47)

First noteworthy gas discovery in Southeastern **New Mexico** is the development of 90,000,000 cubic feet of gas a day at The Texas Production Company No. 1 Rhodes well in the Jal area, Lea County. (9)

The first search for oil in **Norway,** made by Norwegian geologists, Dr. Anders K. Orvin and Dr. Gunnar Horn, in the vicinity of Grenfjorden at Spitzbergen. (45)

The first electric-power, **automatically-controlled pipeline** built in California, the forerunner of present-day lines. (19)

Pittsburgh Equitable Meter Company formed when Equitable Meter and Manufacturing Company purchases Pittsburgh Meter Company. (38)

Plane, First Executive—Standard Oil of Indiana purchases a Ford tri-motor airplane for its executives. This is the first plane ever built for the use of executives of any large company. (13)

For the first time, the cast-iron-type **plug** is replaced with one made of cement. (40)

E. J. Miley's Athens 6 well in Rosecrans field, California, sets **deep production** record flowing from pay bottomed at 7591 feet. (World Oil)

A. O. Smith Corporation introduces high-strength, electrically-welded line pipe. Mass production of large-diameter pipe with less wall thickness now practical. (47)

The State Monopoly on petroleum and products called Campsa (Compania Arrendateria del Monopolio de Petroleos, S. A.) set up by **Spain.** (64)

Pasotex Petroleum Company, later renamed **Standard Oil Company of Texas,** organizes to market in West Texas. This is Standard's (California) first domestic marketing venture outside the seven western states. (50)

Tube Turns founded as Pipe Bending Process Company in Louisville, Kentucky, as manufacturers of forged seamless welding elbows and returns. (50)

Deepest well record set by Chansler-Canfield-Midway Oil Company's Olinda 96 well in Olinda field, California, 8046 feet. (World Oil)

Standard Oil Company of New Jersey and **I. G. Farben** reach an agreement which, in effect, makes available to Standard the immense German experience in a field of chemistry—catalytic—almost entirely unexplored by United States petroleum technicians. (50)

The earliest injection project involving a higher level of injection pressure (1160 psi) instituted by Marland Oil Company in the Seal Beach field of California. Continued until 1928. (1)

Louisiana State University organizes Petroleum Engineering department. (1)

A Mexican Supreme Court decision declares that the right of a company to explore for and produce oil may not be limited to 50 years. The decision negates a 1925 law requiring oil companies to exchange their titles to oil lands for 50 year concessions. (**Mexico Oil Law**) (14)

Standard Oil Company (New Jersey) becomes a holding company, and transfers its refining and marketing functions to Standard Oil Company of New Jersey (now Esso Standard). (50)

1928

January—The first **marsh buggies** built and operated by Ed Arpin in connection with a hunting lodge south of Gueydan, Louisiana; later converted to geophysical use. (Homer Patrick)

February—**Near East Development Company,** composed of Standard Oil Company (New Jersey), Socony Oil Company of New York, Gulf

Oil Corporation, Atlantic Refining Company, and Mexican Petroleum Company, organized. Sinclair and The Texas Company had withdrawn from original seven companies. Later Gulf and Mexican Oil sold their interest to the two Standard Companies. (80)

March 10—The Texas Railroad Commission appoints a committee of six to consider the feasibility of limiting production of the prolific **Hendricks Field** under a **proration** agreement similar to those already effective in the Seminole and Yates Fields. (2)

April 4—Texas Railroad Commission issues **first Texas proration order** based on the conservation statutes—pertains to Hendricks Pool in Winkler County. Hendricks order effective 5-5-28 followed by Yates, Howard-Glasscock. First proration order in Texas issued 7-18-1919 on NW extension to Burkburnett. (58)

April 16—First **Rule 37 Case**—United States Supreme Court holds that the Act of March 31, 1919, conferring authority on the **Texas Railroad Commission** to administer the oil and gas laws is a proper exercise of the police power of the state in controlling the development of natural resources. Rule 37 attacked as violative of the 14th Amendment to the Federal Constitution. (58)

May 9—**Southern Natural Gas Company** formed as Southern Natural Gas Corporation for the purpose of constructing, owning and operating a natural gas transmission system. (50)

June 1—Standard Oil of Venezuela discovers **Quiriquire field** when Moneb No. 1 well comes in flowing 500 barrels of oil per day. This is SOV's first discovery of commercial production in Venezuela. (Creole records)

June 16—A broad program for improving production methods and increasing efficiency of oil recovery instituted at a general meeting of the **API Division of Development and Production Engineering.** (2)

June 19—Midwest Refining Company discovers **Hobbs field** in Lea County, New Mexico, at 4065 feet with a 200-barrel well. In 1929 Humble Oil & Refining Company opens the first large production in the field three miles northwest of the Midwest discovery. (75)

June—**Denver and Pueblo,** Colorado, change to straight natural gas piped by the longest and largest natural gas pipeline in existence at this time. (38)

July 31—**Red Line Agreement** consummated with the organization of the **Turkish Petroleum Company,** which is composed of Anglo-Persian Oil Company, Royal Dutch-Shell Company, Compagnie Francaise des Petroles, and Near East Development Company, each with 23.75 per cent ownership, and **Calouste Gulbenkian** with the other five per cent. It limits activities of the participants to specified Middle Eastern areas marked out by a red line on the map. (80)

July—**Elwood field,** California, discovered. (67)

July—The **Schlumberger** brothers have a crew commercially operating "**electrical coring**" methods in France, the first commercial application (The Petroleum Times, 1936). (73)

September 9—The **first statewide oil proration order** issued by a state regulatory body is Order No. 4430 of the Corporation Commission of Oklahoma. It recites a total demand for the state for 700,000 barrels of oil which is divided 275,000 barrels per day to the settled pools and 425,000 barrels per day to the flush pools (Seminole area). The allocation between the flush pools is based on potentials. (9)

September 26—**Augua Dulce field,** Texas, discovered by Grimm and Morris No. 1 Garrett, completed for 75,000 mcf per day from a depth of 2030 feet. (44)

September—The **API** sponsors a movement to standardize procedure for the measuring, sampling, and testing of crude oil and petroleum products. (1)

September—Seventeen wells are being used for the **introduction of gas into the oil sand** of the Burbank field, Osage County, Oklahoma. (1)

October—**Pipe Line News** first published. (50)

October—**Shell Development Company,** organized to do basic hydrocarbon research, moves into new laboratory in Emeryville, California. (Shell Oil Company)

October—**The Oil Marketer** first published. (50)

November 8—**Kettleman North Dome Oil field** (Kettleman Hills) discovered by Milham Exploration Company's No. 1 Elliott well which comes in out of control. Fresno and King Counties. (74)

November 10—**Getty Oil Company,** Wilmington, Del., incorporated as Pacific Western Oil Corp. Present company name adopted 1956. (50)

November 12—Texaco enters into a contract with **Louisiana Land & Exploration Company** to develop land in southern Louisiana. (50)

November—**Bemis-Shutts field** discovered in Kansas by Phillips Petroleum Company No. 1 Shutts completed for 290 barrels per day at 3569 feet. (70)

November—The **Texas-Empire Pipe Line Company** incorporated in Delaware to operate a pipe line from Oklahoma to the East Chicago area. (Texaco, Inc.)

November & December—California Talc Company sells 32.95 tons of Aquagel to General Petroleum Corporation to stop **caving shale** in their Ochsner No. 2 well at Kettleman Hills, California. (Baroid Division National Lead Company)

December 3—API President **Axtell J. Byles,** at the annual meeting urges foreign producers of oil to curtail production—**warning of tariff** on the import of oil. (2)

155

December 4—**Oklahoma Ciey field** discovered by Foster Petroleum-ITIO on land purchased from Mrs. Celia Hall. The well comes in out of control from 6355 feet and produces 4909 barrels of 40 gravity oil per day when controlled. (75)

December 15—King Mohammed V, of **Morocco,** at recommendation of Erik Labonne, signs law creating Bureau of Mining Research and Participation, dedicated to oil exploration. (45)

December 21—Standard Oil Company of California assumes obligations and commitments of **Eastern Gulf Oil Company's Bahrein option contract** upon payment of $50,000. This is the first all-American oil venture in the Middle East. (80)

December—The API board adopts a **code of ethics for marketing,** subject to approval by the Federal Trade Commission. (12)

Research begins on possible use of gas as fuel for system to produce cold air for summer **air-conditioning.** A. G. A. committee on Natural Gas Research makes 15 installations. (38)

Otis Engineering Corporation formed as Southern States Corporation in Shreveport, La., to engineer, manufacture, and sell well completion and production equipment. (50)

The first **Alchlor treaters** used in the production of lube oils placed in operation at Gulf's Port Arthur Refinery. (50)

Baroid Division National Lead Company founded as California Talc Company in Los Angeles, California, as a service company selling Aquagel and Baroid. (50)

First **butane-air gas plant** installed at Linton, Indiana, replacing a coal-gas plant. (38)

Stray railway currents—instead of being kept off the lines—used as a source of **cathodic-protection current.** (40)

Chiksan Company founded as Chiksan Oil Tool Company in Fullerton, California, as manufacturers of drilling disc bits, reamers, and tong dies. (50)

The first mechanical **drift indicator** run by Technical Oil Tool Corporation on drilling rig in the Dominguez field in the Los Angeles basin. (50)

El Paso Natural Gas Co. organized to transport gas from Lea County, New Mexico, gas fields, to the El Paso area. Builds 208-mile line with delivery capacity of 36,000,000 cu. ft. per day. (5)

The French government draws up a petroleum charter which makes possible the development of the **French oil-refining industry.** (45)

The **Gach Saran** field discovered in Iran. (70)

The **Haft Kel** field discovered in Iran. (70)

Gas-fired unit heater, hung from ceiling joists or beams, introduced to gas industry at A. G. A. convention; heater represents important development for industry. (38)

Houston Oil Field Material Company, Inc., founded in Houston, Texas, as manufacturers of remedial tools for the recovery of packers and liners in wells. (50)

E. O. Bennett calls attention to the increased use of **natural gas injection** into oil reservoirs to aid in the recovery process. (1)

New Orleans receives its first natural gas when the 100-mile, 18-inch extension of the Monroe field-Baton Rouge pipe line completed. (47)

J. C. Paterich invents the rubber-like material, **Thiokol.** (25)

The American Petroleum Institute begins publication of "**Petroleum Facts and Figures.**" (62)

Amerada makes first **bottom-hole pressure** measurements. Runs deviation tests on drilling holes. Determines that slower drilling rates permit reduction in hole deviation. (1)

Reed Roller Bit Company develops and markets the first rotary wire line drilling-coring outfit. (50)

Successful **profiling of salt domes** by **reflection seismograph** first achieved when a good profile is obtained across Barbers Hill Dome. (40)

Cespa (Compania Española de Petroleos, S. A.), a 100 per cent private and independent company, founded in **Spain,** and in 1929-30 constructs the Teneriffe Refinery in the Canary Islands. (64)

A. P. I. records show that the first welded **tank committee** appointed. (1)

Gulf Oil Corporation installs the first fire-wall type **automatic tank gauges** at Sour Lake, Texas, and the first remote-reading automatic tank gauges in 1930 at the same place. Both types of gauges built by Gulf in its Beaumont, Texas, shop. (50)

Tubing first installed in flowing wells against high pressure in the gas fields of northern Louisiana. (47)

Electric-arc welding used on section of Mississippi River Fuel Corporation's line in Louisiana, first major gas pipeline electric welding job. (38)

Deepest well drilled by Texon Oil and Land Company. University 1-B well, Big Lake field, Texas. Depth 8523 feet. (World Oil)

The bulletin on production and development problems in the Powell field, Navarro county, Texas, by **Hill and Sutton** calls attention to the prolific **Woodbine reservoirs** and to the effect of water in obtaining high oil recovery. (64)

The United States Congress repeals the **federal excise tax** on automobiles, motorcycles and buses, entirely withdrawing the federal government from the automotive tax field. (62)

First commercial **pipe coating plant** established to perform mill-coating-and-wrapping of pipe. (38)

The **Texaco-Cities Service Pipe Line Company** lays 10- and 12-inch lines from Seminole, Oklahoma, to East Chicago, Illinois, a Major Joint-Interest Crude System. (40)

Texaco organizes **first Aviation Division.** It is headed by Captain Frank Hawks, who was to make the first non-stop transcontinental flight in 1929. (50)

New Orleans, Louisiana, begins large scale application of **cathodic protection** to its gas distribution system. (38)

Standard Oil Company of New Jersey buys the Venezuelan holdings of **Creole Petroleum Corporation.** (50)

Texaco becomes the **first oil company to market in all the states** of the United States. (50)

Union of California introduces propane-dry **gas injection** idea in wells in Dominguez field, California. (1)

Method for **"reforming" high Btu gases**—such as refinery gas—into gases with Btu and physical characteristics similar to city gases then distributed, is perfected by Perry of the U.G.I. company. (38)

Tia Juana field discovered by Venezuelan Oil Concessions Ltd. but well shut in because of low gravity and small production; activity resumed in 1936 and 1100-barrel well completed at shallow depth. (77)

University of Tulsa organizes Petroleum Engineering Department. (1)

1929

January 1—**Memphis** receives its first natural gas service. The gas supplied from the Monroe field through the **Memphis Natural Gas Company's** 210-mile, 18-inch pipe line. (47)

February 11—American Petroleum Institute Committee, appointed by incoming President Reeser to study and report on **conservation,** adopts resolution recommending state laws to prevent gas waste and protect against dangerous oil waste. (2)

February 18—**Shell Chemical Corporation** organized to manufacture chemicals from petroleum by-products, utilizing processes originated by Shell Development research. (Shell Oil Company)

February 26—California Talc Company negotiates an agreement with Silica Products Company for exclusive sales rights to **bentonite,** for use in cement and oil well drilling on the Pacific Coast. (Baroid Division National Lead Company)

February 27—**Atlas Supply Co.,** partly owned by Standard Oil Company (Indiana), organized. (50)

158

February—**Kerr-McGee Oil Industries, Inc.,** formed as Anderson-Kerr Drilling Company. Subsequent mergers include Fen-Ter Refining Company in July 1948; J. E. Crosbie, Inc., in February 1951; Deep Rock Oil Corporation in April 1955; Triangle Refineries, Inc., in May 1957. (50)

March 12—**President Hoover** closes **public domain** to leasing. (3)

April 2—The **American Petroleum Institute** submits to Federal Oil Conservation Board a proposal for a **world-wide** plan for the **limitation of oil production** to demand, but the Attorney General replies saying Congress has not granted the Federal Board or any other agency the power to grant immunity from the operation of the Sherman Act. (Conservation in the Production of Petroleum, Zimmerman, Yale University Press, 1957)

April 8—U. S. Supreme Court unanimously affirms conviction of **Harry F. Sinclair** on contempt charges in connection with **Teapot Dome oil scandals.** After serving his 3-month sentence and paying $500 fine he is unanimously retained by vote of the board of directors as chairman of the board of Sinclair Consolidated Oil Corporation. (78)

April 9—**J. J. Cabot** invents the **logging caliper.** (1)

April 12—**Ward-Estes, North field,** Texas discovered by Gulf Production Co. No. 4 O'Brien making 1500 barrels a day at 2631 feet. (44)

April—Amerada Petroleum Corp. runs a **bottom hole pressure bomb** in the Earlsboro field in Oklahoma. (50)

April—**Eunice-Monument field** discovered in New Mexico by Marland and California Companies 1-B - 31 Lockhart. (67)

April—The Federal Government begins operation of its **helium** extraction plant near Amarillo, Texas. (44)

May 24—**Drilling and Exploration Company, Inc.,** founded with principal office in New York City. (50)

May 28—**California**'s Governor C. C. Young signs a "new" gas conservation law extending state authority to production of crude oil by granting power to prevent the over-production and waste of natural gas. (2)

May 31—Final report of Navy Department on cancellation of leases at Teapot Dome and Elk Hills in connection with **Teapot Dome oil scandals** results in the collection of more than $43 million by government. (78)

June 11—The **Independent Petroleum Association of America** formed in Colorado Springs, Colorado. (57)

June—**"Super Service Station"** starts publication. (50)

June—Turkish Petroleum Company becomes known as **Iraq Petroleum Company, Ltd.** (80)

July 10—**Darst Creek field** discovered in Guadalupe County, Texas by The Texas Company. Becomes first field in Southwest to undergo **proration** and regulation of output. (41)

August 5—**Societe de Prospection Electrique,** the parent organization of Schlumberger methods in use today, makes the **first electric log in the western hemisphere,** for Shell in **Venezuela** (The Petroleum Times, 1936). Then the following rapid expansion of service is noted: at beginning of year, only in France; a crew in Venezuela in March; in the United States in June; and in Russia in August. (73)

August 17—**First Schlumberger Electrical Log in United States** run in B-Boston Land Company's well in West Haven area of California for Shell Oil Company. (50)

September 14—The Marathon Oil Company's (then Ohio) I. G. Yates "A" No. 30 is the "**largest individual well**" in the oil industry's history. The well drilled to 1070 feet, with a record daily production of 202,224 barrels. (50)

October 7—Secretary of Interior **Albert B. Fall** starts serving jail sentence in Santa Fe Penitentiary in New Mexico (he was permitted to select his own prison) for his part in **Teapot Dome oil scandals.** He had been convicted in July. (78)

October 14—Pure Oil Company completes Jarman No. 1 as the discovery well of the **Van field** in Texas, producing 146 barrels per hour from Woodbine sand at 2656-2710 feet, and unit operation of pool undertaken. This is nation's **first major unitization project,** and first field to be completely unitized. (5) (11) (44)

October 22—A committee of the **American Bar Association** recommends enactment of **federal legislation** on oil and gas conservation. (2)

October 29—**Great Depression** is triggered with crash of stock market.

October—The first issue of **The Petroleum Engineer** published. (50)

November 29—Admiral Richard Byrd makes the first flight over the South Pole. (54)

December 3—The **API** suggests a reduction of refinery **gasoline** production, and officially recognizes and approves the policy of **unitization.** (2)

December 11—The **New Mexico Oil and Gas Association** formed and holds its organizational meeting in Artesia, New Mexico. (57)

December 24—The **Texas Company (Overseas) Ltd.** organized. (50)

December—Chicksan Company introduces the **all-metal rotary hose** for transmitting drilling mud. (50)

December—**Eason Oil Company,** Oklahoma City, begins operations under its present name, concluding a series of reorganizations and mergers that began in November 1913 with formation of the Healdton Oil and Gas Co., the original Eason firm. (50)

160

California—Formation of the **Conservation Committee of California Oil Producers.** (3)

Mid-Continent Supply Company founded in Fort Worth, Texas, with first company store in Houston. (50)

The **fluidized catalyst** concept stems from the **William W. Odell** patent. Rights acquired by Jersey Standard in 1936 when that company filed for re-issue of the patent to cover catalytic cracking of petroleum fractions. (40)

A **ram-type blowout preventer** is invented by W. D. Shaffer and first used successfully this year at Seal Beach, Calif. The device is followed in 1930 by the first 3000 psi blowout preventer and wellhead control, and immediately thereafter by the first 5000 and 6000 psi blowout preventers. (50)

Colorado—Act passed making it the duty of the Gas Conservation Commission to prescribe rules for proper closing of wells drilled for oil and gas. (3)

Continental's **E. H. Griswold** reports on use of acid bottle in **crooked-hole surveys** and draws attention to distortion of subsurface data by crooked holes. (1)

The question of oil field **salt water disposal** covered so competently and thoroughly by **Schmidt and Devine** that their report still dictates modern methods to a marked degree. (64)

One of the most significant advances in **compressor engines** is the introduction of the angle-type unit. (40)

The **Gyroscopic Inclinometer,** a tool which determines deviation from the vertical of a well being drilled, devised by Sun Oil Company scientists. (50)

Esso Research and Development Company, and other firms acquire rights to the I. G. **Farben oil-refining process,** including **Hydroforming.** (40)

Jersey Standard and Ethyl Corporation produce **iso-octane** in small quantity for use in laboratories as the basis for the iso-octane scale. (12)

Lago Petroleum Corporation, using wooden or concrete piles as derrick foundations, sinks wells in five fathoms of water in **Lake Maracaibo,** Venezuela. (45)

The FTC approves a **"fair practice" code** in an attempt to end chaotic competition in **gasoline marketing.** (40)

Michigan passes a general oil and gas conservation statute containing most of the better conservation features of a number of the older oil and gas states. (9)

In **Morocco,** the **Societe Cherifienne des Petroles** is formed, staffed with qualified technicians and adequate equipment. It surveys the Rharb and pre-Rif regions of northern Morocco, also makes general survey of country for its oil potential. (45)

A résumé by **H. C. Miller, "The Function of Natural Gas in the Production of Oil,"** published jointly by the Bureau of Mines and the American Petroleum Institute. (48)

New Mexico—Legislature enacts a law providing for the cooperative development of oil fields. (9)

New Mexico—The first large oil well in New Mexico, completed in Lea County, is the Humble Oil & Refining Company, Bowers No. 1 well, in the Hobbs field which comes in for 9720 bbl. of oil a day. (9)

North Dakota enacts second conservation measure. (3)

The 297-mile pipe line, built by **Pacific Gas & Electric Co.,** of 16-20- and 22-inch pipe, from the Buttonwillow and Kettleman Hill fields to San Francisco, Oakland and San Jose is the first large-diameter, long-distance gas line of all-welded construction. (47)

V. A. Sokolov works out and proposes the **gas survey method of prospecting** for petroleum. (27)

South Dakota—Legislature passes act prohibiting the use of natural gas in any form without fully utilizing its heat units in manufacture or domestic use. (3)

Southern Union Gas Company organized. (38)

First **underground gas-storage** project in the Southwest commenced by Cities Service Gas Co. in Eastern Kansas. (5)

Technical Oil Tool Corporation founded in Los Angeles, California as manufacturers of Drift Indicator, "Totco Recorder." (50)

The Federal Government begins requiring **unit operation** by lessees on public lands. (40)

Viscosity index becomes an important criterion of lube quality. The first viscosity-index chart introduced by Standard Oil Company of New Jersey. (40)

Deepest well, Shell Oil Company's Nesa 1, Long Beach, California, 9280 feet. (World Oil)

West Texas now has 5500 miles of pipeline, costing $150,000,000— considered a new record for any oil area. (5)

West Virginia—Drilling and Plugging Statute passed. (3)

For the first time, crude oil production is over 1 billion barrels a year in the United States. (48)

This is the first year that all 48 states levy a **gasoline tax,** with New York becoming the last to join the list. (62)

Bahrein Petroleum Company, Ltd., wholly-owned subsidiary of California-Standard, formed in Ottawa, Canada. (80)

Medearis Oilwell Supply Corporation founded as California Bettis Company in Los Angeles, California to sell and service drill pipe protectors and mud shakers. (50)

Southern Natural Gas system—from Louisiana fields across the southern states—begins construction. First natural gas delivered in December to a lime kiln near Birmingham, Alabama. (38)

The first refinery in **Spain** built for 500 barrels per day capacity in the town of Cornella (near Barcelona). It is now shut down and the installation used for storage. (64)

Texas A & M College organizes Petroleum Engineering Department. (1)

University of Southern California organizes Petroleum Engineering Department. (1)

Secretary of Interior **R. L. Wilbur** suggests that oil states form an **interstate oil compact** to conserve oil and gas. (40)   **President Hoover's** plea for such a compact is rejected by industry meeting at Colorado Springs. (60)

1929-30—A special research committee of the American Society of Mechanical Engineers designs **automatic stations** using tanks and liquid-level instruments. The stations are exhibited at the International Petroleum Exposition in Tulsa. (40)

1930

January 1—The **Gasoline Retailer starts** publication. (50)

January 1—The **API** Divisions of Production, Refining, Marketing and Statistics organized. (62)

January 18—The **North Texas Oil and Gas Association** formed in Wichita Falls to protest a 25 cents crude price cut and to formulate a plan of action. (57)

January 25—**Keystone field,** Winkler County, Texas brought in by M. J. Bashara and Sons in their No. 2 Fee well. The first well in the field, the M. J. Bashara et al No. 1 Fee blew out and caught fire on May 1, 1929. (41)

January 29—The Independent Petroleum Association of America **(IPAA)** appeals to Congress for   **import tariff,** blaming the surplus of crude brought in from foreign fields. (2)

January—**Calliou Island field,** Louisiana, discovered. (67)

163

February 11—API President Reeser appoints a Central Committee on Unit Operation to guide the Institute's "work in promoting the **unit development** and operation of oil pools." (22)

February 28—**Baroid Sales Company of California** formed. (50)

February—Mississippi—The Mayes No. 1 well of the Jackson Oil & Gas Company, is the discovery well of the **Jackson field.** (9)

February—**World Petroleum** first published. (50)

March 4—The **Federal Oil Conservation Board** suggests a six-day week for gasoline refineries, in effect lowering production one-seventh. (2)

March 10—Secretary of Interior R. L. Wilbur initiates program of government **demand forecasts** of refinery products and through it the demand of crude necessary to yield such products.

March 18—Texas Legislature passes the "**Common Purchaser Act,**" Chapter 36 of the Acts of the 41st Legislature. Act provides in part that a purchaser of oil who is a common carrier or is affiliated with a common carrier should purchase oil ratably with no discrimination. (9)

March 29—**United Gas Corporation,** a holding company, incorporated under the laws of Delaware. Approximately two months later, more than forty associated companies are welded into United Gas Corporation and the new firm starts in business on June 3, 1930. (50)

April 25—**Northern Natural Gas Company** organized in Wilmington, Delaware. Three large holding companies, United Light & Railway Company, Lone Star Gas Corporation and North American Light and Power provide the capital. (50)

April—The **Independent Petroleum Association of America** Monthly first published. (57)

April—The Humble Oil & Refining Company begins **gas injections** in its **Sugarland field.** The gas injected into the field's free gas cap to control reservoir pressure and edgewater encroachment. (40)

May 20—The **Society of Exploration Geophysicists** founded under the name, "Society of Petroleum Geophysicists," in Houston, Texas. Its present name adopted in 1936. (57)

June 17—Standard of California runs a **bottom hole pressure bomb** in the Taft field in California. On Sept. 30 the company runs a second bomb in the Yates field in Texas. (50)

June 30—The **Oklahoma Corporate Commission** acts on a state-wide scale. Production materially restricted, for what proves to be the essential step in waste prevention and protection of property rights. (1)

July 3—A temporary statute adopted authorizing Secretary of Interior to approve **unitization** plans. (3)

July 10—Lagunita No. 1 of Venezuelan Oil Concessions Ltd. completed for 150 barrels daily at 3915 feet as the discovery well of **Bachaquero field, Venezuela.** (77)

August 1—Bahrein oil concession assigned to **Bahrein Petroleum Company, Ltd.,** by Standard of California. (80)

August 9—Construction starts on the first **multi-product, long-distance pipeline.** Extending initially from Borger, Texas, to East St. Louis, Illinois, the line later extended to East Chicago, Indiana. (54)

August 14—Texas Railroad Commission issues its first **"Statewide Proration Order"** with effective date of August 27, 1930, to limit the production of Texas to 750,000 barrels per day, representing a cut in production from previous year of some 50,000 barrels. Order is based on the reasonable **market demand** for same. (58)

August 20—The Ohio Oil Company (now Marathon) buys the assets of **Transcontinental Oil Company,** including: remaining one-half interest in Yates Pool, Texas; producing properties in seven states; transportation and refining facilities; and Transcontinental's marketing subsidiary, the **Marathon Oil Company.** (50)

August—Peoples Gas Light & Coke introduces the first **"therm" rate** in the United States. (38)

September 10—**Cowden, North field,** Texas, discovered by Southern Crude Oil Co. Well completed for 281 barrels per day at 4244 feet (44)

September 22—Standard Oil Company (Indiana) acquires full ownership of a crude oil purchasing company in which Standard already owns a half interest. It was then named **Stanolind Crude Oil Purchasing Co.** (now **Indiana Oil Purchasing Co.**). (50)

September 22—Standard Oil Company (Indiana) acquires full ownership of 6878-mile crude pipeline and names it Stanolind Pipe Line Company (now **Service Pipe Line Co.**). (50)

September 29—**Ventura Tool Company** founded in Ventura, California, engaging in general oilfield repair. (50)

October 5—The **East Texas field,** largest oil reservoir in the Western Hemisphere, discovered by **Columbus Marion "Dad" Joiner** when his **Daisy Bradford 3** well, a rank wildcat and his third "pore boy" effort on the Bradford farm in Rusk County, Texas, comes in at 3536 feet to open a stratigraphic trap in the Woodbine formation loaded with six billion barrels of oil. It is larger than the next 20 fields in the U. S. combined. More than 25,000 wells drilled. This field makes conservation a necessity. It promotes the system of **oil payments.** It promotes numerous changes in engineering and geological thinking and brings numerous landmark legal decisions that will influence oil and gas legislation and regulations all over the world. (56)

Standard Oil Company of New York acquires **White Eagle Oil & Refining Company,** a Delaware corporation. (50)

Magnolia builds Luling-San Antonio **products pipeline.** (44)

Standard Oil Company of New Jersey interests become majority shareholders in **Anglo-American Oil Co.,** the British marketing concern which had been among the companies severed in 1911. (50)

Bentonite brought into the oil fields as a rotary-mud conditioner. (1)

A rectifier first used for **cathodic protection** in New Orleans. Results reviewed in 1956 showed that no corrosion leaks had occurred on cathodically-protected 473 miles of pipe in New Orleans. (40)

Southern Union Gas Company builds 200 miles of 10- and 12-inch line from the San Juan Basin to Albuquerque and Santa Fe, New Mexico; this is the **first gas line to cross the Continental Divide.** (38)

Eastman Oil Well Survey Company founded as **H. John Eastman,** Controlled Drilling and Oil Well Survey Services in Long Beach, California, as manufacturers of **directional drilling equipment** and **oil well survey instruments.** (50)

The Bureau of Mines analyzes **natural gas supply and demand** for the American Gas Association. (48)

The **Kremser Equation** for designing absorbers introduced by Alois Kremser, Standard Oil Company of California. (Natural Gas Processors Association)

Seaboard, the largest individual interest in the Kettleman North Dome Association in California, through KNDA initiates the extensive use of **electric logging.** (1)

A pipe line completed connecting Las Cruces and Los Manueles, Venezuela, fields with the shore of **Lake Maracaibo.** (45)

The Bureau of Mines begins a study of the odorization of natural gas and their report details extensive tests with **ethyl mercaptan** as the odorant. (48)

Continental Construction Corporation, with affiliate Texoma Natural Gas Company (both forerunners of **Natural Gas Pipeline Company of America**), begins construction on the first long-distance, high-pressure, large-diameter natural gas pipeline to Chicago. First use of thin-wall longitudinal pipe as developed by Company and A. O. Smith Corporation, during planning stages for line (1927-30). Line construction also employs electric welding. Line design capacity is 175 MMCF. Deliveries of gas began October 16, 1931. (50)

Dr. Graham Edgar is credited with perfecting the **octane scale** for determining the antiknock performance of motor fuels. (40)

In **Mexico,** the large **Poza Rica field** discovered by the Compania Mexicana de Petroleo—El Aguila—a subsidiary of Royal Dutch-Shell. (14)

Star Petroleum Co.'s Colby 2 well in Long Beach field, California, sets **deep production** record flowing from pay bottomed a 8550 feet. (World Oil)

The electric **submersible pump** brought into use. (1)

166

H. B. Hill's paper on the Williams pool in Texas shows the results of **air repressuring** on leases operated as a unit for increasing recovery by secondary methods. (64)

First natural-gasoline plant on Gulf Coast built at **Raccoon Bend,** Austin County, in connection with **sand-repressuring** project of Humble Oil & Refining Co. (5)

The **Rodessa field** discovered as a gas field but subsequent development proves it to be a major oil and gas field, lying in three states—Louisiana, Texas and Arkansas. (47)

Gulf Oil Corporation builds the first rubber **swab scraper** in its Beaumont, Texas, shop. The swab built and used for swabbing water out of Gulf's West Texas Sour System to reduce internal corrosion caused from the water and sour crude. (50)

K. C. Heald makes careful **temperature measurements** in a number of oil wells in the Tonkawa and Burbank fields of Oklahoma and fails to show any irregularities whatever that would suggest any localization of heat near oil sands. He concludes that abnormal amounts of heat are not associated with deposits of petroleum. (22)

Vernon Tool Co., Ltd., founded in Vernon, California, as manufacturers of tool joints, drill collars, shale shakers and pumping units. (50)

Deepest well drilled by Standard Oil of California's No. 1 Mascot, Midway field, California, 9753 feet. (World Oil)

The **"Wild Mary"** Sudik well on March 26 makes a roaring arrival in Oklahoma City field, defying control for 11 days, and attracting national attention. (5)

Cabot Shops, Incorporated founded in Pampa, Texas, to fabricate carbon black plants. (50)

Cement used in oil fields in Oklahoma, in Kansas, and in Illinois, with a marked increase in oil production and recovery. Earlier use was in Goose Creek by **R. A. Welch** and **L. P. Garrett** about 1905. (48)

Rector Well Equipment Company, Inc., founded in Fort Worth, Texas as manufacturers of casing heads. (50)

First construction of a **solid electric-welded gas line** (without expansion joints or couplings between welded joints) for Cities Service Pipeline Co., in Kansas, by H. C. Price Co. (50)

University of Texas organizes Petroleum Engineering Department. (1)

There are 26,749,853 motor vehicle registrations in the United States. (11)

1931

January 1—**Stanolind Oil and Gas Co.** (now Pan American Petroleum Corporation) organized by combining **Dixie Oil Company** and other producing properties. (Standard Oil Company (Indiana))

January 6—Holders of chief process patents in **thermal cracking field**

167

sign agreement ending 15 years of litigation. Patents assigned to **Universal Oil Products Co.,** which is purchased by Shell and four other oil companies. (50)

January 15 and 16—Representatives of governors of oil-producing states meet in Washington to discuss **proration** in the various states. (2)

January 31—**United Gas Corporation** extends its operations eastward by the purchase of a pipeline approximately 202 miles in length. The line extends from Benton, Mississippi, to Mobile, Alabama, and Pensacola, Florida. (50)

January—The American Petroleum Institute publishes the first issue of the **API Quarterly.** (62)

January—The **El Plan field** of Mexico discovered. (70)

January—The use of the **swivel joint** for making all-metal lines flexible introduced by Chiksan Company. (50)

February 28—On call of Gov. William H. Murray of Oklahoma, governors of Texas, New Mexico, Kansas and Oklahoma meet in Fort Worth and create **Oil States Advisory Committee** "to study the present distressed condition of the petroleum industry and to make recommendations for uniform legislation looking to the relief of said industry and the conservation of oil and gas." (60)

February—**Schlumberger** introduces **electrical logging** into Rumania. (50)

March 4—Congress authorizes Secretary of Interior to enter into oil and gas unit development in the **public domain.** (62)

March 9—First meeting of newly formed **Oil States Advisory Committee** held in Texarkana with representatives from Texas, Oklahoma, California, Arkansas, Kansas, and Wyoming present. Later, committee urges Federal Oil Conservation Board to try to stabilize oil production, curtail imports, asks coordination among the states with federal cooperation, and authorization of an interstate agreement. Committee functioned until NRA code was adopted. (60)

March 15—Proration Act passed by **Kansas** Legislature. (9)

March 17—**Hunt Tool Company** founded by T. N. Hunt in Houston, Texas as authorized Appleman Bit Service Company, Inc. (50)

March—The **Bradford District Pennsylvania Oil Producers Association** formed from the former Northwestern Pennsylvania Oil Producers Association, which had been founded on July 27, 1918. (57)

April 1 to September 30—At the request of the Federal Oil Conservation Board, the Bureau of Mines' first **forecast** of both crude oil and gasoline **supply** and **demand** made for this period. (48)

April 3—**Texas Gulf Producing Company** organized as Nat Hunter Producing Company. (50)

April 4—Texas Railroad Commission issues first proration order for the **East Texas Field** with an effective date of May 1, 1931, providing for an allowable in excess of 1000 barrels per day per well. (Order changed on April 22, 1931 and again on April 29, 1931 prior to effective date.) (58)

April 4—Humble Oil & Refining Company runs a **bottom hole pressure bomb** on the Ben Laird No. 1 well in the East Texas field about the same time the company runs other similar tests on the Peterson 1, and the Crim Nos 2, 3, 5, 9, and 14 wells, all in East Texas field. (50)

April 10—The first drill stem test using an **equalizer valve** in the tool conducted at Belridge in the San Joaquin Valley, California by Johnston Testers. (50)

April 11—A bill establishing the **Drake Well Memorial Park** on the site of America's first commercially successful oil well at Titusville, Pennsylvania, signed by Governor Pinchot of Pennsylvania. (54)

April 12—**K.M.A. field,** Texas, discovered by Deep Oil Development Co. No. 1-A Munger. (44)

April—**Chase-Silica** field, Kansas, discovered. (67)

May 1—First proration order for the **East Texas Field** becomes effective. At this time the East Texas Field is producing one million barrels of oil per day, one-third of the national production, and the price of oil drops to 10 cents a barrel. "There was much unrest with talk of threats of blowing up wells and pipelines." (58)

May 14—First **turbojet plane** flown.

May 19—The **Iraq concession of 1925** to Iraq Petroleum Company amended with the company receiving a single territory of 32,000 square miles, in lieu of the block system, in the Mosul and Baghdad vilayets, east of the Tigris. The company's rights restricted to that single area. (80)

May 21—**Thompson field,** Fort Bend County, Texas, discovered by Gulf Production Company and Cullen and West No. 1-A Lockwood and Sharp well making 400 barrels per day at 3089 feet. Field first called "Clear Lake," then "Rabb's Ridge" before Thompson. (42) (44)

June 10—Legislation passed, revising, recodifying and supplementing the entire mining laws of **Ohio.** (3)

June 23—**Quaker State Refining Corporation** incorporated at Oil City, Pa., consolidating 18 oil companies, some of which date back to the 1890's. (50)

June 27—**Minnesota Northern Natural Gas Company** organized. (50)

June—Humble Oil & Refining Company et al completes Cockrell-Moran No. 4 for 1000 barrels per day from cap rock at **Grande Ecaille,** Plaquemines Parish, Louisiana; is better known as **Lake Washington**

field; extensions made in 1950 to the Southwest by Placid Oil Company and The Texas Company and in 1952 extension of more than two miles to northwest, made by John W. Mecom with well making about 200 barrels per day and considerable gas from 11,872 to 11,890 feet. (42) (50)

July 14—**Governor Sterling** of Texas calls a special session of the state legislature to strengthen the state's conservation powers and to make enforceable its regulations pertaining to proration. (2)

July 23—Attorney General Mitchell advises President Hoover that he is without authority to place an embargo against the **importation of oil** into the U. S. under the provisions of the Hawley-Smoot Tariff Act. (2)

July 28—**Vacuum Oil Company, Inc.,** incorporated in New York. On July 31, 1931, Socony-Vacuum Corporation transfers to Vacuum Oil Company, Inc., all the assets (except $5,626,900 cash) received from Vacuum Oil Company. (50)

July 28—Three-judge federal court holds April 4, 1931 proration order for **East Texas Field** invalid on the basis that the order has no reasonable relation to physical waste, but is based on market demand which affects price fixing and economic waste (which is specifically prohibited by the March 29, 1929 amendment). Macmillian et al. v. Railroad Commission, 51 F.2d 400 (W.D. Tex. 1931) reversed, 287 U. S. 576 (1932). (58)

July 30—**Standard Oil Company of New York, Inc.,** incorporated in New York. Standard Oil Company of New York changes its corporate name to Socony-Vacuum Corporation. Socony-Vacuum Corporation acquired all of the assets of Vacuum Oil Company (incorporated in New York in 1866). This union is usually referred to as the merger of Socony and Vacuum. (50)

July—Phillips Petroleum Corp. designs and operates first **pipeline** for the simultaneous movement of several types of finished **products** over a long distance from Phillips, Texas, refinery to East St. Louis, Illinois. (50)

August 4—**Governor Alfalfa Bill Murray,** Oklahoma, orders **Oklahoma City** and **Greater Seminole** fields shut down by state troops. (9)

August 12—Texas Legislature passes a statute which, by detailed definition, prohibits every conceivable type of physical waste but restates that **market demand** is not to be considered. (9)

August 15—All wells in **East Texas field** close down when Gov. Ross Sterling of Texas declares **martial law** and sends state troops into the field. (56)

August 24—The **Oil States Advisory Committee** adopts a definite program calling for an interstate compact which will let each oil-producing state regulate its own production but coordinate efforts between states. Compact will have to have consent of Congress after adoption. (2)

170

August—Shell Oil Company plant at Shell Point, California, becomes operative. First refinery to use natural gas to make **ammonia.** (6)

September 2—Texas Railroad Commission issues second proration order for the **East Texas field** limiting production to approximately 400,000 barrels per day, but changes materially the method of distribution of the allowable production by allowing each well to produce 225 barrels a day without respect to the potential of the well or the size or productive character of the tract upon which the well is drilled. (Note— prior order of May 1, 1931, distributed allowable on the basis partly on the areas of productive units and partly on the maximum area to be credited to a producing well.) (58)

September 13—Kansas, Oklahoma and Texas agree to enforce proration. Court decisions uphold authority of state governments to use police powers to enforce restrictions and regulations on production. **Temporary compact** partly enforced by martial law declared in Texas and Oklahoma fields. (2)

September 14—The first all-welded, self-propelled sea-going vessel (the **"M.S. White Flash"**) commissioned after development by Atlantic Refining Company. (50)

September—**Texas Gulf Producing Company** acquires the properties of **Humphreys Corporation** which include the Barbers Hill, Texas field. (50)

October—Chicago first receives natural gas when The **Peoples Gas Light & Coke Co.** starts distributing 800 Btu mixed gas. The Natural Gas Pipe Line Co. of America pipes the gas through a 24-inch welded steel line, 1000 miles long, from the Texas Panhandle. (46)

October—Standard of California, after forming **Bahrein Petroleum Company,** spuds in its first well which comes in May 31, 1932, producing 500 barrels of oil per day from a Cretaceous limestone at 2000-2500 feet; this was discovery of production on **Bahrein Island.** (10)

December 8—Cameron Iron Works' pressure type **blowout preventer** patented to J. S. Abercrombie based on an application dated July 1, 1927. This significant new pressure operated preventer was first used in the Oklahoma City field boom. On January 20, 1933, patent (No. RE 18874) was reissued. (50)

December 31—**Conroe field** discovered by **George W. Strake's** South Texas Development Co. No. 1 well in Montgomery County, Texas, producing gas and distillate at 4931-4991 feet. Shallow drilling and numerous geophysical surveys had failed to indicate this deep-seated salt dome structure. Conroe establishes Gulf Coast as major oil province. Starts new trend of exploration and identifies **Cockfield** as prolific oil formation. Strake receives no help from any major interests in spite of lesson East Texas field a year earlier. (Houston Post) (44)

Conrad Schlumberger applies for patent on the **S. P. Measurement** in boreholes to locate permeable strata. It was granted in 1933. (Rust, 1938). (73)

Effective **bottom hole pressure bombs** developed by Amerada Petroleum Corporation and Humble Oil & Refining Company in East Texas field. (50)

Texas Legislature amends the **Common Purchaser Act** to include gas. (9)

George E. Failing Company founded as the George E. Failing Supply Company in Enid, Oklahoma, as manufacturers of portable rotary type drilling rigs. (50)

T. V. Moore and **H. D. Wilde, Jr.,** present both theoretical and experimental results of slippage in the flow of gas-oil mixtures, which is an important factor in the efficiency of the **gas lift system.** (1)

Idaho—Act passed dealing with methods of drilling and plugging. Also deals with log records. (3)

The two-meter lateral **resistivity curve** used up to this time replaced by a short normal; the **standard electric log** thus becomes the S. P. curve and a short-normal resistivity curve. (50)

Texas passes **"Marginal Well Act."** (3)

Natural Gas Processors Association introduces the first test methods and specifications of LP-Gases. (57)

Texas gas made available for distribution to eastern markets for the first time when construction completed on **Panhandle Eastern Pipe Line Company's** line from the Hugoton-Panhandle field, starting at Dumas, Texas, to Rockville, Indiana, and through an intermediate line to Muncie, Indiana, where it connects with the Columbia system. The pipe line consists of 20-, 22-, and 24-inch pipe, and, approximately 900 miles in length, is constructed at an average unit cost of $31,280.00 per mile. Five years later, the line extended to a total of 1200 miles by a branch to Detroit. (47)

F. C. Henderson, Inc. (operating an extraction plant in a gas producing portion of the **Panhandle field,** and extracting gasoline content of the gas, and blowing away about 46 million cubic feet a day) brings suit in federal court and attacks the validity of the statutes which forbid such operations. Three-judge federal court sustains the validity of the statute and enjoins the operations conducted by the company. (9)

The first **polymerization** process using heat and pressure alone, begins operation. (26)

Tide Water Associated Oil Co.'s Lloyd 57 well in Ventura Avenue field, California, sets **deep production** record flowing from pay bottomed at 8823 feet. (Oil) (World Oil)

Sun Oil Company completes one of the first pipe lines built to move refined products directly from the refinery to marketing areas. This **products pipe line** extends from Marcus Hook, Pennsylvania, west to Cleveland, Ohio, and north to Syracuse, New York. (50)

Morris Muskat and **H. G. Botset** publish the first of a series of papers on fluid flow that has been instrumental in advancing the knowledge of **reservoir dynamics** to its present state. (1)

Security Engineering Division Dresser Operations, Inc., founded as Security Engineering Company in Whittier, California, as manufacturers of oilwell reamers. (50)

Sun Shipbuilding and Dry Dock Company, a subsidiary of Sun Oil Company, builds the **first all-welded ship,** a small tanker. (50)

Standard Oil Company of New York and Vacuum Oil Company join together to form **Socony-Vacuum Oil Company.** (50)

The **S. P. curve** introduced commercially into Venezuela. (73)

California—"Town Lot Drilling Act" passed by legislature to prohibit drilling wells to a greater density than one to an acre in new fields. (3)

During this year, the natural gas industry constructs approximately 7700 miles of **transmission lines** at a cost of $318,265,000.00, utilizing about 75 per cent of the total steel pipe tonnage produced in the United States. (47)

Two **deepest well** records set. The first is Chansler-Canfield-Midway Oil Company's Hobson A-2, Rincon field, Ventura, California, drilled to 10,030 feet, world's first well below 10,000 feet. The second is Penn-Mex Fuel Company's Jardin 35, State of Vera Cruz, Mexico, drilled to 10,585 feet. (World Oil)

J. S. Ross, in a report on the Cotton Valley field in Webster Parish, La., states that, during the early development of Blossom sand in 1924, literally "billions" of cubic feet of gas was wasted in efforts to bring oil into the wells. (**Gas Waste**) (1)

Kansas legislature empowers the **Corporate Commission** to administer the Oil Conservation Act. (3)

Societe Franco-Americaine de Raffinage starts building a refinery at Port Jerome, **France.** (Standard Oil Co. of New Jersey)

Texaco engineers begin developing the first **submersible drilling barge** to drill for offshore oil off Louisiana. (50)

Standard of California joins with Kettleman West Dome Association in **unitization** of Kettleman Hills field, California. (1)

First natural gas supplied to **Washington D. C.** through a 20-mile, 12-inch line from Rockville, Maryland. Washington Gas Light Company changes to a mixed gas of 600 Btu. (38)

Virginia—The first successful gas well drilled by the **Bristol Natural Gas Corporation.** It is the discovery well of the Early Grove field in Scott and Washington counties. Other gas fields subsequently found in Buchanan, Dickenson, Wise, Lee and Russell counties. (10)

February 23—**Denmark** enacts a law giving private enterprise the right to explore for and produce oil and natural gas. This law further amended May 8, 1950, by abolishing Law No. 27 of February 19, 1932, through which the government had retained ownership of the country's mineral assets. (45)

February 25—Texas Railroad Commission issues third proration order for the **East Texas field** fixing allowable at 75 barrels per day, giving East Texas field about 325,000 barrels per day, and retaining the flat per-well method of distribution. Note: Order remains in effect, but operators continue to produce as they please, counting on federal judges to strike it down. (58)

February—General Motors introduces the **"Faraday" gas refrigerator.** (38)

February—**Dowell Incorporated** founded as Dow Well Service in Midland, Michigan. The company sells a chemical service to the oil and gas producers. (50)

February—Suit for injunction (**E. Constantin** et al vs Lon Smith et al, in Federal Court for the Eastern District of Texas) reaches opinion. Three judges, after a colorful trial, say that the governor has no right to declare **martial law. Case** appealed to the Supreme Court, where the decree is affirmed. (9)

March 23—Filing of opinion by Court of Civil Appeals at Austin, in the **Danciger Case,** in which the court holds that production in excess of reasonable market demand causes or results in physical waste, and that restriction of production to reasonable market demand prevents or minimizes such waste; consequently, under the Act of 1929, the Commission had properly exercised authority to limit production to reasonable **market demand,** solely as a means of preventing physical waste as defined. It is held that such limitation is not a price-fixing scheme, and not regulation of economic waste as prohibited by statute. (9)

April 4—The **public domain reopens,** but the issuance of prospecting permits and new leases subject to important limitations. (3)

April 15—Eastern Gulf Oil Company relinquishes back to Eastern and General Syndicate, Ltd., all rights pertaining to al-Hasa and the **Kuwait Neutral Zone.** (80)

May 16—The United States Supreme Court upholds **Market Demand Law.** Champlin Refining Co. v. Oklahoma Corporation Commission. (58)

May 20—Amelia Earhart flies across Atlantic.

May 28—Ratification of Agreement granting a seventy-five year concession covering Northern **Iraq** west of Tigris River, by the Iraq Government to B.O.D. Company Limited. (45)

June 1—First oil discovered in Bahrein just south of Awali by **Bahrein Petroleum Company, Ltd.** (80)

June 4—**Ernest O. Thompson** succeeds **Pat M. Neff** as a Texas Railroad Commissioner. (56)

June 21—Gov. **William H. Murray** of Oklahoma takes over the control of the production of crude oil in the Oklahoma City field. Places 30 National guardsmen in field. Creates new proration board with all decisions subject to approval of governor. (2)

June—The United States government re-enters the **automotive tax** field with levies of three per cent on automobiles, motorcycles and buses; two per cent on trucks and parts and accessories; two and one fourth per cent per pound on tires and four cents per pound on tubes. Lubricating oil taxed for the first times at four cents per gallon. (62)

June—**Tariff on imports** becomes effective. Excise tax of 21 cents a barrel on crude and 2½ cents a gallon or $1.05 a barrel on gasoline entering the U. S. to compete with domestic crude and products. This marks a major victory for the IPAA and its president, **Wirt Franklin.** (2)

June—The United States government enters the field of **gasoline taxation** for the first time, with a one-cent levy, scheduled to expire in one year. (62)

September 3—Construction of the 12-inch **Kirkuk-Mediterranean pipelines** begins. (45)

November 1—Standard Oil Company (Indiana) acquires substantial direct interest in **Utah Oil Refining Company,** which became wholly-owned affiliate in 1956. (50)

November 1—**Imperial Oil Company Ltd.,** introduces the five-day, forty-hour week to Canada. (63)

November 12—Special Session of the Texas Legislature hurriedly enacts the "**Market Demand Act.**" Acts 42nd Leg., 4th C.S., 1932, C. 2. (58)

December 2—**Pledger field,** Texas, discovered by Danciger Oil & Refining Company No. 1 Hunt completed for 12 million cubic feet of gas and 200 barrels of distillate per day through ¾-inch choke from a depth of 6782 feet. (44)

December 28—First practical use of **gun perforating** in Union Oil Company's LaMerced No. 17 well in **Montebello field,** California, by Lane-Wells Company. Depth of well is 2665 feet. (50)

December 29—**Aurora Gasoline Company,** of Detroit, now wholly-owned subsidiary of The Ohio Oil Company (Marathon), founded. Later built world's first **Rexformer.** (50)

First **well is acid-treated** in the Southwest on Ackers ranch near Breckenridge, Texas. Production increased ten-fold after treatment. (5)

The **Associated Petroleum Industries of Pennsylvania** formed. (57)

175

Improved **gyro cracking** process is introduced to the Southwest. (5)

Unitized draw works is installed on a drilling rig in Conroe field, Texas. (5)

Pneumatic rotary drilling (pressure drilling) with gasified water tried in the **Big Lake,** Texas, field and then used in **Fitts,** Oklahoma, pool in 1934. (1)

Kentucky—Fairly comprehensive law enacted to regulate the drilling of oil or gas wells in lands known to be underlaid with coal-bearing strata. (3)

Development of **caliper logs** by **M. M. Kinley;** a mechanical tool, recording downhole rather than at the surface. (73)

Electric log operations reopen in the United States in June and the use of well logs as a formation evaluation tool has been **expanding** ever since. (The Petroleum Times, 1936). (73)

"Transitional period" **temperature logs** initiated in Pechelbronn, Alsace, by the Schlumberger Corp. Introduced same service in California in February 1935, and in Mid-Continent in March 1935. (1)

Standard Oil Company (New Jersey) acquires ownership of **Lago Petroleum Corporation.** (50)

Pittsburgh Equitable Meter Company acquires Nordstrom Valve Company; new firm later to become **Rockwell Manufacturing Company.** (38)

Midway Supply Company founded as Midway Tool Company in Saginaw, Michigan, as suppliers of cable tools and fishing tools. (50)

The **Minerals Yearbooks** of the Bureau of Mines replaces and augments the Survey publication. (48)

Legislature of the State of **Mississippi** enacts Senate Bill Number 89 as a conservation law to protect the mineral resources of the state. Law creates the **State Oil and Gas Board,** to be appointed by the governor for a term of four years. (9)

Panhandle Eastern Pipe Line Company places its major gas-transmission line in operation from Texas to Indiana.

A group of owners of sweet gas wells make application for permits authorizing the stripping of gas. Railroad Commission orders operators to close all wells in a certain part of the sweet gas portion of the **Panhandle field,** and restricts daily production of other wells to four per cent. Pipe line companies affected bring suit, and again the federal court grants injunctions, declaring no statutory authority for the Commission's order. (9)

Gun perforating introduced in California by William Lane and Walter Wells who form the **Lane-Wells Company** in Los Angeles, also providing oil well packers.

A 10-inch pipe line 147 miles long built in Mexico from **Poza Rica** near the seacoast through the jungle and over a 10,000-foot elevation to Mexico City. The line uses electric power for pumping. (19)

Tide Water Associated Oil Co.'s Lloyd 83 well in Ventura Avenue field, California, sets **deep production** record flowing from pay bottomed at 9710 feet. (Oil). (World Oil)

Standard Oil Company of New Jersey buys from Standard Oil Company (Indiana), for $50 million cash and $96 million in Jersey stock, the latter's foreign properties, including concessions at Lake Maracaibo, Venezuela, and a refinery at **Aruba** in the **Netherlands West Indies.** (50)

Texas makes violation of its proration orders a felony, enforcing curtailment in East Texas field. (5)

Western Gas Company completes a 275-mile, 12-inch line from El Paso, Texas, to Douglas and Bisbee, Arizona, and to Cananea, Mexico. (38)

Oil States Advisory Committee drafts interstate compact with power to regulate all phases of oil industry. (40)

1933

January 1—The **American Petroleum Industries Committee** of the American Petroleum Institute organizes and functions until August 31, 1958, when it is merged into the **Committee of Public Affairs.** (62)

January—**Petroleum Marketer Magazine** first published as Lubrication and Maintenance. (50)

March 2—The **West Central Texas Oil and Gas Association** formed in Breckenridge, Texas. In 1947 headquarters of the association were permanently located in Abilene, Texas. (57)

March 27 to 29—A three-day conference in Washington between representatives of **oil-state governors** and of the oil industry. Recommends that President Roosevelt call governors and legislatures of principal oil-producing states that have no adequate or no general conservation statutes, to adopt such statutes. (2)

April 3—**President Roosevelt** declares he has no power to declare a moratorium on flush crude oil, and says he might be infringing on state sovereignty if he makes suggestions as to adoption of conservation statutes. Is prepared to recommend Congressional legislation against interstate and foreign commerce of oil or products produced or manufactured in violation of state law. Approves strict enforcement of gasoline and pipeline tax. (2)

April 10—Oklahoma **"Proration Tax Act"** passed by legislature. (9)

April 12—**Oklahoma Corporation Commission** issues and promulgates rules of practice and procedure relating to the conservation of oil and gas. (9)

May 22—**Greta field,** Texas, discovered by Geo. E. Smith et al No. 1 O'Brien completed for 530 barrels per day through 1/4-inch choke from a depth of 4404 feet. (44)

May 26—**East Texas proration order** of Railroad Commission **upheld** by three-judge Federal Court and conditions become somewhat more stable in field. (44)

May 28—Terms of **Anglo-Persian Oil Company's Iran concessions renegotiated** with concession reduced to an area of 100,000 square miles and the company to pay four shillings on every ton of oil sold in Iran or exported. (80)

May 29—Standard Oil Company of California granted a concession over **Saudi Arabia,** said to be 360,000 miles, one of the largest oil grants in the world. (80)

June 16—**NRA** (National Recovery Act) enacted. (N.R.A. 1933, 1935)

June—The one cent per gallon United States federal **gasoline tax** extended for two years and increased by the addition of a one-half cent per gallon temporary levy. (62)

June—**Warren Petroleum** establishes first large-scale tidewater blending, storage and cargo assembling terminal for natural gasoline, on Houston ship channel. Also installs industry's first **radial-cone roof storage tanks** made by **Chicago Bridge and Iron Company.** Then installs C.B.&I.'s first 100,000-barrel Hortonspheroid for natural gasoline at this location. (50)

July 20—General rules, regulations and orders for conservation of oil and gas and **ratable and equitable** takings thereof within **Oklahoma** promulgated. (9)

July 22—First solo global flight.

July—**Fitts field,** Oklahoma, discovered by E. H. Moore et al No. 1 Wirick. (66)

August 19—**Code of Fair Competition** for the Petroleum Industry becomes effective. **Harold L. Ickes,** Secretary of the Interior, Administrator, organizes the **Petroleum Administrative Board** to assist him in administering the Petroleum Code and Section 9C of the **NIRA,** which relates to movements of oil in interstate and foreign commerce. (1)

August 26—**Southern Minerals Corporation** granted Delaware charter to do business in Texas. (50)

September 1—The **Texas** Legislature enacts a statute making it a felony to produce oil in violation of Texas Railroad Commission orders or to bypass oil. (44)

September 7—**Standard-Vacuum Oil Company** organized and incorporated in Delaware. Socony-Vacuum Corporation, Vacuum Oil Company, Inc., and Standard Oil Company of New York, Inc., transfer to the new corporation their respective assets in the Far East and South Africa for which Socony-Vacuum Corporation acquires 50 per cent of its stock. (50)

September 26—Million-acre **King Ranch** in Texas leased for 20 years by **Humble Oil & Refining Company** for $127,824 annually plus one-

178

eighth royalty on recommendation of **Wallace E. Pratt** over opposition of **W. S. Farish,** president, who is later to become president of Standard of Jersey. (12)

October 11—Johnston Testers is the first to use a **Controlled Flow Bean** in conjunction with a drill stem test. This test conducted in Fruitvale, California. (50)

Fall—What are believed to be among the first, if not the first, **offshore geophysical surveys** by boat carried on in Galveston Bay, Texas, first by torsion balance and later by seismograph, by Geophysicists, Inc., later succeeded by Salt Dome Production Co. (Karl F. Hasselmann)

November—**Kuwait oil concession** transferred to Gulf companies by Eastern and General Syndicate, Ltd. (80)

November—In an attempt to reduce drilling time and costs in the North Dome Field, Kettleman North Dome Association brings an "Oklahoma" rig into the field. This rig is believed to have been the first heavy-duty "**balanced**" **rotary-drilling rig** ever assembled. (1)

Act passed creating a board known as "**Arkansas** Board of Conservation." (9)

Bureau of Mines begins publication of **monthly forecasts of supply and demand.** (48)

Franklin Supply Company founded as Franklin Tool Company in Mt. Pleasant, Michigan, as distributors of a complete line of oil field supplies. (50)

V. C. Illing proves that water, oil, and gas can flow past each other in a reservoir rock by experiments using glass tubes with kerosene and water flowing into opposite ends. (22)

Montana—Extraordinary session of 1933 legislature creates an Oil Conservation Board. (3)

Pate Oil Company established in Milwaukee. (50)

Petroleum Equipment Suppliers Association founded to write code for oil equipment industry under NRA. (57)

V. A. Sokolov first publishes results of **geochemical prospecting.** (22)

The first air-cooled **gas refrigerator** unit introduced after lengthy testing. (38)

The first Full Hole **Tool Joint** introduced by Reed Roller Bit Company. (50)

Deepest well record set by North Kettleman Oil and Gas Company's (later Union Oil's Lillis-Welch No. 1), Kettleman Hills, Calif. Depth 10,944 feet. (World Oil)

Chicago first city to go into house gas heating business in big way. Panhandle natural gas is being mixed with manufactured gas to provide 800 Btu gas. First attempt at mass merchandising of gas house heating equipment began at Peoples Gas Light & Coke Company and by July more than 10,000 installations, mostly conversion burners, had been installed. (38)

The **D'Arcy** system for measuring **permeability** is adopted by the industry; unit and name first proposed by R. D. Wyckoff, H. G. Botset, M. Muskat and D. W. Reed. (50)

First **electric welded pipeline** without the use of a backup ring inside the pipe is built for Phillips Petroleum Company from Oklahoma City, Oklahoma to Thrall, Kansas by H. C. Price Co. (50)

Humble Oil & Refining Company builds an expansion **gas porosimeter.** (1)

Michigan Natural Gas Corporation lays a 157-mile gas line from midstate fields to Flint and Pontiac. (38)

First college course in **natural gas engineering** offered by the **University of Oklahoma.** (38)

The first detailed **report on fuel consumption** by types at refineries issued by the Bureau of Mines. (48)

Rangely, Colorado, **field,** where small production from shallow sands had been secured as early as 1902, proven for important production by California Company's well making 300 barrels per day after an 1800-quart shot at 6315 feet. (Colorado School of Mines Quarterly)

1934

January 1—The one-half cent temporary increase in the United States federal **gasoline tax** expires, returning the rate to a one cent per gallon levy. (62)

January 7—**John Eastman,** a California specialist in drilling deviational holes, drills for Humble Oil & Refining Company from its **Conroe** property into an adjoining "runaway" well belonging to Harrison & Abercrombie. The year-old wild well is killed by pumping vast amounts of water into the **deviational hole.** This is probably the first time such a method has been employed for such a purpose. (12)

January 29—The **San Joaquin Valley Oil Producers Association** founded in Bakersfield, California. (57)

January—**Fuel Oil News** first published. (50)

February 2—**Kuwait Oil Company, Ltd.,** formed by the Anglo-Iranian Oil Company (now British Petroleum Company Limited) and Gulf Oil Corporation, who thus become joint and equal partners in the search for oil in Kuwait. (45) (80)

February 6—**Platt's Oilgram** news service started. The Platt's Oilgram price service had started in early June, 1922.

April 24—By presidential order, the **Bureau of Mines** is transferred back to the Department of the Interior. (48)

April—First **wireline bridging plug** set by Lane-Wells. (50)

May 16—The **National Stripper Well Association** organized at a meeting held in Tulsa, Oklahoma. It is designed to be an organization of oil and gas associations in areas having stripper well production, and its aims are to promote and protect the interests of stripper well owners and operators, their employees and the owners of royalties under such wells. (57)

May 31—First **submersible drilling barge** finds successful use in maritime operations of The Texas Co. at Lake Barre, in Terrebonne Parish, Louisiana Gulf Coast. (18)

May 31—Socony-Vacuum Corporation changes its name to **Socony-Vacuum Oil Company,** Incorporated. (50)

May—Oil Administrator H. L. Ickes dispatches **L. R. Glavis,** chief of Investigation Division, to the East Texas oil field to clamp down lid on "hot oil" in that area. (2)

June 8—Hearings on **pipeline divorcement** bills held when arguments of some of the proponents of measure are heard. Congress adjourns with no action. (2)

June 26—**Tom O'Connor field** discovered in Texas by **Quintana Petroleum Corporation.** No. 1 Tom O'Connor completed for 545 barrels per day on ⅜-inch choke at 5580 feet. (44)

June—**Lone Star Gas Company** engineers demonstrate that the residue gas from gasoline stripping plants can be returned to the reservoir by taking gas from a high pressure area and returning it through a well in a low pressure area to the reservoir. In the demonstration, 100 million cubic feet of gas returned to the reservoir through a single well in six days. (50)

July 12—**Clark Oil and Refining Corporation** incorporated under Wisconsin laws. (50)

August 9—**Great Lakes Pipe Line Company** uses newly-completed products line to pump 500,000 to 750,000 gallons of fresh water daily from Kansas City to drought-stricken communities along the line as far as Des Moines. (18)

August 21—The discovery of oil in **Goestring** (Lower Austria), with an initial production of 30 tons daily, is regarded as the beginning of a regular systematic development of oil fields in **Austria.** (45)

September 15—**Schlumberger Well Surveying Corp.,** founded in Houston, Texas, as a service company. (50)

November 1—Maiden run of Union Pacific's new streamlined, Diesel-fueled train cuts 14 hours and 32 minutes from previous record train time from Los Angeles to New York. (18)

November 8—**Old Ocean field,** Texas, discovered by Harrison & Abercrombie No. 1 Bernard River Development Co. completed for 500 barrels per day at 8651 feet. (44)

November 18—**Goldsmith,** Texas, **field** discovered by Landreth Production Company et al No. 1 Scharbauer as a gas-distillate well at 4186 feet followed by completion June 14, 1935 of Gulf Oil Corporation No. 1 Goldsmith making 1140 barrels per day at 4177 feet. (44)

November—Secretary of Interior **Harold L. Ickes** calls for strong **federal controls of the oil industry** and for a declaration that it be held a public utility. (60)

December 3—**E. W. Marland,** governor-elect of Oklahoma, former head of a major oil company, hosts a meeting at his palatial home near Ponca City to begin negotiations for a treaty for voluntary cooperation among oil states and an **Interstate Oil Compact.** Governors of Texas, Kansas and Oklahoma and representatives of five other states attend. Another meeting held a month later. Wide differences of approach make the project seem impossible. (60)

December 4—**German Reich law** specifies mandatory reporting to the Central Government of all geophysical investigations and explorations. (45)

December 13—Exploration and production of minerals belong exclusively to the Central German Government. (This law was reaffirmed in another version of the **German Code,** September 24, 1937). However, the 1934 law does not affect those German landowners who already have production on their properties. (45)

December 23—**Kuwait** grants exclusive 75-year oil concession to the Kuwait Oil Company, Ltd. (80)

December 23—**Hastings field** discovered in Galveston County, Texas by Stanolind Oil and Gas Company well producing 5½ barrels per hour on small choke from 5980 feet. (70)

December 25—A new Texas Statute goes into effect giving the Texas Railroad Commission authority to stop the shipment of products as well as crude when the latter has been illegally produced. (44)

Arkansas Louisiana Gas Company formed by merger of Arkansas Natural Gas Company and Southern Cities Distributing Company. (38)

Austria—Erdol Productions Gesellschaft, drilling near Zisterdorff, on its Goesting No. 2 produces oil. On December 10, the company says that up to November 18, the well has produced 15,600 barrels of oil from three sands. It starts off at 170 barrels per day, but production reaches 240 barrels at year's end, field production totalled 44,000 barrels. In 1944 production was eight million barrels. (10)

Brown Oil Tools, Inc., incorporated in Houston, Texas, as manufacturers of well completion tools, packers and hangers. (50)

Drilling-control panel introduced by Martin-Decker Corporation. (1)

Gas industry exhibit at **Chicago World's Fair** features "gas in the home." (38)

Sun Oil Company engineers develop a system for using low cost **bunker oil as a fuel** in Diesel-powered ships. (50)

Wallace E. Pratt reports that he believes earth movements with resultant friction, are a possible source of the internal **heat of the earth.** (22)

Multi-shot perforator developed by I. J. McCullough of McCullough Tool Co. In this same year McCullough develops the first mechanical firing system for bullet guns. Patent No. 2,154,859 issued April 18, 1939. (50)

Use of long **drill collars** started. (1)

Bowen Company of Texas, Inc., founded in Houston, Texas as manufacturers of releasing and circulating overshot, automatic line wiper safety joint, removable rope sockets, releasing spears, casing cutters and circulating swivels. (50)

Britain's Petroleum (Production) Act, 1934, vests in the Crown the ownership of all mineral oil not discovered up to that date and makes it possible for a person or company to acquire exploration licenses. (45)

The first well into which substantially more **cement** was pumped than could be contained in the hole is a General Crude Oil Company well, with operations under the direction of Thomas W. Pew. (1)

The first experimental work with **drilling-mud** suspensions and cores done in the USSR on the Dagestan formation by the geology expert M. I. Balmazov. (27)

Supercharging of four-cycle engines enters the picture. From this beginning has come the **spark-ignited turbocharged gas engine** in 400-hp. range. (40)

Waste of natural gas is at its peak in the Texas and Oklahoma Panhandles. The low-pressure residue gas is flared to the air at the rate of one and one-half billion cubic feet daily. (56)

The Bureau of Mines begins its studies of gas-condensate fields and fluids, in the earliest stages of **gas-condensate** recognition. (48)

The **South African Torbanite and Mining and Refining Co., Ltd.,** registered. It produces **gasoline from oil shale,** but as a result of mining difficulties supplements the raw material by the importation of crude oil. (45)

The usefulness of bottom-hole measurements appreciably increased by the development of **continuously recording instruments** such as the pressure gauges invented by **P. Comins and Geophysical Research Corp.** With improved instruments, a precision of plus or minus one per cent can be obtained. (1)

The first **iso-octane produced** in commercial quantity is a thousand gallons delivered by the Shell Oil Company to the Army Air Corps. (12)

A 1200-mile, 12-inch system from Iraq's **Kirkuk field** to Haifa, Palestine, and Tripoli, Lebanon, completed, looped with a 16-inch line 10 years later, and with a 30-32-inch line in 1950-52. (40)

President Roosevelt creates the **National Resources Board.** (2)

A research chemist at Du Pont laboratories spins a synthetic fiber called **Polymer 66,** which will soon become famous as **nylon.** (Standard Oil Co. of New Jersey)

Petromex takes over the functions of the National Petroleum Administration. (14)

Martin-Decker Corporation introduces a **drilling-control panel** consisting of five instruments: rig, weight, vernier, mud pressure, torque and tachometer, which is generally known as the "**Quintuplex.**"

The **long-normal resistivity curve** added to the standard log. Schlumberger. (50)

Deepest well record set by General Petroleum Corporation's Berry 1 well, Belridge, Kern County, California, at 11,377. (World Oil)

Well Equipment Manufacturing Corp., Division of Chicksan Company founded as Well Equipment Company in Houston, Texas as manufacturers of wing unions. (50)

1935

January 2—The **Cole Committee Report,** influenced by the interest in an agreement among oil states, recommends no federal legislation but urges upon the states the adoption of an interstate oil compact. (12)

January 3—Representatives of governors and governors-elect of eight oil-producing states meet at Ponca City, Oklahoma and unanimously adopt request to Congress to pass legislation to permit them to set up **Interstate Oil Compact.** (2)

January 7—The Supreme Court of the United States, in the **Amazon and Panama** cases which originated in East Texas, invalidates the subsection of the **NIRA** on which federal hot oil regulation has been based. (12)

February 7—Vulcanized rubber applied to pipe to protect it against **corrosion** and **soil stress** is being tried out for the first time on a section of Lone Star Gas Company's main line in Ellis County, Texas, between Cleburne and Mexia. (18)

February 15—**Katy gas field** in Waller, Harris and Fort Bend Counties, Texas, one of the nation's major reservoirs, discovered by Stanolind Oil and Gas (Pan American Petroleum Corp.) in the Thorp No. 1 well, producing from plugged back depth of 7466. Oil was discovered by the same company in 1943 in the No. 1 Pattison well at 6621 feet. (Five Star Oil Report, Houston)

February 15-16—On call of Gov. **E. W. Marland** of Oklahoma, representatives from Oklahoma, Texas, Arkansas, Colorado, Illinois, Kansas, and Michigan meet and compromise on a compact. The compromise is between Marland of Oklahoma and Gov. **James V. Allred** of Texas. Marland seeks certain controls over production allocations by the states.

Allred opposes economic controls. **W. M. Downing** of Colorado appointed to chairman a subcommittee, composed also of Judge **Elwood Fouts** of Texas and **Tom Anglin** of Oklahoma, to draft the compromise agreement. (60)

February 16—The **Interstate Compact to Conserve Oil and Gas** entered into by Oklahoma, Texas, California and New Mexico and recommended by Arkansas, Colorado, Illinois, Michigan and Kansas. The compact becomes effective upon ratification by three states and is ratified by New Mexico 2-25-35, Oklahoma 3-6-35, Kansas 3-13-35, Colorado 4-15-35, Texas 4-15-35, Illinois 7-10-35, agreed to by Congress 8-27-35 and signed by the President. The **Interstate Oil Compact Commission** provided for in the Compact Agreement is organized September 12, 1935 with the six states which had ratified the Agreement as members. Other states which have since become members of the Commission are: Alabama 6-9-45; Alaska associate 3-26-53 and member 12-27-57; Arizona associate 4-28-51 and member 3-18-55; Arkansas 2-21-41; Florida 6-6-45; Georgia associate 8-10-46; Idaho associate June 1960; Indiana 3-14-47; Kentucky 3-2-42; Louisiana 5-13 and 7-11-40; Maryland 3-25-59; Michigan 3-25-43; Mississippi 4-10-48; Montana 2-24-45; Nebraska 4-1-53; Nevada associate 3-25-53 and member March 1955; New York 4-17-41; North Dakota 2-27-53; Ohio 5-14-43; Oregon associate 9-11-54; Pennsylvania 7-23-41; South Dakota April 1955; Tennessee February 1947; Utah 3-19-57; Washington associate 9-1-53 and member 2-21-58; West Virginia 3-8-45; Wyoming February 1955. (60)

February 22—U. S. Congress passes the **Connally "Hot Oil" Act** to cure the defective drafting of Section 9C of the NIRA. Act prohibits the movement in interstate and foreign commerce of oil (including products by definition) produced or withdrawn from storage in violation of a state statute or regulation. (1)

March 3—**Anahuac field** in Chambers County, Texas discovered by Humble Oil & Refining Company No. 1 Middleton completed for 32 barrels per hour on ⅜-inch choke from pay at 7088 feet. (44)

March 21—First light-weight **portable rotary rig** using constant-torque prime movers starts drilling for **Gypsy Oil Co.** (Gulf) at Eunice, New Mexico. (18)

March 31—Introduction of a **continuously recording temperature instrument.** Schlumberger. (50)

May 1—**Texas** Legislature enacts a comprehensive **gas regulation statute** with detailed provisions for apportioning the reasonable market demand of gas throughout the state. Prohibits the production of gas in such a way as to cause underground waste; blowing to the air of gas from a gas well before or after such gas has been processed for its gasoline content; use of sweet gas for the manufacture of carbon black, but allows sour gas to be used for such purposes. Acts 44th Leg., Reg. Sess., 1935, C. 120. (58)

May 11—Texas Legislature enacts **Texas "Hot Oil Statute"** declaring as contraband any oil produced or transported in violation of statutes or regulations, and providing for the confiscation and sale by the state of such. Acts 44th Leg., Reg. Sess., 1935, C. 246. (58)

May 17—**Qatar**—Seventy-five year concession granted to Anglo-Iranian Oil Co., Ltd., and as result subsequent assignments and conveyances now held by **Qatar Petroleum Co., Ltd.** (45) (World Petroleum Report)

May—By Supreme Court decree, the **NRA** invalidated. (48)

June 29—**Western States Natural Gas Company** is incorporated as Gulf States Oil Company. Present name adopted 1947. (50)

June—**Dr. E. E. Rosaire** and **Dr. Leo Horvitz** start experiments in **geochemical prospecting,** based on an idea first used by Germans in 1929, and in 1932 by Russians in the same field. The Rosaire-Horvitz experiments based on **soil analysis** while the German and Russian ideas are based on air-gas samples. The first field test of the soil analysis system is in Hastings field in Texas in 1938. (Dr. Leo Horvitz—Houston)

July 5—The **Shamrock Oil & Gas Corporation,** Amarillo, Texas, is organized, successor to a series of concerns which began in 1925 as Shamrock Oil Co. (50)

July 11—First use of **butane** as a fuel for engines on a drilling rig in the Mid-Continent region being made on a wildcat test being put down by Amerada Petroleum Corp. and Stanolind Oil and Gas Co. in Coal County, in Southeastern Oklahoma. (18)

July 18—A new motor fuel in the form of a jellylike mass called "**solid gasoline,**" makes its debut in a practical demonstration in New York at the **Daniel Guggenheim School of Aeronautics.** Sponsors claim use of the fuel is safer because it does not ignite except in direct contact with flame and does not spill. (18)

August 1—**Yount-Lee** assets acquired by Standard Oil Company (Indiana) increasing crude oil reserves. (50)

August 18—Johnston Testers is the first to run a **pressure recorder** in conjunction with a drill stem test. This test is in Texas. (50)

August 21—The United States enacts a **Mineral Leasing Act** that eliminates the permit system and institutes the five-year prospecting lease with a minimum royalty of 12½ per cent for all lands which are not known or believed to contain oil and gas deposits. (61)

September 5—**Falcon Seaboard Drilling Company** incorporated in Oklahoma. Subsequently incorporated in Delaware on December 27, 1948. (50)

September 13—**Kaw Pipe Line Company,** a crude oil pipe line in western Kansas, organized in Delaware. (Texaco, Inc.)

October—Oil Administrator H. L. Ickes appoints a **Federal Tender Committee.** Way cleared to control interstate shipment of crude oil and its products, regardless of whether or not Department of Justice prosecutes violators. (2)

December 26—Blowing in of oil gusher 675 feet from the governor's mansion near Oklahoma's capitol grounds launches intensive drilling and development play in prolific north extension area of big **Oklahoma City field.** (18)

The first gas **air-conditioning units** marketed. (38)

Phillip E. Harth, Sales Manager for **National Pigments & Chemical Company,** granted a patent on the use of **bentonite** as a suspending and gelling additive to muds. (Baroid Division National Lead Company)

The Bureau of Mines starts weekly **reports on all crude oil stocks** throughout the United States. The forecasts of supply and demand for crude oil and products, begun in NRA days, are so useful that the states and the industry ask that they be continued after the demise of the NRA in 1935. (48)

A. O. Smith Corporation manufactures the first **welded casing.** (50)

Experimental **cycling operations** first put into effect in the **Big Lake** gas **field** of Texas, where condensate wells, thought to be freak gasoline wells, have been producing large quantities of liquid hydrocarbons for several years. (38)

Britain grants 39 licenses (maximum area 200 square miles each) to the **D'Arcy Exploration Company Limited** (now B. P. Exploration Company Limited), a subsidiary of the Anglo-Persian Oil Company limited. (45)

Probably the first successful **dual completion** in which segregated production from both zones can be obtained simultaneously is the McCarthy, Bertrand well, in Conroe field, Montgomery County, Texas, in the Spring. This well utilizes the now simple technique of producing one pay through the tubing and another through the annulus, with a packer being used to separate the two zones. (40)

100-octane gasoline, manufactured at Baton Rouge, Louisiana, used commercially for the first time at the Southwest Air Races in Tulsa, Oklahoma. (Standard Oil Co. of New Jersey)

Kansas passes gas conservation act. (9)

Myron M. Kinley invents a caliper for determining the size of shot holes, but its design will not permit using it in a hole full of fluid. It is redesigned to operate on an electric cable and is first used in 1940. (1)

Lafitte field, Louisiana, discovered by The Texas Company's No. 1 Bayou St. Denis completed for 2410 barrels per day on ⅜-inch choke at 9558 feet. (70)

The **Naft Safid** field discovered in Iran. (70)

New Mexico Oil and Gas Conservation Act passed. (3)

Oil Workers International Union is one of eight original founders of the Committee of Industrial Organization formed within the AFL, and a charter member of the Congress of Industrial Organizations formed in 1938. (OCAW, Denver) (**CIO**)

Polyforming gains in importance. **Pan American Refining Corporation** awards contract for 2000-bbl. unit at Texas City, Texas. (5)

The first commercial **catalytic polymerization** unit comes into operation. This is the Shell Development Company's sulphuric acid polymerization process. The product from this process is used, after hydrogenation, as a component in producing the first 100-octane aviation gasoline. (39)

American **standard code for pressure piping** first issued, sponsored by the American Society of Mechanical Engineers and approved by the American Standards Association. (38)

The **rotary drilling unit** introduced by Oil Well Supply. This development provides an independent **prime mover** for the rotary, freeing the drawworks engines for other service. (50)

Tide Water Associated Oil Co.'s Lloyd 131 well in Ventura Avenue field, California sets **deep production** record flowing from pay bottomed at 9836 feet. (Oil) (World Oil)

"**Public Utility Holding Company Act**," first introduced as the Rayburn-Wheeler Bill, passed by Congress. (38)

The one cent per gallon United States federal **gasoline tax** extended for another two years. (62)

Texas—Statute passed which specifically authorizes voluntary agreements under certain circumstances for the operation of gas fields or parts thereof. (3)

Texas passes **Transportation Act.** Elaborately controls the movement of oil, gas and products, and calls for **tenders** or other documents to show whether the commodity to be transported is legal. (3)

Unit Rig and Equipment Company founded in Tulsa, Oklahoma as manufacturers of rotary drawworks. (50)

Deepest well is Gulf Oil Corporation's McElroy 103, Gulf-McElroy field, Upton County, Texas drilled to 12,786 feet. (World Oil)

Wilmington field, California, discovered. (67)

1935-37—C. J. Coberly issued many patents for the **Kobe oil-lifting pump.** Though not announced until 1935, the first installation was in 1932 at the Baldwin Hills field near Los Angeles. (40)

188

Association of Gas Appliances and Equipment Manufacturers organized in Chicago, Illinois. (51)

New Mexico Institute of Mining & Technology organizes Petroleum Engineering department. (1)

First well spacing law passed by any state enacted by Oklahoma Legislature; gives Corporation Commission jurisdiction to fix size and shape of drilling units and to locate well within unit; force pools all of the royalty interests within the unit, but does not necessarily force pool the working interest. (60)

1936

January 1—The Bureau of Mines compiles a summary of state specifications for **asphalts for road materials.** (48)

January 9—**Foster field,** Texas, discovered by Barnsdall Oil Co. et al with 167-barrel well at 4310 feet. (44)

January—The first pilot **water-flood** operation in the State of Texas is credited to The Texas Company in the Fry Pool of Brown County, and continues for two years, but is then abandoned because of production of excessive amounts of water in wells adjacent to the water-injection wells. (1)

February 20—**Rotary tools** make debut in **Pennsylvania** and **New York** to combat the problem of high gas pressures encountered in drilling and completing wells in the **deeper Oriskany sands.** (18)

March 16—**Talco field,** Texas, discovered by Housh, Thompson et al. No. 1 Carr pumping 552 barels per day from 4208 feet. (70)

March—**Santa Maria Valley,** California field proven for important production by Union Oil Company No. 1 Adam, completed for 2376 barrels per day at 2576 feet; minor production had previously been secured in 1934. (66)

March—The American Petroleum Institute begins publication of its **Tax Economics Bulletin.** (62)

April 23—**Oil Field Haulers Association, Inc.,** organized. (57)

April 24—The Texas Company acquires part ownership in the **Barco Concession in Colombia.** (50)

May 1—**Wagner Morehouse Inc.,** founded in Los Angeles, California as manufacturers of well servicing equipment. (50)

May 15—**Heyser field,** Texas, discovered by Humble Oil & Refining Company No. 1 Wardner, completed for 126 barrels per day from a depth of 5475 feet. (70)

June 6—The first semi-commercial **Houdry process** unit goes on stream at Paulsboro. (40)

June 30—A country-wide **survey of crude oil stocks,** including both quantity and quality, made by the Bureau of Mines. (48)

June—**Rio Vista-Isleton field,** California, discovered by Amerada Petroleum Corporation No. 1 Emigh completed for 900 mcf per day from a depth of 4485 feet. (66) (67)

July 1—**General American Oil Company of Texas** organized and starts business in Dallas. (50)

July 31—The Ohio Oil Company acquires all assets of subsidiary **Marathon Oil Company,** including "Marathon" trade name. (50)

September 1—**Carthage,** Texas **gas field** discovered by Glassell et al No. 1 Frost Lumber Company completed as gas-distillate well at 5600 feet. (44) (66)

September 13—Introduction of **sidewall coring.** (50)

September—**Trapp field,** Kansas, discovered by Coralene Oil Co. well producing 598 barrels per day. (70)

October 22—The **Slaughter field,** Texas, discovered by Cascade and Honolulu Oil Corporation No. 1-A Duggan, then known as the Duggan field in Cochran County. The field is extended into Hockley County on April 6, 1937 with the completion of Texas Company No. 1 Bob Slaughter Unit and becomes known as the Slaughter field. (41)

November 14—**Richfield Oil Corporation** organized in the State of Delaware. (50)

November 30—Through a series of evolutionary mergers, the Baroid Sales Company of California National Pigments & Chemical Company, Silica Products Company, and the Baroid Sales Department of National Pigments & Chemical Company, a Division of National Lead, become the **Baroid Sales Division** of National Lead Company. (50)

November 30—**Seminole field,** Texas, discovered by Adams et al. No. 1-A Averitt-Ohio completed for 333 barrels per day at 4959 feet. (44) (World Oil)

November—Tide Water Oil Company and Associated Oil Company merge with and into the **Tide Water Associated Oil Company.** (50)

December 21—**Y.P.F.B.,** a Government Oil Authority, created by law in **Bolivia.** It starts its activities in 1937. (45)

The Texas Company purchases a 50 per cent interest in California Arabian Standard Oil Company (later to become Arabian American Oil Company—"Aramco"). (50)

Colonial Oil Company, marketing firm, formed in Jacksonville, Fla., to operate in Georgia and Florida. (50)

California-Texas Oil Company, Ltd. (**Caltex**), organized by Standard of California and The Texas Company. Latter firm obtains half-interest in Bahrain Petroleum in exchange for $27 million in Eastern Hemisphere marketing outlets. Texas Company also purchases half-interest in SOCal's Arabian and East Indies ventures. Corporate name of California-Texas Oil Corporation adopted December 6, 1946. (50)

The Tidewater Oil Company and the Seaboard Oil Company pioneer what is to become the world's **first cycling plant** in Cayuga field in Anderson County, East Texas. (40)

The **DC-3** transport plane introduced. (Standard Oil Co. of New Jersey)

Detroit changeover to straight natural gas completed following extension of Panhandle Eastern Pipe Line Company's system from Zionsville, Indiana. (47)

W. E. Gilbert gives first results of subsurface **dynagraph** studies. (1)

A device, popularly called an **"echometer"** (Depthograph), reported to give good results in measuring static liquid levels. (The original experiments were made in 1932 by Lehr and Wyatt of the Shell Oil Co.). (1)

The first portable **filter press** goes into the field. This instrument makes it possible to check water loss and filter-cake thickness so that they might be kept within bounds. (40)

John Melhase tests crude oils from several oil fields in California and notes a marked difference in the **fluorescence** of oils from different fields and different formations in the same field. (22)

First year in which a greater volume of **cracked gasoline** has been manufactured than straightrun gasoline. (5)

Kentucky—Nearest approach to conservation legislation. Act prohibits the waste or escape of natural gas from a well or pipeline. Law has been of little assistance in waste prevention. (3)

Louisiana—Act passed to conserve oil, gas and sulphur resources of the State, prohibiting production in excess of reasonable market demand. Act 225. (9)

The **Marathon Oil Company** (was Ohio) introduces the first detergent motor oil to general motoring public with Marathon V.E.P. (50)

Petroleum engineering section of Continental Oil Company is the first to make application to the state conservation authorities for **multiple completions** in Texas and Louisiana. (1)

In **Netherlands New Guinea,** oil discovered at Klamono. (40)

Oklahoma Oil Company established in Chicago as retail gasoline and fuel marketer. (50)

R. D. Wyckoff and **H. G. Botset** introduce the term **"relative permeability."** Their data for flow through unconsolidated sands of varied permeabilities indicates that relative permeability to oil does not vary appreciably with viscosity of oil. (1)

Introduction of **photographic recording** by Schlumberger and Halliburton. (50)

The Texas Co.'s Lafitte 5 well in Lafitte field, South Louisiana sets **deep production** record flowing from pay bottomed at 9950 feet. (Oil). (World Oil)

The **lateral-resistivity curve,** with a much longer spacing, returns as a part of the standard electric log. Schlumberger. (50)

Robinson-Patman Act—This amendment to the Clayton Act makes it illegal to "discriminate in price between different purchasers" where the effect may be to substantially lessen competition. It also says nothing shall prevent a seller from showing that his "lower price . . . was made in good faith to meet the equally low price of a competitor"— the troublesome "good-faith" clause that is giving FTC and the courts some headaches now. (NPN)

The **sand-content test** introduced into the field. The alkalinity and pH tests prove to be dependable for treating mud systems. (40)

First use of a **"scraper"** in large-diameter natural gas pipelines made on the 22-inch Amarillo-Denver line. (38)

First use, in a well in Kettleman Hills, Calif. of the **J. E. Gosline-**designed **sliding sleeve** that can be moved to change the number of holes without pulling the tubing. (1)

A. I. Levorsen introduces the term **stratigraphic trap.** (AAPG)

Texas A & I organizes Petroleum and Natural Gas Engineering Section. (1)

Mene Grande Oil Co., C. A. organized to succeed Venezuela Gulf Oil Company which was formed March 23, 1923. On Nov. 12, 1952, Mene Grande Oil Company was rechartered as a Delaware corporation. (50)

England's first deep test well drilled on **Portsdown Hill,** overlooking Portsmouth Harbour. (45)

Hunt Oil Company is organized as a Delaware corporation, by H. L. Hunt, succeeding other Hunt companies. (50)

H. C. Smith Oil Tool Company founded in Compton, California, as manufacturers of conventional core barrels and multi-bladed drag-type drilling bits (4 to 6 blades). (50)

The **Internal Flush Tool Joint** introduced by Reed Roller Bit Company. (50)

1937

February 22—**Deep production**—Harrison and Abercrombie's No. 3 Bernard River well is completed at 10,437 feet in **Old Ocean field,** Brazoria County, Texas. This is the first Gulf Coast field to produce from below 10,000 feet. (Phil Martyn)

February 26—**Clay City field** discovered by Pure Oil Company No. 1 Weiler, completed for 40 barrels oil per day from Cypress horizon at 2608-2613 feet; May 13, 1937, Pure completes its No. 1 Travis making

2462 barrels of oil per day from the McClosky horizon at 2950-2960 to touch off the **Illinois Coal Basin** boom. (70)

February—The first search for oil in **Nigeria** is begun by geologists of the Shell-BP Petroleum Development Company of Nigeria Limited at Owerri, in the Eastern Region. (45)

February—Traces of oil are discovered at **Bahra** on the north shore of **Kuwait.** (45)

March 13—The Government of **Bolivia** cancels the rights to the concession granted to Standard Oil of New Jersey, establishing by this deed a monopoly of all phases of the oil industry in favor of the state owned corporation Y.P.F.B. (Yacimientos Petroliferos Fiscales Bolivianos). Appropriate compensation paid to Standard Oil of New Jersey. (45)

March 18—An explosion of natural gas, piped in for heating purposes, destroys the Consolidated Public School in **New London, Texas,** killing 294. (38)

March 22—**Texas-New Mexico Pipe Line Company** formed in Delaware. (Texaco, Inc.)

April 2—**Cosden Petroleum Corporation** incorporated in Delaware. (50)

April 15—Superior Oil Co., and Pure Oil Co., joint operators, make location for **first well to be drilled in the open waters** of the Gulf of Mexico off the coast of Louisiana. Their No. 1 Gulf (discovery well of the **Creole field,** the first **offshore field**) is a mile from Cameron Parish shore. (18)

April 19—**First commercial catalytic cracking** plant goes on stream at Marcus Hook, Pennsylvania. It has a capacity of 10,000 barrels daily, took four years to build, and cost $11,000,000.00. (54)

April 23—**Stratton field,** Texas, discovered by Camp Drilling Company No. 1 Wardner completed at a depth of 6002 feet. (44) (70)

April 29—The first flow string of **all-welded casing** in the Mid-Continent area is run by Carter Oil Co. (18)

April 29—First large pipeline using "stove-pipe" **method of construction** is laid by Hope Natural Gas Corp. Project involves 94 miles of 12¾-inch line from Hastings to Clendenin, West Virginia. (18)

April—Name of A & K Petroleum Company changed to **Kerlyn Oil Company** and a second corporation, **Kerr-Lynn & Co.,** formed to operate rotary drilling equipment. (50)

April—**Lake Arthur field,** Louisiana, discovered. (67)

May 6—Hindenburg (dirigible) disaster.

May 12—In **West Pakistan,** the **Dhulian oil field** in the District of Attock discovered. On April 9, 1944, the **Joyamair oil field** in the District of Attock discovered. On May 15, 1946, the **Balkassar oil field** in the District of Jhelum discovered by Attock Oil Co./**Pakistan Oil-**

fields Limited. On June 29, 1949, the **Chakwal oil field** in the District of Jhelum discovered and on October 11, 1950, the **Pirajangla oil field** in the District of Jhelum discovered by **Pakistan Petroleum Limited.** On February 5, 1956, the **Karsal oil field** in the District of Jhelum discovered by Attock Oil Co./Pakistan Oilfields Limited. (45)

May 22—**Deep production**—The first well to produce from below 10,000 feet in Louisiana is Humble Oil & Refining Company's No. 1 Ellender well in Lirette field, Terrebonne Parish. Flow is from 11,625 feet. (50)

May 25—Patent to C. J. Coberly. First to produce and successfully operate a **fully-balanced full double acting pump.** (1)

May—Oficina No. 1 of Mene Grande Oil Company completed for 2400 barrels per day at 5995 feet as the discovery well of the **Oficina, Venezuela, field.** (77)

June 19—**Wasson,** Texas **field** discovered by Continental Oil Company and Amon G. Carter No. 1 Wasson completed for 333 barrels per day at 4959 feet; follows small well in area by Davidson and Honolulu Oil Company in September 1935. (44) (66)

June 24—**Minnesota** reports the discovery of oil. A wildcat test near Wheaton in the western part of the state has 37° gravity oil standing within 100 feet of the top of the hole which is bottomed at 864 feet in what is believed to be the Dakota sandstone. (18)

June—The **Petroleum Engineer Magazine's** Continuous Tables first published. (64)

July 8—Secretary of War Woodring approves an application of Humble Oil & Refining Company to drill wells in the Gulf of Mexico. Humble proposes sinking shafts a mile offshore at **McFaddin Beach,** Jefferson County, Texas, eight miles east of High Island. It is the second company to receive permission to drill in the Gulf; Superior Oil Company will drill near Cameron and Creole, Louisiana, nine miles from Calcasieu Pass. (18)

July 15—**Webster field,** Texas, discovered by Humble Oil & Refining Company No. 1 Settegast with an initial production of 650 barrels of 29° oil through 1/4-inch choke from sand at 5802-6009 feet. (18)

August 16—Kuwait—A well at Magwa, south of Kuwait Town, in the Burgan area, marks the opening of the now-famed **Burgan field,** where the oil-bearing horizon is between 3500 and 4500 feet, 1000 feet thick. The Kuwait Oil Company (a joint ownership venture of Gulf and Anglo-Iranian) completes the discovery well. (10)

August 26—Act passed amending **Mineral Leasing Act,** extending for two years the outstanding prospecting permits committed to unit operation. (3)

August—The first complete equipment designed for **mud logging** and built as a result of investigations of **John T. Hayward** used at the Kate Edwards No. 2 well, Lamar Peninsula, Texas. (1)

October 30—Texas Mid-Continent Oil and Gas Association adopts plans for industry-wide **theft prevention** program to be carried out by the Association. (This was and is the only program of its kind in Texas). (57)

November 15—Texas Railroad Commission, by Order No. 6-163, orders the East Texas field closed in for four consecutive Sundays (November 21 and 28 and December 5 and 12) to study bottom hole conditions. This is the first regularly scheduled **shut down day order** in Texas. (99)

December 6—**Seeligson field** in Jim Wells County discovered by Magnolia Petroleum Company on land belonging to the estate of the great wildcatter, **Tom Slick**. In one of the most spectacular blowouts and oil well fires in history, this discovery well had blown out on July 7 and burned until August 9. Well No. 7 completed for 1300 barrels per day through ¼-inch choke at 6582-6694 feet. (41) (44)

December 29—**Butyl**, a synthetic rubber made from petroleum, is invented by chemists at Standard Oil Development Company, and patent filed. (Standard Oil Co. of New Jersey)

December—Cracking patent history made when an agreement is signed by **Universal Oil Products Company** and the Texas Company whereby Universal purchases licensing rights from Texas Company under the patents of the Texas Company, Standard of Indiana, and Gasoline Products, for the benefit of its licensees since 1931 and future licensees for about $1,000,000 in cash and $2,500,000 in D notes. (13)

The **Agha Jari** field discovered in Iran. (70)

Austria enacts "Erdoel-Bergpolizeiverordnung" (Mining Regulations for Oil), as amended BGBI.278/1937. Also enacted is "Bitumengesetz." Gesetzblatt fuer das Land Oesterreich, No. 375/1938. (45)

Patent on **nylon** awarded posthumously to **Wallace Hume Carothers,** research chemist, and assigned to E. I. duPont de Nemours & Co. (65)

Longest and heaviest string of 7⅝-inch casing ever run is successfully cemented by Continental Oil Company in Abbeville field, Vermilion Parish, Louisiana. String is landed on bottom at 11,342 feet in record time of 14 hours. Five-inch casing is run at 11,975 feet. (5)

China—The first commercial oil pool found at Wu Su in Northern Sinkiang, west of Tihwa. (23)

Ralph J. Schilthuis, after analyzing samples of reservoir rocks from three different formations in three fields—East Texas, Anahuac and Tomball—presents his findings on **connate waters** to the API, with practical suggestions on how to determine the proportion of water to oil in an oil sand, thus making possible greater accuracy in estimating the reserves in a field. (12)

H. L. Doherty receives **Anthony F. Lucas Medal** for distinguished achievement in improving techniques and practices of finding and producing petroleum. (1)

The Lee C. Moore Corporation brings out the jackknife **cantilever-type drilling mast.** (1)

Indirect hydrochemical methods of oil **exploration** (in the form of surveys and other works) first used in the U.S.A. (27)

F. B. Nichols, employed as a development geologist in the Seminole area for the Indian Territory Illuminating Company, invents the **Geolograph,** but it does not become generally available until 1943. (1) (73)

Credit for commercial development of modern **catalytic cracking** goes to **Eugene J. Houdry,** of France. (6)

Hungary becomes an oil-producing country for the first time when a promising field is discovered at Budafa-Preszta, in southern Hungary, not far east of the Danube. The first well drilled produces gas with a little oil. (20)

Commercial catalytic hydrogenation for synthetic 100-octane base stocks inaugurated at the Baton Rouge refinery of Standard Oil of Louisiana. (50)

Mexico—The government creates the General Administration of National Petroleum. (14)

Michigan Gas Conservation Bill passed. (3)

Union Oil Co.'s Kernco 85-34 well in Rio Bravo field, Kern County, California sets a **deep production** record flowing from pay bottomed at 11,302 feet. (Oil). (World Oil)

The American Petroleum Institute resumes publication of **"Facts and Figures"** on a bi-annual basis. Publication continued through 1941. (62)

First field use of Halliburton high pressure **power cementing pump** used on Phillips Petroleum Company's Rose No. 1 well at Snow Hill, Arkansas. (50)

Natural gas, accompanied by small quantities of oil, located at Cousland, Midlothian, **Scotland.** (45)

Small-diameter sectional **bullet guns** developed by McCullough Tool Co. Patent No. 2,155,312 issued April 18, 1939. (50)

Sun Shipbuilding and Dry Dock Company builds the first **all-welded ocean-going** tanker. (50)

University of Kansas organizes Petroleum Engineering department. (1)

"Temporary" one cent per gallon United States federal **gasoline tax** again extended for another two years. (62)

1938

January 1—The Bureau of Mines' sixth biennial survey of **natural gasoline plants** reveals a sizeable decrease in number of plants in a 10-year period (741 in 1938, compared with 1,155 in 1928) and the expansion in individual units, since the total capacity in 1938 barely exceeds the 1928 capacity of 11 million gallons daily. (48)

January 10—**Louden,** Illinois **field** discovered by Carter Oil Company No. 1 Miller at a depth of about 1500 feet. (66) (67)

January 14—**Kansas Independent Oil & Gas Association** holds its first meeting.

January 25—**Timbalier Bay,** Louisiana **field** discovered by Gulf Production company No. 3 P.P. State, completed for 304 barrels per day from 6960 feet. (66)

January—**Mohawk Petroleum Corporation,** San Francisco, is organized to acquire assets of a predecessor company of the same name, for exploration, production, refining and marketing. (50)

February 23—Oil in commercial quantities discovered at **Burgan** some 28 miles south of Kuwait Bay and 14 miles from the Gulf Coast of Kuwait. (45)

February 27—The **J. W. Van Dyke,** first high-pressure, high-temperature, steam turbine, electric-driven tanker put into service by The Atlantic Refining Company. (50)

March 18—**Expropriation in Mexico**—President Cardenas, of Mexico, issues a decree expropriating foreign oil properties in Mexico following prolonged labor dispute and litigation. Chiefly involved are American, British and Dutch interests. (2)

March 29—**Magnolia field,** Arkansas, discovered by Kerlynn Oil Company's No. 1 Barnett completed for 350 barrels per day at 7646 feet. (70)

March—The **first commercial cycling plant** starts operation, processing 11 million cubic feet daily in the Cayuga, Texas field; Tidewater Associated Oil Company and Seaboard Oil Company of Delaware, the operators, had secured permit October 19, 1937, to recycle gas. In January 1939 a distillate cycling plant is put into operation in the Agua Dulce field, Nueces County, Texas. (1) (44)

March—**Creole field,** Louisiana, the **first offshore field in the Gulf Coast** discovered one mile out in the Gulf of Mexico by Superior Oil Company and Pure Oil Company joint operators of No. 1 State producing 300 barrels per day from 5110-5130 feet. (70)

April 11—**Brazil** enacts Law No. 366 which establishes the legal principles regulating the ownership of all hydrocarbon and natural gas deposits. (45)

April 29—**Brazil** enacts Law No. 395 creating the Conselho Nacional do Petroleo (National Petroleum Council). (45)

June 7—**Mexico**—The law of this date sets up **Pemex** to carry on exploration, production, refining and all other processes up to marketing; and the **Distribuidora de Petroleos Mexicanos** formed to handle marketing at home and abroad. Both are public corporations. (14)

June 14—Congress passes the **Natural Gas Act** which becomes operative on June 21, 1938. It marks the entrance of the federal government into the field of regulatory control of the natural gas industry. (47)

June 30—Act passed permitting Secretary of the Navy, regarding **Naval Petroleum Reserves,** with consent of the President, to enter into **unitization agreements,** though such agreements do not extend the terms of the affected lease unless so specified in the agreement. (3)

June—Sun Oil Company drills the first **salt water injection** well in the East Texas field. This well, and others drilled later, by Sun and other companies, start the practice which eventually develops into the **East Texas Salt Water Disposal Company,** which plays a major role in keeping the East Texas field producing and in recovering additional billions of barrels of oil. (50)

June—The **Ras Gharib field,** Egypt, discovered. (70)

July 1—**Salem field,** Illinois discovered by The Texas Company at a depth of about 1500 feet. (67)

July 1—**Coalinga East field,** Fresno County, California, immediately adjacent to Eastern Boundary of Coalinga oil field, discovered by Petroleum Securities Co. (now Union Oil Co. of Cal.) with initial production 4776 B/D oil and 2700 Mcf gas. (74)

August 26—**West Ranch field** in Jackson County, Texas discovered by Magnolia Petroleum Company after two previous failures by the same operators; No. 1 West Ranch completed for 132 barrels per day on ¼-inch choke at 5086 feet. (42) (70)

August 30—**Saudi Arabia**—Aramco drills to the so-called Arab Zone, an oil-bearing limestone of substantial thickness, and opens up the **Dammam field.** (10)

August—The first still using Gulf's patented **Polyform process** placed in operation at the company's Port Arthur refinery. This is a combination polymerization and reforming process and is considered the first in the industry. (50)

October 29—W. G. Green, S. A. Scherbatskoy, R. E. Fearson, L. M. Swift, and J. Neufeld of Engineering Laboratories, Tulsa, Oklahoma, make their first **gamma-ray log** in Barnsdall Oil Company's Dawson No. 1 well in Oklahoma City Field. This group, together with Socony-Vacuum, founds **Well Surveys, Inc.** Practical demonstrations given during 1939. (1)

November 11—**Coles Levee field,** California discovered by Ohio Oil Company's F-1 K.C.L. completed for 826 barrels per day at 9365 feet. (70)

November 18—**Jusepin field,** Venezuela, discovered by Standard Oil Company of Venezuela Jusepin No. 1 completed for 750 barrels per day through ½-inch choke after drilling to 5042 feet and plugging back. (77)

198

November 22—**Quintana Petroleum Corporation** chartered in Houston, Texas, to succeed Quintana Petroleum Company formed in May, 1932 by **Hugh Roy Cullen.**

November—**Shaffer Tool Works,** Brea, California, incorporated. The company was founded in 1923 by William D. Shaffer when he purchased the Brea Tool Works. In 1925 the present name of the company was adopted. (50)

December—**Big Piney field,** Wyoming discovered when Wyoming Petroleum Corporation No. 1 Budd blows out of control while shut down for the winter at 1765 feet. (66)

"CP" range introduced by gas appliance manufacturers and utilities, sets new standards in "cooking perfection." (38)

California Legislature passes the **State Land Act.** It is a conservation as well as a leasing act. (31)

Caliper log; Halliburton establishes it as a commercial tool. (73) (50) Halliburton introduces the first **high-pressure-retrievable cementer.** (40)

Centralia oil boom gets under way in Illinois. (6)

Eilerts and Schellhardt report on the investigation of what they call a "**combination**" well, because it produces **distillate.** (64)

First paper published on quantitative interpretation of **electric logs** in terms of relating resistivity to oil productivity. (Martin, Murray, and Gillingham, 1938). (73)

First reports in U. S. A. on application of **gas logging.** (27)

First publication of **Journal of Petroleum Technology**—published irregularly as a bi-monthly or quarterly. (70)

Louisiana State Legislature passes a **boundary-extension act.** (31)

George Miller prepares an **oil-base mud** using air-blown asphalt, with lampblack as a setting inhibitor. Successful on an 8000-foot test in the Ten Sections Field, Kern County, Calif. (1)

First application of **plastics** in production for the purpose of reducing the **water-oil ratio** made in Rodessa field, Marion County, Texas. (5)

Pressure maintenance initiated in the East Texas field. (48)

Fohs Oil Co.'s Buckley-Borg 1 well in DeLarge field, South Louisiana sets **deep production** record flowing from pay bottomed at 13,266 feet. (Condensate). (World Oil)

Drillings in the Bizerta region of **Tunisia** find natural gas. (45)

Continental completes wells in the Ville Platte Field in Louisiana. First instance of one hole serving both as a **producing** well, **and** as an **injection well** into and from the same formation. (1)

The weekly **crude oil stocks report** of the Bureau of Mines revised to show data both on a state and district basis. (48)

First accurate **well depth measuring** system developed by O. J. McCullough of McCullough Tool Co. Patent No. 2,271,742 issued Feb. 3, 1942. (50)

Gulf Oil Corporation acquires an exclusive long-term concession on the entire Kingdom of Denmark, exclusive of the Faroe Islands and Greenland, through the purchase of **Danish-American Prospecting Company** which becomes a wholly-owned subsidiary of Gulf. The concession was disposed of around 1950. (50)

Husky Oil Company organized in Cody, Wyoming, by Glenn E. Nielson. Canadian Husky Oil, Ltd., predecessor formed in 1946; two separate companies now maintain single operating unit. (50)

Michigan Consolidated Gas Company formed by merger of Detroit Gas Company, other gas utilities. (38)

First Appalachian Gas Measurement Short Course held at the **University of West Virginia.** (38)

After three years new **deepest well** record established by Continental Oil Company's KCL A-2 well in Wasco field, Kern County, California at 15,004 feet. (World Oil).

1939

January 20—The **Saint-Marcet,** France natural gas field discovered at a depth of 4920-5250 feet. (45)

January—Standard Oil Company of New Jersey gives all its **information on synthetic rubber** to the Army-Navy Munitions Board, and during 1940 and 1941 tries unsuccessfully to interest the United States rubber industry in its manufacture. (50)

January—The Atlantic Refining Company employs a surface-active agent, its own product "Ultrawet", along with acid in the **acidization of** several **wells.** (50)

March 22—H. R. 491 enacted. General Code amended to permit **water flooding** operations upon the written approval of the Chief of the Division of Mines of the State of **Ohio.** (3)

March 31—Shell Oil Company, San Francisco, merges into Shell Petroleum Corporation, St. Louis, to form new operating company, **Shell Oil Company, Inc.,** which a month later also takes over Shell Eastern properties. (50)

April 30—First public TV broadcast.

May 31—Standard of California executes supplemental agreement with **Saudi Arabia** increasing **concession** by 80,000 square miles, to make a total of 440,000 square miles. It also includes the Saudi Arabian undivided half interest in the two Neutral Zones of Kuwait and Iraq. (80)

June—**Butane-Propane News** begins publication. (50)

June—Baroid Co. obtains an exclusive license on **mud-logging** process and enters the field with one unit in August, 1939. (1)

July 11—Superior Oil Company No. 2 Fitton completed pumping 60 barrels per day from 3000 feet as discovery **New Harmony field,** Illinois. (66) (67)

August 10—**Associated Publishers, Inc.,** incorporated in Texas. (50)

September 1—Germany invades Poland; President Roosevelt proclaims a limited national emergency on September 8. (38)

September 1—Standard Oil Company (Indiana) buys the assets of **Standard Oil Company (Nebraska).** (50)

September 3—Britain and France enter World War II.

September 5—Union Producing Company completes **J. C.** Woodruff No. 1 in Yazoo County, **Mississippi,** as discovery of **Tinsley field.** It produces 300 barrels daily of 35° gravity oil from 4455-4700 feet. **First commercial oil well** in the state. (10)

October—**Chocolate Bayou field,** Texas, discovered by McCarthy and Plummer No. 1 Houston Farms completed for 25 barrels per day at a depth of 9865 feet. (66) (67)

October—The Bureau of Mines inaugurates a special **survey of aviation gasoline** to cover production, stocks, and domestic demand on a monthly basis. (48)

November 1—**Nebraska**—Pawnee Royalty Company completes a well that produces 100 barrels a day for three days. Heavy paraffin clogs the well and forces a shutdown. This is on the Boice farm in Richardson County about two miles west of **Falls City.** The well produces at only 2276 feet and is 2285 feet deep, in the Hunton limestone. (10)

November 10—**Drilling Magazine** first published. (50)

November 18—**Johnston Testers** develops and first uses its own **shut-in pressure tool** in a test conducted in California. (50)

November 21—Lobato No. 1 completed not far from Bahia's capital city, Salvador, as discovery well of **Lobato-Jonas** field and **Brazil's** first commercial producer. (10)

Alabama—Conservation bill passed. Introduced by Senator Oliver Young of Lamar County. Forbids waste, calls for proper plugging of dry wells; requires a permit with fee, and makes mandatory the filing of logs with the supervisor. Power to limit production of any well or pool or field specifically denied until the total average daily production exceeds 50,000 bbl. per day for a period of 90 consecutive days, and no provision made for unit operations, voluntary or enforced. (3)

The Arkansas Legislature passes Act 105, creating the **Arkansas Oil and Gas Commission** to administer the conservation and production control sections of the Act. Duties of the Commission, in short, are to prevent waste and protect correlative rights of owners of underground oil and gas deposits. For the first time, Arkansas imposes sanctions against illegal oil and gas and illegal product. (3)

A 263-mile pipe line connecting the **Barco Concession** in Colombia with Covenas on the Caribbean completed. (Texaco, Inc.)

Southwest—First use of **hydraulic torque converter** on drilling rigs. Purpose is to provide flexibility approaching that of the steam rig without sacrificing fuel economy. (5)

Fluid catalytic cracking invented by Standard Oil Company of New Jersey. (50)

A 43-mile pipe line completed between the **Dammam field** in Saudi Arabia and Ras Tanura on the Persian Gulf. (Texaco, Inc.)

Dominican Republic—Dominican Seaboard Oil Company completes one well, depth 1197 feet, in the Azua Valley; initial production of 200 barrels a day, 21° gavity. (H. G. S. Bulletin)

In **England,** oil discovered in commercial quantities in the Eakring District of Nottinghamshire and to a smaller extent at Formby, Lancashire. Natural gas located at Eskdale, Yorkshire. (45)

Introduction of the **gamma-ray log** by **Well Surveys, Inc.;** the first commercial use of radioactive properties in logging. (73)

Although not classed as a commercial oil-producing state, **Iowa** enacts certain control laws relating to oil and gas drilling. (3)

The first **airborne magnetometer** developed by Gulf Research, but before it can be used to help find oil it goes to war to help Allied airmen detect enemy submarines. (50)

Michigan passes Oil Conservation Act. (3)

First small refinery built at Sidi-Kacem, in the north of **Morocco,** to handle local production. (45)

Well-treating mixture, now known as **"mud acid,"** used successfully by Texas Gulf Coast operators. (1)

First use of **pollen and spores** in oil geology by Shell Oil Company in Venezuela. (GeoTimes)

The French Government creates the **Regie Autonome des Petroles (RAP),** a government agency. (45)

Exports begin from **Saudi Arabia.** (Review)

South Dakota—Legislation enacted for the purpose of furthering and encouraging the development and exploitation of oil and gas permits counties to sell or lease their public lands, and Boards of Schools and Public Lands and Rural Credits authorized to enter into agreements on behalf of the State of South Dakota to pool acreage under their several jurisdictions with other acreage for unit operations and to apportion oil or gas royalties on an acreage or equitable basis. (3)

Trade agreement with Venezuela. **Excise tax on imports** of crude petroleum, topped crude, fuel oil, and gas oil reduced from 21 to 10½ cents per bbl., continuing the tax-free entry of products for supplies of vessels. (3)

Falcon Seaboard Drilling Company is the first in the contracting industry to offer and acquire a **footage basis contract** beyond 10,000 feet. Contract is with Gulf Oil Corporation for a 12,000-foot test in shallow water south of New Orleans, Louisiana in the Gulf of Mexico. Rig is powered by steam, set on pilings with the boilers on a barge. (50)

In Venezuela, the original **Oficina-Puerto La Cruz** oil pipe line, 100 miles of 16-inch pipe, is the industry's first larger than 12 inches. (40)

Reed Roller Bit Company introduces the **Reed Super Shrink-Grip tool joint.** (50)

"Temporary" one cent per gallon United States federal **gasoline tax** extended again for another two years. (62)

A new process for producing **synthetic toluene** for **TNT** is devised at **Standard Oil Development Company.** (50)

In **Venezuela** a 16-inch pipe line one hundred miles long laid across the jungles from Oficina to Guanta. (19)

The first commercial **"wall scratchers"** run in California. Based on the design of **Kenneth Wright** and **Bruce Barkis.** (1)

1940

January 1—**Uniform System of Accounts** formulated for natural gas companies over which the Federal Power Commission has jurisdiction. (59)

April 1—First commercial **radioactivity well log** run by Well Surveys (later acquired by Lane-Wells) in Polo Field, Oklahoma. (50)

April 4—**Erath,** Louisiana **field** discovered by The Texas Company No. 1 Vermillion Parish School Board completed for 120 barrels per day on 12/64-inch choke at 11,378 feet. (67)

April 19—Introduction of the **photoclinometer** for measurement of hole deviation from the vertical. Schlumberger. (50)

May 9—**Nebraska—Pawnee Royalty Company** completes its second well, one on the Bucholz farm southeast of the first well. This well too, is in the Hunton limestone, and wins the company a state bonus for a well that will produce 50 or more barrels a day for 60 consecutive days. $15,000 bonus. (10)

May 25—**Sheridan field,** Texas, discovered when Shell Oil Corporation completes its No. 1 Plow as an oil well at a depth of 8200 feet. (66)

June 3—United States Supreme Court upholds the "substantial evidence rule" as applied by federal courts to Texas Railroad Commission orders, the court saying that it is not a proper function of the federal courts to resolve fact issues contrary to Railroad Commission findings and that whatever rights the State statutes may afford are to be pursued in the state courts. **Railroad Commission** v. **Rowan and Nichols Oil Co.,** 310 U. S. 573 (1940), modified 311 U. S. 614 (1940), rehearing denied 311 U. S. 727 (1940). (58)

June 12—**Frontier Refining Company** organized at Cheyenne, Wyoming. Later relocated headquarters in Denver, Colo. (50)

June 29—The Federal Power Commission in **Columbian Fuel Corporation,** 2 F.P.C. 200, first considers indirectly the question of whether the **Natural Gas Act** in fact covers initial sales by producers and gatherers, and determines that it does not have such jurisdiction. (59)

June—The **Magnet Cove Barium Corporation** plant at Malvern, Arkansas, is the first to use **froth flotation** for beneficiating barite. (50)

July 8—**Plantation Pipe Line Company** incorporated under the laws of the State of Delaware. (50)

July 31—The National Socialists, occupying **Austria,** declare all existing concessions null and void; oil becomes a state monopoly, and a number of concessions granted to various German companies for the production of Austrian oil. (45)

August 6—Two 10,000-gallon tank cars of toluene leave Esso's Baton Rouge refinery. This is the first use of **Hydroforming in** the **making** of **toluene** for TNT. (40)

August 8—Mexico—The General Administration of National Petroleum and the Distribuidora abolished and their assets and functions transferred to **Pemex.** (14)

September 30—Department of Justice files suit against 22 "major" oil companies and several hundred subsidiaries and the API, charging that by unity of action, through the institute, methods to restrict production and to eliminate competition are promoted. This becomes known as the **"Mother Hubbard"** or "umbrella" case. (2)

October 15—**American Association of Oil Well Drilling Contractors** organized in Dallas, Texas. (57)

December 20—**Hawkins field** in Wood County, Texas discovered by **Bobby Manziel's** No. 1 Morrison producing 40 barrels per day from Woodbine at 4318 feet. (41) (66) (70)

December 30—**API says federal control unwarranted** in year-end statement by Axtell J. Byles, president. (2)

Gypsum cement introduced by Halliburton Oil Well Cementing Co. (1)

Bureau of Mines initiates a **survey of aviation gasoline content** of crude oils. (48)

Seismograph Service Corp. develops **radioactivity well-logging** method, consisting of gamma-ray-surveying instrument containing gamma-ray detector, amplifier, and equipment for transmitting indications over a cable. (5)

Louisiana Legislature adopts Act 157, containing provisions revolutionary in the conservation field at this time, many of which are still unique in administrative law. (3)

Magnet Cove Barium Corporation founded in Jamestown, Tennessee, as manufacturers of mud chemical or additive for oil well drilling known as Barite (barium sulfate). (50)

The first oil field for **Morocco** is **Ain Hamra.** (70)

Standard Oil Company of New Jersey is producing **Perbunan,** a synthetic rubber, at the rate of 2000 tons yearly. With Perbunan, a bullet hole in a hose or fuel cell will close within twenty seconds. (50)

The Marathon Oil Company (then Ohio) puts into operation at its Robinson, Illinois, refinery completely new concept—a light ends recovery unit with a **polymerization plant.** (50)

In **Qatar,** oil discovered at Dukhan. (40)

Russia—The specialized oil-gas-survey office organized for prospecting work. The scientific director is **V. A. Sokolov.** (27)

The United States federal **gasoline tax** "temporarily" increased to one and one half cents per gallon and other "temporary" increases enacted in the "temporary" levies on lubricating oil, automobiles, motorcycles, buses, trucks, parts and accessories, tires and tubes. (62)

Tennessee Gas and Transmission Company chartered for the purpose of taking gas to Tennessee. It did not become operational, however, until 1943 when it was acquired by the **Chicago Corporation.** (50)

The Houston, Texas refinery of Shell Oil Company, using a process originated by Shell Development, begins extracting **nitration-grade toluene** from crude oil. (50)

In **Yugoslavia,** oil discovered at Selnica. (40)

There are 32,453,233 motor vehicle registrations in the United States. (48)

A survey of the **aviation gasoline content** of all important crude oils initiated by the Bureau of Mines. (48)

It is believed that this is the first year the Internal Revenue Service sanctioned an **ABC transaction.** This type of transaction did not become prevalent until after World War II. An ABC transaction is one wherein A, the owner of an oil and gas lease, conveys his entire working interest in the lease to B, the ultimate purchaser, reserving to himself (A) a production payment payable out of the interest assigned to B, and the simultaneous conveyance by A to C of the reserved production payment. In other words, A to B and to C, selling to B the working interest subject to production payment, and selling the production payment to C. (Arthur Anderson & Co.)

When waterflooding comes into prominence as a means of secondary recovery, Oil Well Supply develops a line of horizontal **triplex power plunger pumps** specifically for this service. (50)

205

1941

January 1—**Logging caliper service** to the industry commercially introduced by Halliburton Oil Well Cementing Co. (1)

February—**Abqaiq field,** Saudia Arabia, discovered. (66)

March 25—The **first Texas offshore well** reported in the discovery of oil 9000 feet off **Sabine Pass** at a producing depth of 4980-95 feet by Hall Jordan and British American Oil Company. After producing 12,000 barrels of oil this well was abandoned on January 22, 1942. (42)

May 16—**Entire mining laws** of **Ohio** again revised and codified. Contain all of the provisions of the statutes of Ohio which by any stretch of the imagination could be considered as intended for the conservation of oil or gas. (3)

May 23—Hitler sends Stalin a secret memorandum calling for joint exploitation of **Russian oil wells.** Stalin refuses. (Standard Oil Co. of New Jersey)

May 27—**California**—From this date to the end of the war, production in California controlled, first by the Petroleum Coordinator for National Defense and within a year by the Petroleum Administrator for War. (3)

May 27—President Roosevelt declares a state of "unlimited emergency" and makes Secretary of Interior Harold L. Ickes **Petroleum Coordinator for National Defense.** (2)

June 20—**Illinois** passes **Conservation Act.** (3)

June 22—Germany invades Russia.

September—A Shell Chemical plant goes on stream at Houston, Texas, the first plant in America to produce **butadiene** on a commercial basis. (50)

September—**Neutron logging** perfected and described by **Bruno Pontecorvo.** (1)

November 1—The Texas Corporation merges into itself The Texas Company (Delaware) and causes The Texas Company (California) to transfer all assets to it and then dissolve. The Texas Corporation then becomes **The Texas Company.** (50)

November 15—The **Empire State Petroleum Association** formed. Its purpose is to serve its members and to assist in improving their operating methods and to encourage high standards of practice in the marketing of petroleum products in New York State. (57)

November 29—Seventy-eight leaders from all branches of the industry appointed to the **Petroleum Industry Council** for National Defense by Petroleum Coordinator Harold L. Ickes. (54)

December 2—The **S. P. dipmeter** introduced, incorporating the photoclinometer. Schlumberger. (50)

December 7—Japanese attack Pearl Harbor. United States enters World War II December 8. (38)

December 11—**Petroleum Industry War Council** created by Secretary of the Interior for purpose of mobilizing most effectively the resources and abilities of the petroleum industry to deal with the emergency conditions under which it must operate; dissolved December 31, 1945. (61)

December 11—Germany and Italy declare war on U. S.

December 16—A presidential order in **Mexico** specifies the detailed regulations of the petroleum industry. The basic law, as amended, asserts the "inalienable and imprescriptible" ownership rights of the state over petroleum deposits and all forms of hydrocarbons, whatever their physical state. The law declares the petroleum industry a "public utility." (14)

Arkansas Legislature adopts an act permitting the execution of cooperative joint study agreements of reservoir control between U. S. Bureau of Mines, Department of the Interior, and the **Arkansas Gas & Oil Commission.** (3)

New **Continental Oil Co.,** refinery at Lake Charles, Louisiana, sets **record yield** with 27 gallons of gasoline recovered from each 42 gallons of stabilized crude. (5)

The Office of **Coordinator for National Defense** created to cooperate with industry to solve petroleum problems caused by World War II. Shortly after 1941, the agency becomes the Office of Petroleum Coordinator for War; and, on December 2, 1942, the agency is called Petroleum Administration for War. (1)

Lucas Medal presented to **Schlumberger Brothers.** (50)

The **neutron-gamma log,** developed by Well Surveys, Inc., is introduced. (73)

First automatically stabilized **airborne magnetometer** flown in the United States. (5)

Starch introduced to cut down **mud-filtrate loss** and protect water-sensitive formations. (40)

Nebraska—Legislation provides law concerning exclusion of water from oil- or gas-bearing strata before abandonment, filing of notice, and plugging of well. (3)

North Dakota enacts broad conservation law with power in hands of State Industrial Commission. (3)

The United States creates the **Office of Production Management,** sets up priorities on acquisition and use of materials, supplies and equipment that vitally affect the gas industry. (38)

The **Portland-Montreal line,** dual 12- and 18-inch, laid. (40)

South Dakota—Bill passed which embodies the best features of conservation legislation in effect in states where oil and gas is found in commercial quantities. (3)

The United States **federal excise taxes** on motor vehicles, parts and accessories, tires and tubes again increased for the national defense program and made permanent parts of the revenue structure. (62)

The "temporary" United States federal **gasoline tax** made permanent at the one and one half cent rate. (62)

Texas—Section of law (1932) providing for termination of Conservation Act at the end of two years, repealed. (3)

First shipment of **nitrate-grade toluene** made from Baytown Ordnance Works. (5)

Turkey—Oil discovered at Raman. (40)

Pressure gas-welding first used near Tucson, Arizona, on two miles of six-inch line. (38)

The two **deepest tests east of the Mississippi** River are drilled by Falcon Seaboard Drilling Company for the Hope Natural Gas Company, near Clarksburg, West Virginia. The first, in 1941, goes to 10,000 feet, and the second, in 1954, to 13,324 feet. (50)

Sun Shipbuilding and Dry Dock Company, a Sun Oil Company subsidiary, designs and constructs the first **T-2 tanker,** the standard World War II tank ship. (50)

Agha Jari and **Gach Sarin fields** brought into production in Iran. (70)

1942

January 8—Charter for **East Texas Salt Water Disposal Company** drawn up, following several meetings on proposed formation of salt water company. (First salt water injection by company on October 1, 1942) (East Texas Engineering Association)

February 7—Section 7 of the **Natural Gas Act** amended, which provides, among other things, that a **certificate of public convenience and necessity** be required for the engagement in transportation or sale of natural gas, subject to Federal Power Commission jurisdiction, or to undertake the construction or extension of any facility thereof, or acquire or operate any such facilities. This new requirement changes the original 1938 provision in Section 7 (c) which called for a certificate to be issued only for construction or extension of facilities or extension of service to a market in which natural gas was already being served by another natural gas company. (59)

March 3—**Fullerton field** in Andrews County, Texas, discovered by Fullerton Oil Corp. No. 1 Wilson completed for 682 barrels per day after acidizing pay topped at 7250 feet. Secondary recovery program authorized estimated to recover 32.4 million barrels of additional oil, December 1953. (42) (70)

March 16—The United States Supreme Court rules that the sale of natural gas originating in one state and its transportation to another state is interstate commerce, which is subject to regulation as to price by the Congress under the Fifth Amendment to the Constitution. The lowest reasonable rate is not confiscatory in the Constitutional sense. **Federal Power Commission** v. **Natural Gas Pipeline Company** 315 U. S. 575. (59)

March—The **Neches Butane Products Company** organized and its plant in complete operation on May 25, 1944. (Texaco, Inc.)

April 8—**Lone Star Steel Company** founded in Texas during World War II to be operated by the U.S. Government. From 1944 to the end of 1947, it was operated under lease from the Defense Plant Corporation and War Assets Administration. On January 1, 1948, the company purchased all plant facilities including East Texas ore lands and Oklahoma coal mines. (50)

April—George Miller starts a concern known as **Oil Base, Inc.,** which is the first to offer an **oil-base drilling mud** to the industry. (1)`

April—The United States Army orders initial manufacture of **military portable pipe line,** designed and developed by Shell products pipe line department. Military line used extensively in North Africa, Italy, France, and China-Burma-India Theater. (Shell Oil Company)

April—The Bureau of Mines opens a new field office at Franklin, Pennsylvania, to assist in increasing and improving production of **Pennsylvania grade crude oil** to meet military needs for quality lubricating oils. (48)

May 7—The first commercial oil well in **Virginia** is the Fugate No. 1 in Lee County, drilled by R. Y. Walker of Baton Rouge, Louisiana, and is the discovery well of the Rose Hill field. Initial flow is 60 barrels per day, and for five years it produces at the rate of eight barrels daily. (10)

May—The **first fluid catalytic cracking** unit goes on stream at the Baton Rouge, Louisiana, refinery of the Standard Oil Company. (50)

June—War Production Board approves construction of **"Big Inch"**— 24-inch pipeline to run from Texas to Norris City, Illinois. The line later extended to the New York-Philadelphia refinery areas and completion date scheduled for February, 1943. (2)

July 22—Government imposes **gasoline rationing** and introduces the coupon system. (2)

July 31—The Petroleum and Natural Gas Branch of the U. S. Bureau of Mines makes a report to the office of the Petroleum Coordinator for War on the suitability of crude oils and refinery distillates as sources of **toluene.** (64)

August 3—The construction of the "Big Inch," the War Emergency 24-inch crude oil pipe line begins and the first oil arrives at Philadelphia on August 21, 1943. The 1340-mile pipe line costs the Federal government $78.5 million. (47)

December 2—**Petroleum Administration for War** established by Executive Order No. 9276, issued by President of the United States. PAW established to coordinate and centralize war policies and actions of the U. S. Government relating to petroleum with a view toward providing adequate supplies of petroleum for the successful prosecution of the war and other essential purposes. This Order abolishes the Office of Petroleum Coordinator for War and its personnel, records, property and funds are transferred to the PAW. PAW terminated 5-3-46 by Executive Order No. 9718. (61)

December 24—The first plant for commercial production of **hydrofluoric acid alkylate** placed in operation at Phillips, Texas, by Phillips Petroleum Corp. (50)

December 25—The **HF alkylation process** patented by Universal Oil Products, and Phillips Petroleum Company develops, engineers, and constructs the world's first commercial unit at Borger, Texas. It goes on stream on this date with a capacity of 1950 bbl. per day of aviation alkylate. (40)

Central Asia—Oil found at Palran Tash and Andijan, near Tashkent, a city of Asiatic Russia. (23)

Consolidated Natural Gas Company incorporated under the laws of the State of Delaware. (50)

Holland—Oil discovered in the province of Drente, in the Coervorden field near the German border. (23)

The United States federal **tax on lubricating oil** increased to six cents per gallon to help raise revenue for the war effort. (62)

Tennessee Gas Transmission Co. granted permission to construct "Big Inch" line from Texas to West Virginia. First major outlet from Gulf Coast to Atlantic Seaboard states. (5)

United Gas, Coke and Chemical Workers Union formed from several locals which secede from District 50, United Mine Workers. Later (1955) merged with OWIU to form OCAW. (OCAW)

The **War Emergency Pipelines, Inc.,** organized. (Texaco, Inc.)

Enrico Fermi develops **atomic reactor.**

Lone Star Gas Company reorganized into two companies—Lone Star Gas Company and **Lone Star Producing Company.** (50)

In the United States, the War Production Board issues order prohibiting use of gas for new heating installations in 17 states and District of Columbia. Order to be effective elsewhere whenever gas supply shortage occurs. (**Natural gas use prohibited**). (38)

The Bureau of Mines begins monthly **reports on natural-gas liquids.** (48)

1943

February—The Atlantic Refining Company is the first to use the **mass spectrometer** in petroleum research. (50)

March 4—Announcement made of the **Cycloversion process** for the manufacture of high-quality aviation-fuel ingredients. Naphthas produced in thermal operations are converted catalytically to aromatic-rich stocks. (40)

March 9—Probably the **first triple completion** comes as a war expedient. Superior Oil Company No. 5 McWhorter, Lake Creek field, Montgomery County, Texas, completed to produce gas from three separate zones through concentric tubing strings and the casing annulus. (40)

March 14—The **War Production Board** prohibits new installations of oil-burning equipment and encourages the conversion of heating equipment from oil to coal. (2)

April 23—Construction of the **"Little Big Inch,"** the War Emergency 20-inch oil products pipe line begins. The line originates in Beaumont, Texas, and terminates at the New York area. Total length of 1475 miles. Cost is $67.3 million. (47)

May 24—United States Supreme Court, in effect, orders federal courts not to take jurisdiction in suits against the Texas Railroad Commission in matters which, under State statutes, the Railroad Commission has a duty to act, even though diversity of citizenship exists. **Burford v. Sun Oil Co.,** 319 U.S. 315 (1943). (58)

August 19—The plan of reorganization under which the properties and operations of Lago Petroleum Corporation, **Creole Petroleum Corporation** and Standard Oil Company of Venezuela were consolidated under Creole Petroleum Corporation takes effect. (50)

September 8—Italy surrenders to Allies.

September 24—**Tennessee Gas Transmission Company** (then known as Tennessee Gas and Transmission Company and at that time a subsidiary of the Chicago Corporation) receives certificate from FPC for construction of **first pipeline in history to transport natural gas from the Texas Gulf Coast area to markets in the Appalachians.** (50)

September 26—**First oil discovery** made in **Florida** at Sunniland in Collier County by Humble Oil & Refining Company in a well which produces 100 barrels per day of 25 gravity crude from a 13-foot porous limestone topped at 11,626 feet. Humble accepts a $50,000 prize offered by the state for the first commercial oil well, adds $10,000 to it and divides the $60,000 equally between the University of Florida and the Florida State College for Women. (10)

October 13—Italy does an about face and declares war on former ally, Germany.

October—Members of a subcommittee of the Special Senate (Truman) Committee Investigating the National Defense Program return from a visit to the war theaters and revive the ghost of the **"John Bull" scare,** implying that Great Britain is holding out on oil and using U. S. oil in war. (2)

December 25—First shipment of **furnace carbon black** for use in tiretype rubber produced and shipped from Phillips Petroleum Corporation's Borger, Texas, plant. This new process increases overall recovery efficiency ten times over the channel process. (50)

A thermodynamics laboratory established at the Bartlesville, Oklahoma, station of the Bureau of Mines, having been proposed originally as a source for needed basic data for developing a single-stage process for converting **butane to butadiene.** (48)

G. L. Hassler makes one of the first reported **capillary-pressure measurements.** (1)

DDT used for the first time against mosquito larvae and found effective. (39)

Pioneer high-pressure flood launched as a cooperative project in Arkansas' Midway field, Lafayette County. (40)

The double coat, **double wrap machine** developed and used for the first time in applying protective coatings to pipe. (38)

Trade agreement with Mexico. Tax reduction extended to include kerosene and liquid asphalt. (3)

The first **"moving bed" process** for regeneration of the catalyst (Thermofor) comes into operation. (39)

Dowell, Inc., markets a **phenol-formaldehyde** thermo-setting plastic, the polymerization time of which can be controlled. (1)

Union Producing Co.-Fohs Oil Co.'s Fitzpatrick-Vizard 1 well, DeLarge field, South Louisiana, sets **deep production** record flowing from pay bottomed at 13,490 feet. (Condensate). (World Oil)

South Dakota—Act passed creating a Conservation Commission. (3)

Tennessee passes comprehensive oil and gas conservancy code. (3)

The Atlantic Refining Company is the first to use **radioactive tracers** in motor oils to determine engine wear. (50)

First use of **radioactive tracer** (carnolite) **log.** Lane-Wells. (73)

Venezuela enacts a Petroleum Law. It is the intent of the government that the revenue accruing to it from royalties and other taxes should equal the net profits of the oil companies. (**First 50-50 Law**) (45)

The **Arkansas** Legislature passes Act 302. This Act defines primary and secondary recovery, water and gas drive, water and gas injection, water flooding, etc. The Act also states that the Arkansas Oil and Gas Commission must make secondary recovery studies to ascertain their desirability. (3)

Consolidated Natural Gas Company formed to acquire five gas utility properties held by Standard Oil (New Jersey). (38)

Underground storage of LPG begun by Carter Oil Company. (1)

1944

January 3—The United States Supreme Court rules that the Federal Power Commission is justified in rejecting reproduction cost to determine a rate base in the fixing of a "just and reasonable" rate, and it is proper to accept original cost of the properties less depreciation as the rate base. **Federal Power Commission v. Hope Natural Gas Company** 320 U. S. 591.

January 11—**Independent Natural Gas Association of America** formed and holds its organizational meeting in Kansas City, Missouri. (57)

January 26—**"Little Big Inch"** products pipeline from Beaumont and Houston, Texas, to Linden, New Jersey, starts operation carrying seven different refined products. (54)

February 17—**Gilbertown field,** Choctaw County, **Alabama,** discovered by H. L. Hunt No. 1 Jackson producing from a depth of 2563 feet; first field for state. (10) (54)

March 3—**American Society of Lubrication Engineers** organized in Illinois. (50)

April 21—**Rolo Manufacturing Company** formed in Houston to build well checkers. (50)

April 30—**Canol,** the $130,000,000 American-financed **oil project** in northern Canada, opens. (2)

June 1—The **Petroleum Industry Research Foundation, Inc.** (PIRINC) established. It is a non-profit organization, devoted to economic research and the dissemination of information concerning the oil industry. (72)

June 6—The Allies invade Normandy on "D-Day." **"Operation Pluto,"** a pipeline to fuel the forces, laid across the English Channel. (54)

July 1—The Office of **Synthetic Liquid Fuels** of the U. S. Bureau of Mines organized. (64)

August 1—The United States Government grants a **subsidy** or compensatory payment of 35 cents per barrel **on stripper well production.** Thousands of marginal wells enabled to continue on the pump instead of being subject to abandonment. The subsidy is cancelled by the Government July 1, 1946. (National Stripper Well Association)

August 8—An international oil agreement signed by representatives of the British and United States governments provides among other things, an orderly development of oil reserves. This agreement, commonly called the **Anglo-American Treaty,** was never ratified by the United States Senate. (80)

August 11—**Gwinville field,** Mississippi, discovered when Sid Richardson makes a dual gas well completion at 7855-7880 and 8075-8132 feet for a total production of 7000 mcf per day. (66)

September 22—The Federal Power Commission initiates the **Natural Gas Investigation** in Docket No. G-580 to consider problems relating to the production, transportation and utilization of natural gas. The hearings begin on September 18, 1945 and are concluded on August 2, 1946. (47)

October 20—Explosion and fire wreck liquefied natural gas plant of **East Ohio Gas Company** in Cleveland, Ohio, killing 135 persons. Plant had produced first **liquefied natural gas** in 1940, based on experiments started in 1937. (38)

October 31—**Tennessee Gas Transmission Company** completes and places in operation its first natural gas pipeline, which extends 1265 miles from South Texas into West Virginia. (50)

October—The **Mississippi-Alabama division** of the **Mid-Continent Oil and Gas Association** formed. Offices are opened and activities started May 1, 1945. (57)

November 22—**Jefferson Chemical Company,** Inc., organized. (Texaco, Inc.)

December 31—**TXL field** discovered in Ector county, Texas, by Shell and Cities Service in their No. 1 TXL well completed for 1911 barrels per day at 7996 feet. This discovery is in the Devonian series, later discoveries made in the field in the Wolfcamp, Tubb sand, Upper Clear Fork, San Andres, Silurian, Waddell, and Ellenberger formations. (42) (67)

Discovery allowables initiated in New Mexico, apparently the first state to do so. (Handbook of Oil and Gas Law, Sullivan, Prentice-Hall, 1955)

The shortage of crude oil becomes so serious on the West Coast that the Congress authorizes the opening of the **Elk Hills Naval Reserve** in the San Joaquin Valley; and by VJ Day, the costly tank-car shipments of crude oil from West Texas to the West Coast average 35,000 barrels a day. (1)

The **Schoonebeek** oilfield discovered in **Holland.** (45)

The operating organization in Saudi Arabia takes the name of Arabian American Oil Company (known as **Aramco**).

The United States Congress adopts federal highway aid bill of $500,-000,000 annually. It also authorizes a 40,000-mile network of key primary routes to be known as the **National System of Interstate Highways.** (62)

Lime mud introduced. It is still unique for its low viscosity and gels, resistance to contamination, and low upkeep cost. (40)

The $48,000,000 **Neches Butane Products Company** plant operated by Gulf Oil Corporation and four other oil companies and located near Port Arthur, Texas, begins operating to supply butadiene needed for the manufacture of synthetic rubber. (50)

Union Producing Co.-Fohs Oil Co.'s Buckley-Bourg 2 well in DeLarge field, South Louisiana, sets **deep production** record flowing from pay bottomed at 13,503 feet. (Oil). (World Oil)

An oil shale program initiated under the **Synthetic Liquid Fuels Act.** (48)

Mississippi Legislature passes a **Severance Tax** of six per cent of the value of oil or six cents per barrel, whichever is the greater. (Mississippi-Alabama Division of Mid-Continent Oil and Gas Association)

For the second time in history two **deepest well** records set in same year. Phillips Petroleum Company's Price 1, a wildcat in Pecos County, Texas, drilled to 15,279 feet. A few months later Standard of California returns the record to California with a 16,246-foot hole in its KCL 20-13 well in South Coles Levee field, Kern County. (World Oil)

Automobile and truck registrations in the United States decline to 30 million units. (48)

Texas Gulf Producing Company acquires **Snowden and McSweeney Company** with producing properties in West Texas and in the East Texas area. (50)

1945

February 23—The **Levelland field,** Texas, discovered by The Texas Company No. 1 Montgomery producing 75 barrels per day from a depth of 4927 feet. (70)

February—**Anglo-American treaty** is submitted to Senate for ratification and referred to Committee on Foreign Affairs, where it finally dies. Domestic oil industry defeats this treaty on ground that it would make their industry subject to a proposed **International Petroleum Commission,** forcing a form of federal control with international overtones. (2)

April 2—The United States Supreme Court rules that the Federal Power Commission may include production and gathering facilities in the rate base and refuse to let the pipeline treat the "fair field price" as an expense in determining rates for such pipeline. **Colorado Interstate Gas Company v. Federal Power Commission** 324 U. S. 581. (Vinson, Elkins, Weems and Searls)

April—**Qatif field** discovered in Saudia Arabia. (67)

May 7—Germany signs unconditional surrender in Rheims headquarters. (38)

May 29—**Tidelands litigation** starts when U. S. Dept. of Justice files suit against Pacific Western Oil Corporation for extraction of oil from submerged Elwood field in **California.** On October 29, U. S. drops action against Pacific Western and files an original action against State of California in U. S. Supreme Court. (31)

July 16—First A-Bomb exploded as test.

July 24—The **Trans-Arabian Pipe Line Company** incorporated in Delaware. (Texaco, Inc.)

July 31—**Rationing of gas ranges** and heating equipment ends. (38)

August 6—**Atomic bomb** dropped on Hiroshima.

August 14—The **first offshore lease sale** by the State of Louisiana held. (38)

August 14—Japan surrenders. (38)

August 15—**Louisiana** governor dissolves the Natural Gas Conservation Committee and transfers its functions to the Director of Natural Gas Conservation. (3)

August 15—Gasoline and fuel oil **rationing** ends. (54)

September 3—VJ Day.

September 14—The first commercial producer from the **Ordovician Formation** in Southeastern Lea County, New Mexico, completed by Neville G. Penrose, Inc. (50)

September 28—**President Harry S Truman** issues a proclamation laying claim (for the U. S.) to the natural resources of the subsoil and the sea bed of the **continental shelf.** (15)

September—Extraneous fresh-water injection into the Hill sand reservoir, New Hope field, Franklin County, Texas, started, thus marking the initiation of **pressure-maintenance** operation of reservoirs without benefit of primary water encroachment. (1)

December 7—**Texas Gas Transmission Corporation** incorporated. Predecessor Companies were Memphis Natural Gas Company, incorporated on June 11, 1928; Missouri-Kansas Pipe Line Company, organized May 1928; and Kentucky Natural Gas Corporation, organized October 5, 1933. (50)

December 29—First producing oil well in **Chile,** Springhill No. 1, brought in at Manantiales, Magallanes Province, at the southern tip of the country, producing from a depth of 7410 feet. (45) (70)

December—**Borregas field,** Texas, discovered when Humble Oil & Refining Company completes its King Ranch-Borregas for 104 barrels per day through a ¼-inch choke from pay at 6895 feet. (66)

Alabama passes oil and gas conservation act. (1)

Barker Creek dome in San Juan County, New Mexico, discovered to initiate a major gas development in the San Juan basin. (5)

The **Chicago Corporation** divests itself of its interest in **Tennessee Gas and Transmission Company** by sale to a group which later resold the stock to the public. In 1947 the company moves its charter to Delaware and drops the "and" in the name to become the **Tennessee Gas Transmission Company.** (50)

Florida passes oil and gas conservation act. (1)

Jack DeMent reports that the slightest trace of oil will **fluoresce** under ultra-violet light. (22)

216

Georgia passes oil and gas conservation act. (1)

The Petroleum and Natural Gas Branch of the U. S. Bureau of Mines begins the study of **jet fuel.** (64)

North Carolina adopts Oil and Gas Conservation Act. (3)

The Oklahoma Legislature amends the 1935 well spacing law so that, for the first time, a state has the authority to force the pooling of the working interest, whether divided or undivided. This amendment gives the Corporation Commission the power and obligation to fix the equities of the various interests, if they are unable to agree. The act also provides that only one well can be drilled on a drilling unit as fixed by the Corporation Commission. (**Pool-wide compulsory pooling**) (60)

Shell Oil Co.'s Smith-State Unit 1-1 well in Weeks Island field, South Louisiana sets **deep production** record flowing from pay bottomed at 13,520 feet. (Oil). (World Oil)

Deepest well in world drilled by Phillips Petroleum Company. It is the Schoeps 3, a wildcat well in Brazos County, Texas, taken down 16,665 feet. (World Oil)

El Paso Natural Gas Company announces plans to build a 1200-mile system, including a 720-mile, 26-inch line from the Permian Basin in West Texas to California. (38)

A law is passed in **Maryland,** to control acts pertaining to water, oil or gas wells. (60)

McCullough develops and introduces first free-point finder, the **Magna-Tector,** for locating stuck pipe. This instrument, along with the company's string shot back-off, is estimated to have saved the industry some $5 million annually. Patent No. 2,530,308 issued Nov. 14, 1950. (50)

1946

January 1—The **Division of Transportation** of API organized. (62)

January 17—One of the first treatments involving use of **plastics for sand consolidation** performed on Gulf's E. R. Taylor No. 37 well in Pierce Junction field, Harris County, Texas. Initial results are encouraging, and by 1947, the treatment is being used extensively along the Louisiana-Texas Gulf Coast. (1)

January 26—**Sprayberry field,** Dawson County, Texas, discovered by Seaboard Oil Company of Delaware. (42)

January—"**Pipeline Construction**" first published. (50)

March 15—Texas Independent Producers and Royalty Owners Association (**TIPRO**) organized with headquarters in Austin, Texas. (5)

April 1—**Black, Sivalls & Bryson, Inc.** organized as a Delaware corporation to acquire the business of Black, Sivalls & Bryson, Inc., a Maine corporation which was the outgrowth of a business established in 1893 by A. H. Black to manufacture wooden tanks for oil storage. Principal offices are in Kansas City, Mo. and the company engages in oil field production and natural gas processing equipment. (50)

April 10—Texas Court of Civil Appeals upholds the Railroad Commission proration order of August 3, 1944, saying that the Railroad Commission has the discretion to assign allowables to small tracts which will result in drainage to smaller tracts, and away from adjoining areas drilled in accordance with the spacing regulations. Court says in dictum that an allowable for a small tract cannot be cut down to the point where it can not be drilled and operated at a reasonable profit. Railroad Commission v. Humble Oil & Refining Company, 193 s.w. 2d 824 (Tex. Civ. App. 1946), error ref'd, n.r.e. "Hawkins Case." (58)

May 3—Formal order terminating **Petroleum Administration for War.** (1)

May 6—The **Oil and Gas Division** is established by the Secretary of the Interior pursuant to the President's letter of May 3, 1946, with a view to the conservation of the oil and gas resources of the Nation and the achievement of petroleum security. OGD also winds up the affairs of the Petroleum Administration for War, and establishes the channel of communication with the petroleum industry. (61)

June 3—Administration of **"Connally Hot-Oil Act,"** transferred to the Oil and Gas Division, by Executive Order No. 9732. The Acting Secretary of the Interior transfers Connally Act functions to the Geological Survey, Department of the Interior, February 14, 1958. (Effective at the close of February 21, 1958). (61)

June 18—**National Petroleum Council** established by the Secretary of the Interior to provide advice and counsel to the Secretary of the Interior with respect to national oil and gas matters and to serve as channel of communication and liaison between the Federal Government and the petroleum industry. (61)

June 30—**First oil is exported from Kuwait** aboard the S. S. British Fusilier. (80)

July 1—**CATC** Group organized to explore and drill for oil and gas in the offshore waters of the Gulf of Mexico. Participating companies are Continental Oil Company, Atlantic Refining Company, Tide Water Oil Company, and Cities Service Company. (50)

July 8—**Interdepartmental Petroleum Committee** appointed by the Secretary of the Interior to function under the chairmanship of the Director of the **Oil and Gas Division** as a focal point for consideration of oil and gas problems affecting more than one department or agency of the Government in the field of oil and gas. The Committee has been inactive since mid-1950. (61)

August 8—The United States makes a major revision of the oil and gas **leasing policy** for **public lands.** Royalty retained at 12½ per cent; annual rentals at 25 cents an acre; and, because of prior acts, non-competitive leases require no rental payment for the second and third years. (61)

September—First plant in U. S. equipped with refrigerated reactors capable of making a "cold" rubber to produce commercial **tire-type synthetic rubber** from principal raw material (butane) to finished product. (Phillips Petroleum Corp.)

September—A new type of porosimeter, known as the **Kaye-Freeman Porosimeter,** to determine the porosity of reservoir rocks by use of air, developed by The Atlantic Refining Company. (50)

November 13—**El Paso Natural Gas Company** makes first deliveries of natural gas through its 26-inch line from the Permian Basin in Texas to the California border at Blythe to serve markets in Southern California. (38)

November 27—Texas Supreme Court upholds the **"substantial evidence rule"** as applied by State courts to Railroad Commission orders and findings, saying that any order of the Railroad Commission will be sustained by the Court if its action in reaching the conclusions embodied in the order are reasonably supported by substantial evidence. Trapp v. Shell Oil Co., 198 S.W. 2d 424 (1946). (58)

November—The American Petroleum Institute Board of Directors approves the formation of a committee, composed of representatives from member companies, which is known, at this time, as the Public Relations Operating Committee. Its name is eventually changed to the **Oil Industry Information Committee.** (62)

December 5—Gas turned into the **"Little Big Inch"** pipeline. (Tennessee Gas Transmission Company)

December 9—Gas turned into the **"Big Inch"** pipeline. (Tennessee Gas Transmission Company)

December 11—Natural gas from the **Big Inch pipeline** delivered in commercial quantities to consumer points in Ohio. (Tennessee Gas Transmission Company)

Carter Oil Co. devises the **"oil pool analyzer"** to predict the production history of certain types of fields 25 years or more into the future. (5)

Camco, Inc., founded in Houston, Texas, as manufacturers of gas lift equipment. (50)

Phillips develops and introduces sodium carboxmethylcellulose (**Driscose**) to the industry for treatment of drilling mud, particularly to obtain low waste cost and stability. (1)

The first commercial operations with **induction logging** takes place in wells drilled with oil-base muds. (1)

Kerlyn Oil Company becomes **Kerr-McGee Oil Industries, Inc.** (50)

Perforating Guns Atlas Corp., founded as Atlas Research Corp., in Houston, Texas, as a service company. (50)

Shell Oil Co.'s Smith-State Unit 1-2 well in Weeks Island field, South Louisiana sets **deep production** record flowing from pay bottomed at 13,778 feet. (Oil). (World Oil)

Mississippi—**A Documentary Stamp Tax** enacted into law. This law is in lieu of the old antiquated method of advalorem tax of mineral interests and has been advantageous both in the counties and in the state. (57)

Deepest well record returns to Kern County, California, as Pacific Western Oil Corporation's National Royalties 1 in Miramonte area is drilled to 16,668 feet, only three feet deeper than 1945 record well. (World Oil)

The first **Gas Technology Short Course** held at **Texas A & I College.** (38)

Texas Gulf Producing Company acquires **Fohs Oil Company** with principal producing properties in South Louisiana. (50)

Gas Appliance Manufacturers Association name adopted by the Association of Gas Appliance and Equipment Manufacturers, founded in 1935. (38)

Overseas Tankship Corporation incorporated in the Republic of Panama. (Texaco, Inc.)

Peace River, Alberta, in Canada, becomes northernmost natural gas outpost with granting of franchise to S. Hector. (38)

The name of Asiatic Petroleum Company, Ltd., changed to **Shell Petroleum Company,** Ltd. (50)

The "**shaped charge**" used in Texas well completions to perforate pipe. (5)

1947

January—Construction of the **Trans-Arabian pipe line** authorized. (Texaco, Inc.)

February 3-12—The First Session of the **International Labor Organization** held in Los Angeles, California. The Petroleum Committee is one of the committees established pursuant to a decision of the 94th Session of ILO held in London, England, in 1945. (61)

February 13—**Leduc, Canada field** discovered by Imperial Oil Company well producing at rate of 1000 barrels per day from Devonian dolomite at 5029-5066 feet. (66)

March 12—**Trunkline Gas Company** organized as Trunkline Gas Supply Company. (50)

March 17—Texas Railroad Commission issues "**Seeligson Order**"— Restricts the production of gas and oil wells completed in the various reservoirs underlying the Seeligson Field by prohibiting the production of oil and gas in the entire field unless and until all of the casinghead gas produced with the oil is utilized for one of the beneficial purposes enumerated for sweet gas in #7 (1) of art. 6008, Title 102 of the Civil Statutes. Order upheld by Texas Supreme Court in First **Flare Gas Case** on December 31, 1947. Other shut down orders follow promptly. All upheld. (58)

March 29—Pursuant to Presidential letter of May 3, 1946, Military Petroleum Advisory Committee, later changed to **Military Petroleum Advisory Board,** established by the Secretary of the Interior, to provide expert counsel, advice and information on oil and gas matters relating to national security and defense. The Board's functions were transferred to the Petroleum Administration for Defense during the existence of that agency. (61)

March 29—The Secretary of the Interior designates the Director of the **Oil and Gas Division** as the Department of the Interior official representative to the Interstate Oil Compact Commission. (61)

April 16—**Texas City, Texas, disaster.**

April 30—Tennessee Gas Transmission Company's lease with the War Assets Administration to operate the **Big Inch and Little Inch pipelines** expires and Tennessee Gas ceases operation of the two converted lines. (50)

May 15—The Oil and Gas Division of the U. S. Department of the Interior and the Interstate Oil Compact Commission jointly sponsor a **Secondary Recovery Forum** designed to develop ways and means whereby the Division and the Commission can assist in the promotion of research programs to increase secondary production of oil. This marks the initial step by the Department of the Interior and the Interstate Oil Compact Commission in coordinating and correlating secondary recovery activities of the nation. (61)

May—First departure curves for R_t-correction in quantitative studies introduced by **Schlumberger** (1947). (73)

June 6—**Reda Pump Co.** demonstrates first working model of **Electrodrill Corporation's downhole drilling** unit in Bartlesville, Oklahoma. (Oil and Gas Journal)

June 14—The Atlantic Refining Company puts in use a novel system of **offshore seismic exploration,** by which both shooting and recording of records are done simultaneously in the same boat. (50)

June 16—The Interstate Natural Gas Company, a producer and gatherer of natural gas, makes a sale of natural gas in the field to pipeline companies for transportation to other states. The Federal Power Commission orders it to reduce its prices. The United States Supreme Court holds that these are sales in interstate commerce and subject to regulation under the Natural Gas Act. **Interstate Natural Gas Company v. Federal Power Commission et al** (Vinson, Elkins, Weems and Searls)

June 23—**Tidelands Litigation**—The U. S. Supreme Court decides that California can not claim rights to the continental shelf beyond the

3-mile limit. Similar decisions affecting Louisiana and Texas made on June 5, 1950. (15)

June 28—Spurred by criticism of oil shipments to Russia, the **Office of International Trade** of the Department of Commerce reinforces wartime controls on exports on petroleum products—requiring shippers to obtain licenses. (2)

July 1—The Oil and Gas Division of the Department of the Interior initiates the action for placing major petroleum products under **export control** because of impending scarcity of petroleum products, and advice and counsel is given to the Department of Commerce in its administration of export controls. (61)

July 7—**World Oil** succeeds The Oil Weekly, which had been founded April 20, 1918 to take over from an earlier publication, Gulf Coast Oil News, started December 16, 1916. (50)

August 4—80th U. S. Congress enacts bill revising the provisions of the federal statutes applicable to the control of oil and gas lessees holding leases on land of the **Five Civilized Indian Tribes** to permit the Commission's orders to be operative as to federal lands. (3)

October 11—**First LP-Gas tanker,** the **S. S. Natalie O. Warren,** christened. Placed in service by Warren Petroleum Corporation. (50)

October 17—Sound barrier broken.

October—**Washington, D. C.,** joins the ranks of straight natural gas users when Washington Gas Light Company completes its conversion from mixed gas service. (18)

November 5—The **San Ardo field,** California, discovered by Texas Company's No. 1 Lombardi. (67)

November 14—The **"Big Inch** and the **"Little Big Inch"** pipelines sold to **Texas Eastern Transmission Corporation** for $143,127,000. The original costs as reported by the War Assets Administration were $145,800,000. (61)

November—Well No. 7 of Societe Cherifienne des Petroles completed for 125 barrels per day as the discovery well of the **Baton field**, an important deposit in the Oued Beth region of **Morocco.** Small fields discovered earlier are Ain Hamra and Tselfat, discovered in 1932, and Bou Draa, discovered in 1936. (45) (66)

December 13—**World's first offshore producing well out of sight of land** completed by Kerr-McGee, as operator (Phillips and Stanolind also participate) when the No. 1 State Lease 754 in Block 32, Ship Shoal area, 12 miles off Terrebonne Parish, Louisiana comes in flowing 922 barrels of oil per day through an 11/16th inch choke from pay topped at 1732 feet. Depth of water is less than 20 feet. (67)

December 26—Industry's **first large scale LP-gas marine terminal** and distribution center, located in Newark, New Jersey, placed in service by Warren Petroleum Corporation. (50)

The **Chinese Petroleum Corporation**'s Kaohsiung Refinery at **Taiwan** begins operation with a simple crude unit. (45)

First high-pressure centrifugal compressors for gas transmission intalled by Texas Eastern Transmission Corp. at Little Rock, Arkansas, marking revolutionary development in natural-gas movement. (5)

Holland grants a State concession to the N. V. Nederlandse Aardolie Maatschappij (N.A.M.), in which the Bataafse Petroleum Maatschappij (Royal Dutch-Shell Group) and the Standard Oil Company (New Jersey) (Esso) each have a 50 per cent interest. (45)

Indiana passes Conservation Act. (3)

Important oil deposits discovered near Oued Beth dam in **Morocco.** (45)

Jet Perforation of wells deveoped by **Robert H. McLemore,** and **R. C. Armstrong,** founders of **Welex Jet Perforating Company,** and **Gulf Research and Development Company.** First successful **jet perforating** performed in Baxterville, Mississippi, on a Gulf well by Welex working in conjunction with Gulf Research and Development Company. (50)

The **Ohio Oil and Gas Association** organized by the merger of the Ohio-Pennsylvania Grade Producers Association and the Ohio Natural Gas Producers Association. (57)

Oklahoma assembly rewrites **spacing law,** to eliminate percentage consent requirement as a condition precedent to the order, and vests control exclusively in the corporation commission. (3)

Shell Oil Co.'s Smith-State Unit 1-3 well in Weeks Island field, South Louisiana sets **deep production** record flowing from pay bottomed at 13,888 feet. (Oil). (World Oil)

The Texas Co.'s Lafourche Basin Levee Dist. 1 well in Queen Bess Island field, South Louisiana sets **deep production** record flowing from pay bottomed at 13,904 feet. (Condensate). (World Oil)

Oklahoma—Proration acts passed expressly authorizing Oklahoma Commission to consider acreage as a factor in allocating production, proration to prevent waste and to restrict production to prevent drainage uncompensated by counter-drainage. (3)

Russia—The method of **deep gas survey** developed. (27)

West Edmond becomes the first field to be unitized under Oklahoma **compulsory unitization** law. (5)

Deepest well is Superior Oil Company of California's Weller 15-11 wildcat in Caddo County, Oklahoma down 17,823 feet. This is the first time Oklahoma has ever had deep well title. (World Oil)

Texas H. B. 590 passed to permit the organization of corporations "for the purpose of **fighting fires** and blowouts in oil wells and gas wells, and oil and gas wells." (3)

McCullough develops sonic **collar locator** to give continuous and instant information on movements of tools deep in well bore. (50)

Oil Tools, Inc., organized in Houston, Texas. (50)

The **resistivity dipmeter** is commercially introduced, by Schlumberger. (50)

J. Ray McDermott & Co., Inc., constructs first **template type offshore platform.** (50)

University of Houston Petroleum Engineering department organized. (1)

1947-48—The **Basin Pipe Line System** (Shell, Texaco, Sinclair and Cities Service) lays 20- and 24-inch lines from Jal, New Mexico, to Cushing, Oklahoma. Major Joint-Interest Crude System. (40)

1947-48—The **Ozark Pipe Line System** (Shell, Texaco) lays 20- and 22-inch lines from Cushing to Wood River, Illinois. Major Joint-Interest Crude System. (40)

1948

January 3—The President of the United States, by **Executive Order No. 9919,** delegates to the Secretary of the Interior full authority with respect to fuels, including petroleum and petroleum products, and natural gas and manufactured gas, following passage of Public **Law 395 (80th Congress)** relating to industry agreements and plans for the allocation of scarce commodities which basically affect the cost of living or industrial production. A temporary plan to alleviate consumer hardship and to promote equitable distribution of petroleum products is in effect from January 28 to June 15, 1948, during periods of shortages of heating oils during the severe winter of 1947-48 and the tractor fuel shortage in the Middle West the following spring. The National Petroleum Council assisted in this program upon request. (61)

January 23—**Pipe Line Contractors Association** organized in Dallas, Texas.

February—**Basrah Petroleum Company**'s first test wells begin at Zubair and Nahr Umr, **Iraq.** On September 28, 1948, oil in commercial quantities found at **Zubair.** On December 19, 1951, the first tanker loaded with Zubair oil at Fao Terminal, Iraq. (45)

February—The **induction log** introduced commercially, by Schlumberger. (50)

March 23—**Phillips Chemical Company,** a wholly-owned subsidiary of Phillips Petroleum Company, incorporated in the State of Delaware. (50)

April 28—Report by the Federal Power Commission of its **Natural Gas Investigation,** Docket No. G-580, transmitted to the Congress. The Report consists of two volumes, one by Commissioners Nelson Lee

Smith and Harrington Wimberly, and the other by Commissioners Leland Olds and Claude Draper, covering, among other things, divergent views on the jurisdictional status of producers and gatherers of natural gas. (59)

May—The Federal Power Commission authorizes the construction of the 1840-mile, 30-inch **Transcontinental Gas Pipe Line** from South Texas to New York. (38)

June 28—Kuwait enters into a Concession Agreement with the **American Independent Oil Company.** (45)

June—**Ghawar field,** Saudia Arabia, discovered. (70)

July—Discovery of new field about five miles east of old **Digboi field** starts new exploration program for **India** which results in discoveries at Nahorkatiya in June 1953, Moran in October 1956, Cambay on September 9, 1958, Ankleshwar on May 14, 1960, at Rudrasagar on January 1, 1961 and at Nagar on June 10, 1961. (45)

August 1—**Old Ocean field** of Brazoria and Matagorda Counties, Texas Gulf Coast, unitized. This is the largest **voluntary domestic unit operation.** (5)

September 8—**India** enacts Oilfields Act (Regulation and Development) and it goes into effect on October 25, 1949. Petroleum Concession Rules adopted on January 5, 1950, and Petroleum and Natural Gas Rules adopted on November 25, 1959. (45)

September 23—**Utah—Equity Oil Company** drills the No. 1 Meagher, with an initial production of 300 barrels per day of 33 degrees gravity oil. It is drilled in the depleted Ashley Valley gas field near Vernal in Uintah County. Discovery well taken down to 4152 feet, with production coming from 4136-4152 feet. (10)

September—The Atlantic Refining Company is the first to make available to motorists **high-detergency motor oil.** (50)

October 4—**Transcontinental Gas Pipe Line Corporation** chartered in Delaware; succeeding a Texas charter issued to Trans-Continental Gas Pipe Line Company, Inc., on February 16, 1946. (50)

October 10—**First large scale LP-gas terminal and distribution center,** located in Little Rock, Arkansas, placed in service by Warren Petroleum Corporation. (50)

October 14—**Oil Progress Day** proclaimed. (54)

October 23—The first use of an **X-ray** machine for **testing** pipeline welds takes place on a 20-inch loop north of Northern Natural Gas Company's Clifton, Kansas, compressor station. A power-driven X-ray machine able to travel up to 1800 feet inside the pipe used and it stops and takes pictures at each weld. (50)

October 28—The **Federal Power Commission** issues an order directing an investigation to be held to determine if Phillips Petroleum Company is a "**natural gas company**" within the meaning of the Natural Gas Act. (Docket No. G-1148). (59)

October—The first plant to make **alcohol by direct hydration of ethylene** goes into operation at Shell Chemical Company's Houston, Texas installation. (50)

November 5—**Kelly field,** Texas, discovered when Magnolia Petroleum completed No. 1 Winston Brothers for 67 barrels per day from pay topped at 7429 feet. (67)

November 20—**Magnetic collar locater** introduced, by Schlumberger. (50)

November 21—**Snyder field,** Texas, discovered by completion of Standard of Texas No. 1 Brown et al for 532 barrels per day on ¼-inch choke from pay topped at 6260 feet. (67)

December 6—**Socony-Vacuum Oil Company,** Incorporated acquires a 10 per cent stock interest in the Arabian American Oil Company and a 10 per cent stock interest in Trans-Arabian Pipe Line Company. (50)

December 13—In **Tunisia,** a decree on petroleum prospection amended to introduce the fifty-fifty sharing formula (Law No. 58-36 dated March 15, 1958) and raise the percentage fee to be paid from 10 per cent to 15 per cent of the value of the hydrocarbons. (45)

December 16—The Ohio Oil Company (Marathon) joins with Continental Oil Company and Amerada Petroleum Corporation to form **Conorado Petroleum Corporation** to investigate oil prducing prospects and engage in initial exploration activities in foreign areas. (50)

Development of an **acoustic impedance log** by Humble Research. (73)

Standard Oil Company of New Jersey and Socony-Vacuum Oil Company purchase 30 per cent and 10 per cent respectively, of **Aramco** stock. SOCal and Texas Company retain 30 per cent of each. (50)

First experiments in **automatic custody transfer** made by Shell Oil Company in the Antelope Field, Clay County, Texas. (1)

Humble Oil & Refining Company rig No. 30, described as a **drilling equipment field laboratory,** placed in operation in the Sugar Valley field on the Texas Gulf Coast. (12)

World's first **synthetic-glycerin plant** starts production at Shell Chemical Corp.'s Deer Park refinery. (5)

December 18—The **Microlog** introduced by Schlumberger. (50)

Mississippi Legislature passes a modern **Conservation Law** regarded as one of the best in the country. (Mississippi-Alabama Division of Mid-Continent Oil and Gas Association)

The **sonic pump** developed by **A. J. Bodine** of Los Angeles. The method is similar to gas lift in that no rods, pumps, or other such conventional means are used. (40)

Denver Producing & Refining Co.'s School Land 1-A well in Cogar field, Caddo County, Oklahoma sets **deep production** record flowing from pay bottomed at 15,510 feet. (Gas). (World Oil)

Pure Oil Co.'s Unit 1 well in West Spider field, Wyoming sets **deep production** record flowing from pay bottomed at 14,307 feet. (Oil). (World Oil)

The **Redwater field** in Canada discovered. (Brit. Amer. Oil Co.)

Foreign oil properties in **Rumania** confiscated. (Review)

Scurry Reef area field discovered in Texas. (5)

Mississippi Legislature passes a **Severance Tax on Natural Gas.** (Mississippi-Alabama Division Mid-Continent Oil and Gas Association)

Standard Oil Company of New Jersey acquires a 30 percent interest in **Arabian American Oil Company.** (50)

The Bureau of Mines begins monthly reports of operations in the **carbon black** industry. (48)

A formal project in cooperation with industry inaugurated by the Bureau of Mines on **sulphur in petroleum.** (48)

Virginia passes a law pertaining to plugging of wells. (60)

McCullough develops electronic **weight indicator,** a super-sensitive device for indicating on a meter weight of line and tools at all times and depths. Patent No. 2,589,599 issued March 18, 1952. (50)

In **Tunisia,** a gas field discovered at Cap Bon. (40)

1949

February 3—Two **offshore drilling structures,** largest yet built with space for drilling one vertical and four deflecting wells to 20,000 feet, are being fabricated for Gulf of Mexico by Superior Oil Company. (18)

February—An administration bill for federal control of the **tidelands** oil resources sent to Congress with a request for prompt enactment signed by Defense Secretary James V. Forrestal, Attorney General Tom C. Clark, and Secretary of the Interior J. A. Krug. (2)

March—**Bay Marchand** Block 2 field discovered off the coast of Lafourche Parish by California Company. (70)

April—A small group of women employees of the oil companies in New Orleans, at the invitation of **Mrs. Inez Awtry Schaeffer,** form the first Desk and Derrick Club. In June, 1951, the **Association of Desk and Derrick Clubs** formed when Houston, Los Angeles, and Jackson, Mississippi clubs, all inspired by the New Orleans example, decide to unite and hold a national convention in Houston. The stated purpose of the Association is to promote educational programs to the end that the members may increase the scope of their services. (57)

May 4—**Cuyama, South, field,** California discovered by Richfield Oil Company's Homan No. 81-35 completed for 4888 barrels. (70)

May 16—The U. S. Department of Justice files **tidelands suit** against the States of **Texas and Louisiana.** (31)

May 24—Texas Legislature authorizes operators to submit **voluntary unitization** agreements to the Railroad Commission for their approval—and where approval granted, parties to the unitization agreement gain benefits under the State anti-trust laws. Acts 51st Leg., Reg. Sess., 1949, C.76 (58)

May—**Transcontinental Gas Pipe Line Corporation** begins construction of its $235,000,000.00 pipe line from Hidalgo County, Texas, to New York City. (47)

June 18—The **Philippines** approves Republic Act No. 387, otherwise known as "The Petroleum Act of 1949." (45)

June 20—In **Federal Power Commission** v. **Panhandle Eastern Pipe Line Co.,** 337 U. S. 498, the U. S. Supreme Court again holds that Federal authority can not be extended to cover production or gathering of natural gas as such. These remain under state conservation jurisdiction. (59)

June 25—**Realitos, East field,** Texas, discovered when Southern Minerals completes its No. 1 Denman for 37,000 mcf per day from pay at 4179-4185 and 62 barrels per day on 9/64-inch choke from pay at 4253-4256 feet. (67)

June 27—**Duralde field,** Louisiana, discovered by S. W. Richardson No. 1 Soileau, completed for 85 barrels per day on 1/8-inch choke from pay topped at 11,301 feet. (67)

June 30—The Atlantic Refining Company begins the first high-pressure **gas miscible displacement** secondary operation, in the Block 31 Field of Crane County, West Texas. (50)

June—The 20- and 24-inch crude oil **pipeline from Jal,** New Mexico, to **Cushing,** Oklahoma is completed. (Shell Oil Company)

July—The 22-inch crude oil **pipeline** from **Cushing,** Oklahoma **to Wood River,** Illinois is completed. (Shell Oil Company)

August 8—The first **Driltrol Drillable Wing Stabilizer** built and used on an experimental basis on a well in the Wilmington, California field. Its use is considered a success. (50)

August 9—The Marathon Oil Company (then Ohio) completes discovery well (No. 1 Mary Egging) in Gurley field, Cheyenne County, Nebraska. Opens up **Denver-Julesberg Basin** oil province. (50)

August 22—The first natural gas to be delivered to **New York City** arrives at Staten Island, placing the **New York and Richmond Gas Co.** first among northeastern seaboard utilities to convert from manufactured to straight natural gas. (47)

September 12—The first gas well in **Maryland** to yield production in commercial quantities comes in. It was drilled by the **Cumberland & Allegheny Gas Co.,** near Oakland. (47)

October 5—The Atlantic Refining Company presents at an AIME meeting, and later publishes, a specific method of determining **permeability** and average pressure of a reservoir by analysis of a **pressure build-up curve.** (50)

October 13—Shell Oil Company becomes first in petroleum industry to own jet-equipped airplane. Plane, bought from U. S. Air Force, to be used for **testing various types of fuels.** (18)

October 16-22—First annual **Oil Progress Week** held. (54)

October 28—210 days following the announcement of the availability of the (UOP) Universal Oil Products Platforming process, the first commercial unit placed on stream at the **Old Dutch Refining Company** plant at Muskegon, Michigan. (40)

November 17—**U. S. Geological Survey** embarks on **biggest oil-geology study** in history. More than 70 geologists engage in intensive investigations covering 22 states and Alaska to delimit areas favorable for occurrence of oil and natural gas. (18)

December—Production of oil in **Qatar** begins. (45)

AIME reorganized into three branches, Mining, Metals, and Petroleum. A headquarters office for the Petroleum Branch opened in Dallas. **"Petroleum Technology"** has been published continuously since on a regular monthly basis. (57)

At Wu-Tung Chiao of Szechuan Province, **China,** a considerable amount of crude oil produced from a salt well at the depth of 4000 feet. (45)

Hugoton, world's largest dry-gas field, **has amazing development,** with gas being found in various areas of 4,000,000-acre field. Original gas-reserve estimates vary from 22 to 29 trillion cubic feet, or 15 per cent of the known U. S. reserve. (5)

Halliburton Oil Well Cementing Company first commercializes the **hydraulic fracturing process** using napalm soap, under exclusive license from Pan American. (1)

Stanolind Oil & Gas Co. (now Pan-American Petroleum Co.) perfects and patents a process called **"Hydrofrac"** for creating fractures in oil-and-gas-producing strata and used sand as a propping agent to keep the fractures open. (1)

The **Lacq field,** near Pau, France, discovered at a depth of about 2130 feet. (45)

The Lake Shore Pipe Line Company organized. (50)

Petrochemicals industry produces nearly five billion pounds of crude chemicals. Texas and Louisiana Gulf Coast plants account for 85 per cent of U. S. petrochemical capacity. (5)

Louisiana's **deepest producer** to date is completed by Humble Oil &

Refining Co. in Lake Raccourci field, Lafourche Parish, Louisiana. Producing depth: 14,434 feet. (5)

Standard Oil Co. of California's Mushrush 5 well in Wasco field, Kern County, California sets **deep production** record flowing from pay bottomed at 15,530 feet. (Oil). (World Oil)

First production of "cold rubber" begins at Baton Rouge plant of **Copolymer Corporation,** using process developed by Phillips Petroleum Co. in cooperation with tire companies. (5)

Jacket type steel foundations used for marsh operations in the drilling of a well in the Pointe-a-la-Hache field, Louisiana. (5)

Beginning of **underground storage** movement, both mined cavities and salt dome solution. (Natural Gas Processors Association)

Texas Illinois Natural Gas Pipeline Company incorporated. (Natural Gas Pipeline Company of America)

Two **deepest well** records go to Superior Oil of California in breaking its own previous record. First the company drills the Limoneria 1 wildcat 18,734 feet to return the depth record to California in Ventura County. Then it gives Wyoming its first depth title in the same year by drilling the Unit 1, another wildcat, in Sublette County to 20,521 feet as the world's first to go below 20,000 feet. (World Oil)

West Tepetate field, Louisiana, becomes **first field dually pressure maintained and completely unitized.** (5)

World Petroleum Statistics inaugurated by the Bureau of Mines on a monthly basis. (48)

Algonquin Gas Transmission Company, Boston, Massachusetts, organized. (Texas Eastern Transmission Corporation)

Largest gas-processing plant built to date begins operation in Carthage field of Panola County, Texas. Operated by **Carthage Corp.,** it is the largest plant built for delivery of dry natural gas for pipeline transportation. (5)

The **downhole camera** is introduced by Dowell. (73)

First gas turbine engine installed at Wilmar, Arkansas, on 22-inch line of Mississippi River Fuel Corporation. (38)

1949-50—The **Mid-Valley Pipe Line Company** (Sun, Sohio) lays 20- and 22-inch lines from Longview, Texas to Lima, Ohio. Major Joint-Interest Crude System. (50)

1950

January 1—The **Oil Information Committee** of the American Petroleum Institute organized. It functioned until August 31, 1958, when it was merged into the **Committee on Public Affairs.** (62)

January 12—**Aztec Oil & Gas Company,** Dallas, organized as a Delaware corporation by Southern Union Gas Company; was a wholly-owned subsidiary until January, 1954, when it became public corporation. (50)

January—**Salt Dome Production Co.**, organized as a Texas corporation and acquires assets of Salt Dome Oil Corporation which had earlier (1934) acquired through Salt Dome Oil Company the assets of Geophysicists Inc. (50)

February 2—Inauguration of **Qatar Petroleum Company**'s production by the Ruler, Sheikh Ali bin Abdulla Qasim al Thani. (45)

February—First well in **Abu Dhabi,** Iraq spudded in at Ras Sadr. (45)

April 19—Rumors of **illegal directional drilling** in East Texas field reported to Texas Railroad Commission by District Engineer Edwin G. Stanley, who also suggests definite steps for tighter controls. On May 2 the Commission issues a memorandum to all East Texas field operators in accordance with Stanley's recommendations. The Commission also authorizes the Kilgore district office "to conduct inclination surveys on all questionable wells." (58)

April 25—**South Pass Block 24 field,** Louisiana, discovered by Shell Oil No. 1 State completed for 49 barrels per day on 11/64-inch choke from pay topped at 6530 feet. (67)

May 1—The name Stanolind Pipe Line Company changed to **Service Pipe Line Company.** (50)

May 1—**API Division of Technical Services** organized. (62)

June 8—U. S. Supreme Court rules oil-bearing tidelands off the coasts of Texas and Louisiana are subject to paramount rights of Federal government. (18)

June 19—**Chile creates** its governmental **Empresa Nacional del Petroleo** (National Petroleum Enterprise) through passage of Public Law No. 9618 to intensify search for oil. The agency is known by its Spanish initials, ENAP. (45)

June 30—US Troops ordered to Korea.

June—Barnsdall Oil Company merged into **Sunray Oil Corporation.** (50)

July 20—First **tidelands drilling in Germany** gets under way off Cuxhaven on the North Sea at the mouth of the Elhe River. Three companies—Preussag, Deutsche Erdoel, and Deutsche Vacuum—share operation from steel platform one and one half miles offshore. (18)

August 1—Four companies form **Platte Pipe Line Company** to build and operate crude oil trunk line from northwestern Wyoming to Wood River, Illinois. (The Marathon Oil Company)

August 3—**Arabian American Oil Company**'s Abqaiq field in Saudi Arabia is proclaimed **world's largest oil producer** with daily output up to 450,000 bbl. It takes the place once held by the East Texas field which produced up to 1,230,000 barrels daily in its heyday. (18)

August 17—The **first man-made underground storage reservoir** for propane and butane is placed in operation at the Sid Richardson gasoline plant in Keystone field, near Kermit in Winkler County, West Texas. Initial reservoir, leached out of thick salt bed 2000 feet below surface, has storage capacity for 7500 barrels. (18)

September 28—Newly formed **United States Pipe Line Co.** reveals plans for the first independently owned and operated **common-carrier pipeline for petroleum products.** New line, originating from feeders in the large Houston-Beaumont-Port Arthur refining area will serve the St. Louis-Chicago consuming areas. (18)

September—The **South African Coal, Oil and Gas Corporation,** Ltd. (SASOL) incorporated. Its main object is the **production of oil from coal** and it has opened up its own coal mine which is one of the most highly mechanized mines, and probably the most efficient coal mine in the world. (45)

October 3—The **Petroleum Administration for Defense** established by the Secretary of the Interior, pursuant to the Defense Production Act of 1950. Terminated April 30, 1954. (61)

October 5—U. S. Department of the Interior takes over control of California **tidelands** oil fields under the revised stipulation recently agreed to by the federal and state governments. State to turn over to federal government all rentals, royalties and other receipts from leases. (18)

October 12—**Yacimientos Petroliferos Fiscales, Argentine** Government oil agency, reports discovery of first oil production on the Argentine side of **Tierra del Fuego,** at the south tip of the South American continent. Initial well produces 62 barrels daily from depth of 6690 feet. (18)

October—First laterolog introduced. (50)

October—**Trunkline Gas Company's** original stations are the first to use the so-called **unitized station design** with all auxiliaries driven from the engines themselves without depending upon outside power. (50)

November 3—**Austral Oil Company** incorporated. (50)

November 23—First crude from Alberta fields crosses international boundary by way of **International Pipe Lines Company's** newly completed 1150-mile pipeline to Lakehead Pipe Line Company's terminal at Superior, on Lake Superior. (18)

November—Construction of 30-inch **pipeline** from **Kirkuk to Banias** begins. (45)

December 2—The first cargoes taken from the **Trans-Arabian pipe line.** (Texaco, Inc.)

December 3—The first wash-over of the **Driltrol** Drillable Wing stabilizer performed by Loffland Brothers in the Wilmington, California field. (Driltrol)

December 12—**First LP-Gas inland waterways barge,** the City of Mobile, placed in service by Warren Petroleum Corporation. (50)

December 28—First natural gas deliveries through **Transcontinental Gas Pipe Line Corporation's** new 30-inch line from Texas reach New York. (18)

December 30—The **Fifty-Fifty basis of sharing profits** comes into the oil industry of the Middle East with the signing of an agreement by Saudi Arabia and the Arabian American Oil Company—similar in many respects to the fifty-fifty basis which has been in vogue for several years in Venezuela. (80)

December—The first pipe line crossing of the **Hudson River** made. (Transcontinental Gas Pipe Line Corporation)

Atomic Energy Commission selects Phillips Petroleum Corp. to operate **Materials Testing Reactor** and other facilities at the **National Reactor Testing Station** near Idaho Falls, Idaho. (50)

First commercial synthesis of **high-purity benzene** from petroleum is now an established operation at Texas City, Texas, refinery of **Pan American Refining Corp.** Operation of benzene-production facilities incorporates hydroforming unit. (5)

The Cochabamba refinery, largest in **Bolivia,** put into operation. (45)

First steam-turbine-driven centrifugal-compressor equipment ever to be installed on a natural-gas pipeline announced by **Transcontinental Gas Pipe Line Corporation,** for its 1800-mile line from Texas to New York City. (5)

Densilog introduced by Lane-Wells. Developed concurrently by McCullough (with California Research Co.). (73)

The Bureau of Mines begins an annual survey of the **quality** of **Diesel fuels.** (48)

Driltrol founded in Long Beach, California as manufacturers of rotary drilling stabilizers. (50)

The **Federal Power Commission** wins two victories in its campaign to extend jurisdiction to cover natural gas production and distribution. In the **East Ohio case,** the Supreme Court rules that a natural gas distributor, operating solely within a state, but selling gas that moves interstate, is subject to FPC control. The **Kerr Bill** vetoed by President Truman. (47)

A new type combination **gamma ray and neutron log** made in a well in the Dickinson field, Texas, by Pan Geo Atlas Corporation. (50)

Pioneering **aluminum gas line** installed near Listerhill, **Alabama,** to supply natural gas to **Reynolds Metals Company** plants. (50)

In **Holland,** the Caltex Petroleum Maatschappij (Nederland) N. V.'s refinery put into operation. (45)

United States Supreme Court upholds Oklahoma Corporation Commission's authority to set **minimum natural-gas price.** (5)

Neutron-neutron log introduced by P.G.A.C. recorded simultaneously, with the gamma-ray log. This is the first use of simultaneous recording of these radioactivity curves. (73)

Submarine drilling begins in **Peru,** when **Douglas Oil Company** drills several productive oil wells directionally from the Pacific shore. (World Oil)

The **ball pump** invented by engineers of Stanolind Oil and Gas Company. This method uses two parallel tubing strings in which a synthetic rubber ball is circulated as the means of lifting the oil. (40)

Great Britain ends **gasoline rationing** when Standard Oil Company of New Jersey and another United States company offer to meet the resultant increase in demand without additional dollar cost to Britain. (Standard Oil Co. of New Jersey)

Gas from the **San Juan Basin** is moved through the **El Paso Natural Gas Company** 24-inch line and the Pacific Gas and Electric 34-inch line to San Francisco. (38)

Shell builds four unattended stations on its eastern products system. They are designed for push-button control over a dispatching **tele-type system** with operation based on line hydraulics. (40)

The first **all-concrete platform** installed in the Gulf of Mexico by **J. Ray McDermott & Co., Inc.** (50)

McCullough introduces **glass jet casing perforators.** Patent No. 2,796,833 issued June 25, 1957. (50)

Lone Star Gas Company makes financial history with an $85 million loan closed at Dallas, Texas. It is considered the largest financial transaction ever closed in Texas. In October 1952, the company completed a $110 million loan which set another Texas financial record. (50)

Murphy Corporation chartered in Louisiana, succeeding C. H. Murphy & Co., an outgrowth of the Murphy family petroleum interests which began in 1907 in the Caddo Pool. (50)

Pacific Gas and Electric begins operation of 34-inch gas pipeline from Topock, Arizona, to San Francisco; gas is supplied by El Paso Natural Gas Company through new 24-inch line from San Juan Basin. (38)

The Bureau of Mines begins monthly issuance of **World Petroleum Statistics.** (48)

There are 49,161,691 motor vehicle registrations in the United States.

1951

January 16—**Transcontinental Gas Pipe Line Co.** delivers gas to New York City. First pipe line to do so in any volume. It is the longest single project pipeline in the world at the time—1840 miles. (50)

January 18—Drilling begins on first full-fledged **offshore drilling** venture in the **Persian Gulf.** Arabian American Oil Co. deep test located in 19 feet of water, three miles from shore and 20 miles south of Ras del Misha'ab. (18)

January—**Agua Grande** field, Brazil, discovered. (66)

February 1—Petroleos Mexicanos (**Pemex**) lays **first coast-to-coast pipeline in** the **Western Hemisphere,** extending from its Minatitlan refinery on the East Coast to Salina Cruz on the West Coast. The new 155-mile 10-inch line will transport initially 15,000 barrels of gasoline, kerosene and Diesel oil daily. (18)

February 15—**Celanese Corporation of America** forms Canadian subsidiary, **Canadian Chemical Company, Ltd.,** to build western **Canada's first petrochemical plant.** (18)

March 9—**Gas Industry Advisory Council** established by the Secretary of the Interior to obtain the advice and counsel of the gas industry, both natural and manufactured, in connection with the discharge of the defense responsibilities with respect to gas, delegated to the Secretary of the Interior under the Defense Production Act of 1950. The Secretary of the Interior dissolved this Council March 5, 1957. (61)

March 22—**Iran nationalizes oil properties** of **Anglo-Iranian Oil Company, Ltd.** by unanimous vote of legislative body. Action causes crisis, closes world's largest refinery at Abadan, removes 610,000 barrels of available oil from world market in critical time of Korean War. US also sees threat to Marshall plan and organizes **Foreign Petroleum Supply Committee** to provide crude and products from other countries to replace Iran oil in free world nations where need is critical. Nineteen American companies invited to join in effort. (2)

April 3—Hearing by Federal Power Commission in the **Phillips case** begins and continues to May 23, 1951. (59)

April 4—**Williston Basin,** largest oil-bearing sedimentary deposit in nation, opens when **Amerada Petroleum Corp.** discovers oil at **Beaver Lodge field** on Clarence Iverson farm, south of Tioga in Williams County, **North Dakota** from sands between 1130 and 1160 feet in the upper Devonian oil zone. (10)

April 15—The discovery well of the **Medicine Hat gas field,** Alberta, Canada brought in by **Deep Rock Oil Corporation** (Crescent Petroleum Corporation). (50)

May 14—The **National Association of Oil Equipment Jobbers** organized in Louisville, Kentucky. (57)

May 24—The **Illinois Oil & Gas Association** becomes affiliated with The Mid-Continent Oil & Gas Association. (57)

June 2—Texas Legislature establishes the **Liquefied Petroleum Gas Division** as a separate department within the **Texas Railroad Commission**—requiring the use of malodorants and regulating storage and distribution,

235

for protection of the public safety (the principal gases regulated are butane for fuel, iso-butane for manufacture of rubber and explosives, and propane for internal combustion engines.)—Acts 52nd Leg., Reg. Sess., 1951, C. 363. (58)

June 25—The **Foreign Petroleum Supply Committee** established by the Secretary of the Interior under a Voluntary Agreement Relating to Foreign Petroleum Supply pursuant to Section 708 of the Defense Production Act of 1950. The Agreement was amended May 8, 1956, and again on Ocotber 24, 1961. (61)

July 13—Shell Oil Company brings in successful well at Richey, Montana, extending **Williston Basin** producing area. (50)

September 4—Transcontinental **television** inaugurated. (54)

September 10—The **Philippines** grants the **first** Petroleum **Exploration Concession,** PEC No. 1, under the Petroleum Act of 1949 to **Philippine Oil Development Company.** PEC No. 1 is located in Central Luzon. (45)

September 20—The first deep-test well in **Nigeria** spudded in at Ihuo, ten miles northeast of Owerri. This well contains a little gas but no oil. (45)

September 28—**Northeastern Gas Transmission Company,** a subsidiary of Tennessee Gas Transmission Company, brings New England its first natural gas service following completion of 290 miles of a 520-mile pipeline system. (50)

October 3—First issue of **Oil Daily** published in Chicago; **Keith Fanshier,** editor. (50)

November 7—Colonel **Ernest O. Thompson** awarded the American Petroleum Institute Gold Medal for Distinguished Service to the American Petroleum Industry and the American people. (Houston Post)

November 9—**Costa Rica's** public law No. 1382 approves the government's exploration contract with Union Oil Company (subsidiary of Gulf Oil Corporation), the only exploration enterprise in the country, for a four-year term which is renewable. Costa Rica has no refineries, pipelines or petrochemical industry. (45)

November 30—**Microlaterolog,** introduced by Schlumberger. (50)

November—**Kuwait** secures a **50-50 agreement** with Kuwait Oil Company, Ltd., and concession extended for an additional 17 years. (80)

November—The United States federal **gasoline tax** increased by one-half cent—to two cents per gallon. This increase scheduled to expire on March 31, 1954. Also increased at this time are the excise taxes on automobiles, motorcycles, buses, trucks, trailers, and parts and accessories—with similar provisions for the expiration of these increased rates on March 31, 1954. (62)

December 20—First oil well in state of **Washington** is completed near Ocean City, Grays Harbor County. The well, Tom Hawksworth-State,

236

flows 35 bbl. of 49-gravity oil with 300 MCF of gas from a Miocene zone at 3714 feet, but soon abandoned as non-commercial. (10)

December—**Murphy Oil Company of Oklahoma** formed as wholly-owned subsidiary of Murphy Oil Company of Pennsylvania. (50)

Arizona passes oil and gas conservation act. (Arizona Revised Statutes Annotated, Sections 27-501 to 27-527, 1956.) (1)

Fawley, the largest refinery in Europe, opens at Southampton, **England.** (Standard Oil Co. of New Jersey)

The largest natural gas deposits in Europe discovered at an average depth of 13,120 feet in the **Lacq, France field.** (45)

Continuous velocity logging first announced by the Magnolia Field Research Laboratory and licensed for commercial application to Seismograph Service Corporation. (73)

The Federal Power Commission by a 4 to 1 vote in **The Matter of Phillips Petroleum Co.,** 10 F.P.C. 246, finds that Phillips, a producer of natural gas, is not a "natural gas company" within the meaning of Section 1 (b) and 2 (6) of the Natural Gas Act. The Commission holds that it has no jurisdiction since Phillips' relevant operations are found to consist of production and gathering, or incidents of or activities related to those functions which require their inclusion within the exemption of Section 1 (b) of the Act. (59)

Sun Oil Company unveils its new high-speed **electronic reservoir analyzer at** Beaumont, Texas, which predicts future behavior of oil fields. (5)

U. S. Supreme Court follows California case, rules government has paramount rights to **tidelands** areas **off** both **Louisiana** and **Texas** coasts. (5)

Oklahoma Supreme Court upholds constitutionality of state's **unitization law.** (5)

Washington passes oil and gas conservation act. (1)

The **West Texas-Gulf Pipe Line Company** (Gulf, Sohio, Cities Service, and Pure) lays a 26-inch line from Colorado City to Beaumont, and a 20-inch line from Wortham to Longview. Major Joint-Interest Crude System. (40)

Creole opens a 60,000-barrel-daily refinery at **Amuay, Venezuela.** (45)

A new refinery opens at Edmonton which gives Alberta, Canada, its first **catalytic cracking** unit. (British American Oil Co., Ltd.)

The first large diameter **concrete coated pipeline** for offshore production laid in the Gulf of Mexico by J. Ray McDermott & Co., Inc. (50)

The **continuous physical dipmeter** is introduced by Carter Research Laboratory. (73)

More than 100 underground **gas storage fields** reported, having capacity of approximately 600 million Mcf. (38)

Safaniya field discovered in Saudi Arabia. (67)

The Atlantic Refining Company installs near Corpus Christi, Texas the first fieldwide unitized **glycol injection** low temperature separation facility. (50)

The **magnetic susceptibility log** is introduced by Magnolia Field Research Laboratory. (73)

Natural Gas Storage Company of Illinois incorporated. (Natural Gas Pipeline Company of America)

Oil Well Supply patents the **Nitrocycle** process for bore-hardening alloy-steel barrels to a uniform depth without distorting the barrel. (50)

Shell opens a 60,000-barrel-daily refinery at **Punta Cardon** on the Paraguana peninsula, Venezuela. (45)

All Sinclair crude and products pipe lines are put under one firm. **Sinclair Pipe Line Company,** making it world's largest carrier system. (5)

Construction begins on 1300-mile, 26- and 30-inch **Texas-Illinois Natural Gas Pipe Line** system from Gulf Coast to Chicago. (38)

1951-53—The **Cushing-Chicago System** (Pure and Sinclair) lays 22- and 24-inch lines from Cushing to Chicago. Major Joint-Interest Crude System. (40)

1952

January 10—Inauguration of **Basrah Petroleum Company's** production from Zubair, **Iraq.** (45)

January—**Colorado Oil and Gas Corporation** organized as subsidiary of Colorado Interstate Gas Company; operations separated from Interstate since 1954. (50)

February 17—Ratification by **Iraq** Government of profit-sharing agreements with companies (effective from January 1, 1951). (45)

March—**Peru** promulgates a most progressive oil law which prompts an intensive search for oil both in the coastal sedimentary areas and the huge **Amazon basin.** (45)

April 4—**First** full-fledged drilling experiment using **natural gas** instead of liquid **as a circulating medium** proves highly successful in deep test being drilled by **Great Western Drilling Company,** in Val Verde County, West Texas. Drilling time and number of bits reduced as compared with mud-drilled well. Previous use of **gas in drilling** has been confined to drilling in or completion attempts. (18)

April 22—The 30-inch **Kirkuk-Banias pipeline** completed. (45)

April 28—First discovery of natural gas in **Nova Scotia** is reported by the province's Industry Department. Flow from depth of 400 feet uncovered accidentally while exploring salt and limestone deposits on south side of Antigonish Harbor. (18)

April 29—**Milwhite Mud Sales Company** incorporated in Houston to succeed the drilling mud division of the Milwhite Company. (50)

May 2—British passenger jet flies from London to Johannesburg, South Africa, in less than 24 hours. **First** commercial **jet passenger service.**

June 15—**Deep Lake field,** Louisiana, discovered by Superior Oil Company No. 1 Rockefeller-State completed for 7881 mcf of wet gas per day through 22/64-inch choke from pay topped at 10,965 feet. (67)

June 16—Construction started on an island structure for **California's** first **offshore** well to be drilled from an over-water surface location. The project is in 45 feet of water one and one half miles offshore from Seal Beach. Previous offshore wells along the Pacific Coast have been in deflected holes drilled from onshore locations. (18)

June 26—The **Israel Petroleum Law** approved by the Knesseth (Parliament). (45)

August 12—**Puckett Ellenberger field,** Texas, discovered by Phillips Petroleum Company No. 1 Glenna completed for 12,260 mcf per day through 1-inch choke from pay topped at 13,700 feet. (67)

October 14—**Pacific Lighting Gas Supply Company** chartered as a California corporation. The corporate history of predecessor companies goes back to 1919. The company commences operations as a regulated utility January 1, 1953. (50)

October 25—In **West Pakistan,** the **Sui gas field** discovered by Pakistan Petroleum Limited. On May 13, 1954, the **Zin gas field** discovered by Pakistan Petroleum Limited. On March 29, 1955, the **Uch gas field** discovered by Pakistan Petroleum Limited. On September 27, 1956, Pakistan Petroleum Limited brings in the **Khairpur gas field.** On April 8, 1957, the **Mari gas field** discovered by Standard Vacuum Oil Company. On January 23, 1959, the **Mazarani gas field** discovered by Pakistan Petroleum Limited. On April 15, 1959, the **Khandkot gas field** discovered by Pakistan Petroleum Limited. On December 6, 1959, construction starts on the **Dhulian-Wah gas pipeline,** 6-inch diameter, 35 miles long; completed July 27, 1960. In January 1962, the **Morgah oil pipeline** was completed. (45)

October—First exports of crude oil from Ail Zalah, **Iraq.** (45)

November 1—First **Hydrogen Bomb** testing.

The biggest natural gas field in **Austria** discovered at Zwerndorf (Vienna Basin) near the Czechoslovak border when Austria is still occupied by the Russians. (64)

Brooklyn Union Gas Company converts to natural gas, the largest gas conversion undertaking; involves 925,000 customers. (38)

In **Bulgaria,** oil discovered at Kavarna. (40)

Paley Commission, independent fact-finding body appointed by the President of the US, gives full endorsement of percentage **depletion** for oil and gas producers. (72)

239

The United States Congress enacts the **Federal-Aid Highway Act** of 1952 which, for the first time, approves a separate allocation of funds for the 40,000-mile **Interstate System.** (62)

Annual production from **gas-injection** projects is estimated to have reached 175,000,000 barrels. (1)

The Bureau of Mines publishes complete **natural gas statistics** for the period 1936-1950. (48)

Development of **Herscher Dome** near Joliet, Illinois, as an underground gas storage project, is begun. (38)

The **Independent Refiners Association of America** becomes active. (57)

The **Platte Pipe Line Company** (Ohio Oil, Sinclair, Continental, British-American, and Pure) lays 16- and 20-inch lines from Chatham, Wyoming to Wood River, Illinois. Major Joint-Interest Crude System. (40)

Polonium-Beryllium neutron source for **nuclear well logging** developed by McCullough. (50)

1953

February—Gulf places in operation **first pipeline distribution system for handling ethylene** along the Gulf Coast of Texas concurrent with initial operation of Gulf's first commercial ethylene plant at Port Arthur, Texas. (50)

March 1—**Sprayberry Trend** area, Texas, formed by Railroad Commission consolidating Germania, Midkiff and Tex-Harvey (Floyd sand); Germania and Midkiff were discoveries of 1950 and Tex-Harvey discovered February 24, 1949 by Tex-Harvey No. 1 Floyd completed for 133 barrels per day at 8180 feet after having been drilled to 12,063 feet. (58) (70)

March 25—Texas Railroad Commission enters order shutting in all the wells in the **Sprayberry field** until all casinghead gas produced in the field can be devoted to one of the four uses specified in Article 6008, Texas Civil Statutes. At this time the casinghead gas produced from 468 of the wells in the field is being sold for light and fuel purposes and within the statutory requirements; some of the remaining 1800 wells are connected with gasoline plants which flare the residue gas; and others have no connection with a plant and their raw residue gas is being flared. A total of 220 million cubic feet of gas is being flared daily in the field. "**Sprayberry Order.**" Order struck down by Supreme Court of Texas on June 30, 1953. (58)

April 15—**Neutral Zone**—Wafra No. 4 brought in from the rich Burgan sands by the **American Independent Oil Company** and J. Paul Getty's **Pacific Western Oil Corporation** of Los Angeles. AIOC had obtained a concession from Kuwait, and Getty a concession from Saudi Arabia, and AIOC is the well operator. (10)

April 25—22-hour, 26-minute speech by **Senator Morse** against pending offshore land bill sets Senate record for **filibuster.**

April—**Rancho Pipeline System** (Shell, Sinclair, Crown Central, Nantucket, Phillips, Ashland, and Service) from McCamey, Texas to Houston completed. A 24-inch Major Joint Interest Crude System. (40)

Tidelands Bill passed by House May 5, by Senate May 13 and signed by President Eisenhower May 22.

May 12—**Texas** Legislature authorizes cooperative construction and operation of facilities for conservation and utilization of gas to include facilities for extracting and separation of hydrocarbons from natural and casinghead gas. Acts 53rd Leg., Reg. Sess., 1953, C. 117. (58)

June 10—**Israel** grants its first concession, to **Lopidoth Israel Petroleum Co. Ltd.** (45)

June 14—First field test of **well fluid sampler** made in Blue Ridge field, Texas. (1)

June 20—The **Philippines** grants the first Petroleum Refining Concession under the Petroleum Act of 1949 to **CALTEX** (Philippines), Inc., for a capacity of 13,000 to 26,000 barrels per day. Refinery inaugurated at Bauan, Batangas, December 11, 1954. (45)

June 29—**Neville G. Penrose, Inc.,** successfully completes its No. 1 Stella Zimmerman in the **Queen Sand Formation.** This well kicks off a major drilling boom resulting in more than 800 producers from this formation. This well is located in the NW/4 NW/4 of Section 15, T-14-S, R-31-E, Chaves County, New Mexico. (50)

July 16—Texas Railroad Commission issues second **"Sprayberry Order"** as a result of the June 30th Rowan Decision, shutting in all the wells in the field for 20 days per month and fixing the field allowable of the oil which can be produced in terms of the market outlet for casinghead gas. Order goes unchallenged. (58)

July 27—Korean War ends.

July—**Pembina field,** Canada discovered by **Socony-Seaboard.** (70)

August—Monsanto Chemicals (Australia) Ltd. Polystyrene plant, West Footscray, near Melbourne, Victoria, Australia, opens **Australian petrochemical industry.** (45)

September—The **Southwestern Pennsylvania Oil and Gas Association** organized for the purpose of helping producers find better and cheaper means to produce more oil from oil and gas formations. (57)

October 3—**Brazil** enacts Law No. 2004 creating **Petrobras** as the entity designated to implement the government's oil policy. In 1954 Petrobras acquires the assets of the National Petroleum Council. (45)

October 16—In **Peru,** a Supreme decree extends temporary free-entry privileges to firms under contract to do geophysical, exploration, or drilling work. (45)

October—**Ragusa** discovered, is the first and only field for **Sicily.** (66)

November 5—Oil first discovered in a well drilled at Akata, Calabar Province, **Nigeria.** This well proves non-commercial. (45)

November 7—**Libya** proclaims terms for Reconnaissance Permit. (45)

November 9—Invention by staff of Standard Oil Company of Ohio, proposes to float a layer of tiny hollow plastic spheres called "**micro-balloons**" on the surface of oil in tanks to form a kind of "foam," to aid in reduction of loss through evaporation. (1)

November 23—**First seagoing LP-Gas barge** placed in service by Warren Petroleum Corporation. (50)

November—**Wolverine Pipe Line Company** begins operation of 16-inch products line from East Chicago through Michigan to Toledo, Ohio. (Shell Oil Company)

December 11—**Rayne field,** Louisiana, discovered by Continental Oil Company No. 1 Pettijean completed for 618 barrels of oil and 479 mcf gas per day through 3/16-inch choke from pay at 11,908-11,920 feet. (67)

December 15—**South Dakota**—Shell Oil Company strikes oil in Harding County, 14 miles north of Buffalo, the county seat. Oil found in two zones of the Red River formation 8587 to 8600 feet, and 8715 to 8728 feet. Careful acidizing and production tests complete the well a producer (the two zones as one) which settles down by April 7, 1954 to 80 barrels of oil per day. (10)

December—**Texas Eastern Penn-Jersey Transmission Corporation** organized. (Texas Eastern Transmission Corporation)

December—**West Australian Petroleum Co. Pty. Ltd.** (WAPET) strikes the first significant flow of oil (500 barrels a day) at Rough Range, Western **Australia.** Subsequent drilling fails to prove a field. (45)

December—First commercial operation of **Synthesis Gas Generation Process** begun by Texaco. (50)

Chevron Oil Company formed by Standard Oil Company of California to carry on geophysical work for the parent company and subsidiaries in North America. (50)

Columbia Gulf Transmission Company organized as Gulf Interstate Gas Company and construction begun. (50)

The United States Congress passes the **Outer Continental Shelf Leasing Act.** (61)

Noyly Development Company and Leidy Prospecting Company, both incorporated in the early 1950's, consolidate into Devonian Gas & Oil Company of Pennsylvania, Devonian Gas & Oil Company of Delaware in 1958 and **Devonian Gas & Oil Company of Delaware** was the surviving corporation. (50)

A record for **exploratory drilling** established—13,313 exploratory wells drilled in one year. (54)

North Dakota passes oil and gas conservation act. (1)

The Continental Shelf zone of **Peru,** originally set aside as a government reserve, opens to exploration and exploitation. (45)

In **Wisconsin** v. **Federal Power Commission,** 205 F. 2d. 706 (D.C. Cir. 1953), the D. C. Court of Appeals holds **Phillips Petroleum Company** to be a "natural gas company" within the meaning of the Natural Gas Act. (59).

Halliburton Oil Well Cementing Co. introduces **"Pozmix,"** a mixture of pozzolan and Portland cement. (1)

Shell Oil Company's Gonsoulin Minvielle-State 2 well in Weeks Island field, South Louisiana sets **deep production** record flowing from pay bottomed at 17,306 feet. (Oil). (World Oil)

Richfield Oil Corp.'s Cole Levee "A" 67-29 well in Coles Levee, North field, California sets **deep production** record flowing from pay bottomed at 17,892 feet. (Oil). (World Oil)

The **Sararenda structure** is discovered below the Camiri structure allowing Y.P.F.B. (the Bolivian state-owned oil corporation) to supply the total internal demand of **Bolivia** for by-products of petroleum and to export oil in limited quantities to Argentina, Brazil and Chile. (45)

Tryad Service Corporation founded in Long Beach, California to provide the service of mill slot perforating and prepacking casing to customers' specifications. (50)

Laclede Gas Company initiates use of **McIlroy Network Analyzer** to make gas distribution system design calculations. (38)

1954

January 5—**First shipment of Kuwait Neutral Zone** oil loaded on tanker bound for Japan. (80)

January 21—Nautilus, first **atomic submarine,** launched at Groton, Connecticut. (54)

March 1—**Turkey** enacts Petroleum Law No. 6326 to promote the oil resources of Turkey through private enterprise and investments. (45)

March 10—**Camrick District gas field** in Panhandle of Oklahoma discovered by Texas Company No. 1 Cook, completed for 22,250 mcf per day from pay topped at 6812 feet. (67)

March—First commercial **velocity log** under Magnolia license, by Seismograph Service Corporation. (1)

May 6—The Ohio Oil Company is the first company to add variable speed **fluid drive units** at automatic pumping stations along pipelines. (50)

May 18—**Tuloma Gas Products Company** formed. (Standard Oil Company (Indiana))

May—**Trunkline Gas Company** places in service the first high-capacity, low-loss, **dry line type scrubbers.** (50)

May—**Ultraforming,** pioneer process in regenerative platinum-catalyst reforming, introduced with startup of El Dorado, Arkansas plant by American Oil Company. (Oil and Gas Journal)

June 7—**Phillips Case Decision**—The United States Supreme Court rules that the sales of natural gas by the producer in interstate commerce are subject to jurisdiction of and regulation by the Federal Power Commission. The "production or gathering" exemption applies to the physical facilities and properties used in production, and sales of natural gas in interstate commerce do not fall within this exemption. Phillips Petroleum Company v. State of Wisconsin et al, 347 U. S. 672. (Vinson, Elkins, Weems and Searls)

June—Associated Australian Oilfields (A.A.O.) and associated companies strike gas at the rate of 1½ million cubic feet a day at Hospital Hill near Roma, **Queensland, Australia.** (45)

June 18—**Nevada gets first commercial oil** discovery when Shell Oil Company completes a well in Railroad Valley, Nye County, in a **porous volcanic ash formation** which produces 330 barrels per day from a hole bottomed at 6730 feet. (10)

July 16—**F.P.C. Order No. 174** blankets under its control all producers selling gas entering into interstate commerce.

July—**Cameron West Block 192 field,** offshore Cameron Parish, La., discovered by CATC group with Continental Oil Company as operator, for gas-condensate production. (Oil & Gas Journal) (67)

July—**Pipe Line Industry** magazine starts publication. (Gulf Publishing Company)

August 5—**Iran** signs agreement with eight large companies to resume production of Iranian oil.

August 16—The election to deduct **intangible drilling and development costs** first becomes a matter of law with the enactment of Section 263(c) in the Internal Revenue Code of 1954. The Revenue Act of 1918 allowed taxpayers the option to expense certain incidental drilling expenses, and subsequent regulations have confirmed this. Since 1942, however, the election, once made, has been binding; until November, 1962 when legislation was enacted permitting taxpayers to change their election, if desired, effective with the filing of 1962 returns. (Arthur Andersen & Co.)

August 17—Pan American Petroleum and Transport Co. merges into parent company, The **American Oil Company** becomes the new parent of the group of former Pan American Petroleum & Transport subsidiaries. (Standard Oil Company (Indiana)

August 26—**Mobil Producing Company** incorporated as a wholly-owned subsidiary of Socony-Vacuum Oil Company, Inc., to explore and produce in the United States portion of Williston Basin and in the Northern Rocky Mountains. (50)

September 3—**Northeastern Gas Transmission Company** merged into Tennessee Gas Transmission Company. (50)

September—The **Sacroc Unit** project in **Kelly-Snyder field** of Scurry County, Texas, launched. It covers more than 50,000 acres, with about 1240 wells, and holds the title of the **world's biggest unitized pressure-maintenance project.** (40)

September—President Eisenhower appoints an **Advisory Committee** on a **National Highway Program** with General Lucius Clay as its chairman. (62)

October 13—**Arizona** becomes the **thirtieth oil producing state** in the US when Shell Oil Company's East Boundary Butte No. 2 well in the northwest corner of the state and a mile south of the Utah line in the **Paradox basin** makes 2.2 Mcf gas and 11 barrels of oil per day on initial flow. (50)

October—Trunkline Gas Company is the first to lay **two pipelines simultaneously** across the Mississippi River. (50)

November 1—The **Toronto** area of Canada receives its first natural gas service when Tennessee Gas Transmission Company completes a 45-mile pipeline from its system near Buffalo, New York to the Niagara River. (50)

November 15—A **gas line construction record** set when 628-mile line completed from Ft. Laramie, Wyoming to Freeman, Missouri in 61 days by Service Pipe Line Company. (50)

December 6—**Apache Corporation,** Minneapolis, Minn., incorporated, as tax-planning and investment management service; begins oil, gas exploration and production after first year. (50)

December 31—The Ohio Oil Company is the first to drill a **well below four miles,** setting world **depth record** at 21,482 feet, with exploratory well (No. 1 KCL-A-72-4) a dry hole, in Paloma, California, field. (50)

Vacuum Oil Company opens an oil refinery near Durban, **South Africa.** (45)

Arapahoe Pipe Line Company (Sinclair, Pure) lays 18- and 20-inch lines from Merino, Colorado, to Humboldt, Kansas. Major Joint-Interest Crude System. (40)

Austria enacts the Allgemeines Berggesetz (General Mining Law) BGBI, Nr. 146/1854, as amended. (45)

Bureau of Mines' scientists design, build, and prove both a **well-bore caliper** and a well **liquid-level gauge.** (48)

Refinery at Concon, **Chile** is put on stream. (45)

The **United States Federal-Aid Highway Act** of 1954 provides a new formula for matching Interstate system grants. In place of the traditional 50-50 matching this act provides for a 60 per cent federal contribution and only 40 per cent of state funds for construction on Interstate routes. (62)

International Consortium begin operations in Iran. (Review)

Iranian Oil Participants organized. (Standard Oil Co. of New Jersey)

First catalytic cracking unit put on stream in **Morocco,** with annual capacity of 160,000 metric tons. (45)

Oil discovered at a depth of 7872 feet in the **Parentis, France field** by the French subsidiary of Esso Standard. (45)

Field tests of a new **percussion rotary drill** indicate that this tool will be useful in drilling hard formations and for straightening crooked holes. (Gulf Oil Corporation)

McCullough Tool Company's **Scintillation Counter** for well logging is patented, after development begun in early 1950 by company on **scintillation logging.** In usage in oilfields, replaces previous Geiger-Muller Counter. (50)

The "temporary" increase in the United States federal **gasoline tax** and the added "temporary" automotive excise levies renewed for another year. (62)

Legislation returning title of offshore lands within historic boundaries to states upheld by Supreme Court. (**Tidelands**) (38)

In **Tunisia,** natural gas discovered by the SEREPT in the region of Djebel Abderrahmane of the Cap Bon (Northeast of the Gulf of Tunis). (45)

The first telescoping **aluminum mast** built for Ray's Well Servicing, Maysville, Oklahoma, by Franks Manufacturing Division, Cabot Shops, Inc. (Reynolds Aluminum Company)

Champlin Oil & Refining Co., Fort Worth, organized through purchase of Champlin Refining Co. (founded 1917) assets, by Chicago Corporation. (50)

Golden Trend producing district of Oklahoma formed by consolidating about 15 producing areas in Garvin and McClain Counties, the earliest discovery of which had been Antioch Southwest in 1946. (67)

Gulf Interstate Gas Company begins laying 30-inch line from Louisiana to West Virginia; is first pipeline to serve solely as a "transportation company" transporting gas for Columbia Gas System companies. (38)

Solution isotope injector, first tool for subsurface tracer service, dis-

246

pensing isotopes at any depth, developed by McCullough Tool Co. (50)

The Bureau of Mines begins publication of a **quarterly natural gas report.** (48)

J. Ray McDermott & Co., Inc. constructs the first **offshore platform** in 100-foot water depth. (50)

The Bureau of Mines issues a summary of oil developments in the **Williston Basin,** including parts of Montana, North and South Dakota, and Canada. (48)

1955

January 10—**Delhi-Taylor Oil Corporation** formed by a merger of Delhi Oil Corporation and Taylor Oil and Gas Co. Delhi Oil Corporation incorporated in the state of Delaware on October 27, 1945. Taylor Oil and Gas Co. incorporated in Delaware on December 20, 1919. On May 31, 1961, Delhi-Taylor purchased the assets of the Three States Natural Gas Company. (50)

January 13—**Oklahoma Independent Petroleum Association** formed in Oklahoma City.

January 24—**Induction—electric log combination** commercially introduced, by Schlumberger. (50)

January 27—**Steelman field,** Canada discovered by Imperial 1-8 Steelman. (70)

February 21—The **name of AIME** officially **changed** to American Institute of **Mining, Metallurgical, and Petroleum Engineers** (although initials remain AIME). (57)

February—BP Refinery (Kwinana) Ltd. goes on stream at Kwinana, Western **Australia.** Current capacity 48,500 barrels a day. (45)

March 14—**Emperor Devonian field** discovered by Stanolind Oil & Gas Company No. 7 Cowden "A" completed for 65,000 mcf per day from pay topped at 8990 feet. (67)

March—The **Military Petroleum Advisory Board,** in cooperation with the Office of Oil and Gas, Department of the Interior, and the Office of Petroleum Logistics Policy, Department of Defense, prepares the first worldwide petroleum supply and demand report that considers enemy attack damage resulting from the use of ultra-modern weapons of warfare. (61)

April 4—The **Sui-Karachi gas pipe line** in Pakistan, 16 inches in diameter and 347 miles long, completed; it had commenced November 2, 1954. (45)

April 29—Socony-Vacuum Oil Company, Incorporated changes its name to **Socony Mobil Oil Company, Inc.** (50)

April 30—**American Association of Petroleum Landmen** organized at

247

Fort Worth, Texas. In November, the first edition of The Landman issued. (57).

April—**Benfica,** the first field for **Angola** discovered. (67)

April—**Trunkline Gas Company** is the first to use the two-stage series or **parallel centrifugal gas compressor.** (50)

May 16—Mid-Continent Petroleum Corporation merged into Sunray Oil Corporation. The resultant corporation is known as **Sunray Mid-Continent Oil Company.** (50)

June 15—**British Petroleum Canada Limited** formed. (50)

July 15—**Libya** enacts a Petroleum Law. (45)

July 28—**Turkey** enacts a Petroleum Regulation in connection with its **Petroleum Law** No. 6326. (45)

August 13—The Austrian **oil industry,** which up to now had been under Russian administration, **returned** to **Austria** under the State Treaty, and is now administered by the "Austrian Petroleum Administration," the shares being owned by the nationalized "Industrial and Mining Administration Company, Ltd." (45)

August 16—**Alabama**—The discovery well of the **Citronelle field** comes in near Citronelle, a village of 1600 in Mobile County. Gas pressure blasts a spray of oil 180 feet into the air, and the well tests 640 barrels of oil per day. Within two years the Citronelle field produces more than 5½ million barrels of oil from 97 wells, and 41 of the wells are within the city limits. (10)

September 1—The Byron Jackson Company, founded in Woodland, California, in 1872 by Byron Jackson, becomes the **Byron Jackson Division, Borg-Warner Corporation.** The company has pioneered in various oil tools and equipment, particularly pumping equipment and shaped charge for jet perforating wells. (50)

September 23—The **Heletz-Brur field,** 40 miles south of Tel Aviv, Israel, discovered. (45)

October 10—The Dhulian-Rawalpindi gas pipe line in **West Pakistan,** 6-inch diameter, 35 miles long, started on August 23, 1955, is completed. (45)

October 17—**Gabon**—The PG5 completed at 4897 feet in the Upper Cretaceous and produces 50 barrels per day of 20 degrees gravity oil. It is on the eastern flank of a shallow salt dome west of Port Gentil, the chief port of Gabon, a territory in French Equatorial Africa. (10)

November 1—**Jet Research Center, Inc.** established as a subsidiary of Welex Jet Services, Inc., of Fort Worth and Byron Jackson Division, **Borg-Warner Corporation** of Los Angeles. (50)

November 17—**Microfocused dipmeter** survey commercially introduced, by Schlumberger. (50)

November 20—**Libya** grants its first concession to **Libyan American Oil Co.** (45)

November—Imperial Oil Company of Canada succeeds in installing the first **automatic custody transfer** system to receive governmental approval, in the Red Water field of Alberta. (1)

December 5—AFL and CIO merge.

December 15—The Washington, D. C. Circuit Court rules that the use of the fair field price is not prohibited in rate making and it is not mandatory to use the traditional **rate-base method** in determining "just and reasonable" rates. However, the use of the **fair field price** must be justified in the record as being in the public interest and rate-base method should be used as a point of departure. **City of Detroit v. Federal Power Commission,** 230 F. 2d 810 (D.C. Cir.), cert. den., 352 U. S. 829. (Vinson, Elkins, Weems and Searls)

Alaska passes oil and gas conservation act. H. B. 75, Session Laws of 1955, Chapter 40. (1)

American Louisiana Pipe Line Company begins construction of 1000-mile 30-inch line from south Louisiana to Detroit area. (38)

The **Butte Pipe Line Company** (Shell, Murphy Corp., Conoco and Northern Pacific) lays 10-, 12- and 16-inch lines from Poplar, Montana, to Fort Laramie, Wyoming. Major Joint-Interest Crude System. (40)

Wireline **formation fluid tester** introduced by Schlumberger. (50)

The **"Geograph"** developed by **McCollum Laboratories** first used commercially. The "Geograph" embraces a method of seismic exploration which generates the seismic waves by dropping a heavy weight instead of by use of explosives. (50)

The Oleum, California, refinery of the Union Oil Company of California, installs one of the first **in-line blending** systems. It uses mechanical transmissions throughout. (Petroleum Week)

Syria's first commercial oil field, **Karatchuk field,** discovered. (Oil and Gas Journal)

The International Oil Workers Union merges with the United Gas, Coke and Chemical Workers Union to form the **Oil, Chemical and Atomic Workers International Union.** (OCAW, Denver)

The United States **President's Advisory Committee on a National Highway Program** recommends a $101 billion road program. (62)

The Batman Refinery of the **Petroleum Corporation of Turkey** put into production in Turkey. (45)

Cumulative receipts of the federal **gasoline tax** (first levied in 1932) hit $10 billion, or as much as the federal government's total tax revenues during the country's first 100 years. (54)

Trans-Canada Pipe Lines, Ltd., granted authority by Alberta government to export natural gas; plans made to build a 2250-mile line across Canada. (38)

Utah passes oil and gas conservation act. (1)

Humble Oil & Refining Company licenses its **velocity logging** instrument to Schlumberger. (1)

Ambassador Oil Corporation incorporated in Fort Worth, with F. Kirk Johnson as president. Began operations January, 1956. (50)

Shell Petroleum Company Ltd., takes over the business and properties of **Anglo-Saxon Petroleum Company, Ltd.,** which is thereafter discontinued. (50)

Barnsdall Industries, Inc., formed. (Falcon Seaboard Drilling Company)

The Bureau of Mines begins an annual survey of the quality of **fuel oils.** (48)

Jalmat gas area of New Mexico created by Commission order combining certain gas pools in the general Jal area, the earliest gas discovery there having been Eaves gas field in 1928. (67)

Texas Gulf Producing Company organizes **Libyan American Oil Company,** wholly owned subsidiary, which acquires concessions in Libya. (50)

Exploration activities intensified in the Oued Draa region in southern **Morocco.** (45)

The **multiple-spaced neutron log** is introduced for gas detection, by Petro-Tech Service Company. (73)

Neutron generator, first successful heavy particle accelerator or atom smasher, to produce fast neutrons in well bore for **nuclear logging** of oil wells introduced by McCullough. (50)

The first fabrication yard, solely for the assembly of **offshore structures,** built by J. Ray McDermott & Co., Inc. (50)

American Gas Journal, purchased by The **Petroleum Engineer Publishing Company,** moves to Dallas, Texas. (38)

J. Ray McDermott & Co., Inc. constructs the first 250-ton full **revolving derrick barge** for offshore use. (50)

Sho-Vel-Tum producing district of Oklahoma formed by consolidating some 16 producing areas in Carter, Garvin and Stephens Counties, the earliest discovery of which had been "Wildcat Jim" in 1914. (67)

Total motor vehicle registrations in the United States are 62 million. 52 million of these are passenger cars. (48)

1956

January 1—**API Division of Finance and Accounting** organized. (62)

January 31—**Johnston Testers** purchased by **Schlumberger Well Surveying Corporation.** (50)

January—**American Gas Journal** becomes first publication to be edited exclusively for the billion-dollar gas distribution industry. (38)

January—The first commercial oil well in **Nigeria** discovered at **Oloibiri** in the heart of the Niger Delta by **Shell-BP Petroleum Development Company of Nigeria, Ltd.** (45)

January—**Algeria**—"CREPS (Compagnie de Recherches et d'Exploitation de Pétrole au Sahara) a company owned 35 per cent by Shell, 55 per cent by Régie Autonomes des Pétroles (a French company) and 10 per cent by the French Government brings in the Edjele No. 101 producing 35° gravity sweet oil at 1475 feet. On production tests from March 22 to March 30, it flows 465 barrels a day. Other earlier discoveries of lesser importance were **Ain Zeft** in 1895, Tliouant in 1914 and Oued Gueterine in 1949. (10)

February 27—In **United Gas Pipe Line Company** v. **Mobil Gas Service Corporation,** 350 U. S. 332, the U. S. Supreme Court holds that Section 4 of the Natural Gas Act does not provide a mechanism for changing a contract unilaterally, and that a natural gas company cannot change a pre-existing contract rate by filing without the consent of its purchasers. (59)

April 11—**Nebraska Oil and Gas Association** (Division of Rocky Mountain Oil and Gas Association) organized. (57)

April 18—**American Petrofina, Inc.,** incorporated under sponsorship of Petrofina, S.A., Brussels. Absorbed Panhandle Oil Co. in October. (50)

April 30—Libya—First well spudded in Concession 18 of **Libyan American Oil Company.** (45)

May 4—**Tidewater Oil Company** adopts present name; preceding name, Tide Water Associated Oil Company (formed by merger of Tide Water Oil Company and Associated Oil Company). (50)

May 7—The first oil well in **Costa Rica** completed near Panamanian border by Union Oil Company. It turns out to be non-commercial, yielding just a few barrels per day. The well is known as Cocoles No. 1. (45)

May—The **Tiguentourine field** in eastern **Sahara discovered.** (50)

June 4—**San Andres field,** Poza Rica District, Mexico, discovered by Pemex No. 1 San Andres completed for 2302 barrels per day on 33/64-inch choke from total depth of 10,520 feet and San Andres No. 3 completed for 767 barrels per day on 25/64-inch choke from total depth of 10,519 feet. (70)

June—The **Hassi-Messaoud field,** 400 miles southeast of **Algiers,** discovered. (45)

July 12—**Utah Oil Refining Company** becomes wholly-owned subsidiary of the Standard Oil Company (Indiana). (50)

July 26—**Egypt** seizes the **Suez Canal.** United States oil companies cooperate with the federal government to organize an "oil lift" that prevents European fuel shortages. (54)

September 1—Service Pipe Line Company acquires the pipeline facilities of the **Pan-Am Southern Corporation** in Arkansas and Louisiana. (50)

September 25—First trans-Atlantic telephone cable begins operation. (54)

November 7—**Schlumberger Limited** incorporated. (50)

November 14—**Schlumber Well Surveying Corporation of Texas** incorporated. (50)

December—The dredging of the **Lake Maracaibo sand bar** at the entrance of the lake completed, thus facilitating the passage of tankers up to 28,000 tons. (45)

The **Association of Oilwell Servicing Contractors** formed to serve the general interest of the oilwell servicing industry. Membership is composed of servicing contractors and those firms and individuals who have an interest in contract well servicing such as manufacturers, suppliers, banks and others servicing the needs of this segment of the oil industry. (Oil and Gas Journal)

In **Bolivia,** Pipeline Cochabamba-Oruro-La Paz built. (45)

Exploration is started in the provinces of Tarapaca, Antofagasta and Atacama, **Chile** by ENAP. (45)

Super-premium octane automobile **gasoline** introduced. (54)

Guatemala awards a 394,000-acre exploration concession to Continental Oil Company of Guatemala. This acreage will be combined with concessions granted subsidiaries of Ohio Oil Company and Amerada Petroleum Corporation for unit operations. (Oil and Gas Journal)

The United States Congress adopts the **Federal-Aid Highway Act of 1956** which provides for a 13-year construction program to be financed over a 16-year period (fiscal 1957 to 1972). The federal gasoline tax increased to three cents per gallon, a new use tax imposed on heavy trucks and buses, a new tax levied on retread rubber, and some of the existing automotive excise taxes increased. (62)

Construction begins on 1487-mile **Pacific Northwest Pipeline** system from the San Juan Basin to the Canadian border, bringing gas to the Pacific Northwest. (38)

John W. Mecom et al's Humble-LL&E 1-L well in Lake Washington field, South Louisiana sets **deep production** record flowing from pay bottomed at 21,465 feet. (Oil). (World Oil)

Sonar caliper log for measuring cavity dimensions for storage introduced, by Dowell. (73)

In **Syria,** oil discovered at Karatchok. (40)

"Burner with a brain" developed and demonstrated. (38)

252

Eumont gas area of New Mexico created by Commission order combining certain gas pools in the Eunice Monument areas, the earliest gas production there having been discovered in 1929. (67)

The **microlaterolog continuous dipmeter** is introduced. (73)

J. Ray McDermott & Co., Inc. launches the first **jacket from a barge** at location in the open gulf. (50)

The first all-aluminum **offshore platform** built by J. Ray McDermott & Co., Inc., in Lake Maracaibo, Venezuela. (50)

Construction begins on 1487-mile **Pacific Northwest Pipeline system,** from San Juan basin to Canadian border, bringing natural gas to the Pacific Northwest. (38)

Louisiana gets **deepest well** title when John W. Mecom, Richardson & Bass, and Freeport Sulphur's No. 1-I Humble-LL&E well is taken to 22,570 feet in the Lake Washington field, Plaquemines Parish, Louisiana. (World Oil)

1957

January 18—Three United States Air Force eight-jet bombers complete round-the-world flight in 45 hours, 19 minutes. (54)

February 1—Service Pipe Line Company merges with **American Oil Pipe Line Company** in Texas. At the same time, the facilities of the **Yount-Lee Pipe Line Company** are acquired. (50)

February 1—**Standard Oil Company (Indiana)** completes reorganization of nine principal affiliates, consolidating them along functional lines into four operating companies. (50)

February 6—The oil industry warned of **possible White House action** unless it voluntarily steps up emergency oil shipments to Western Europe. (2)

February 11—Cosden Petroleum Corporation's unique process for separation of **ethylbenzene** from mixed **xylenes** goes into operation; styrene monomer plant completed at Big Spring Refinery. (50)

March 1—AIME reorganized into three constituent societies, **Society of Mining Engineers of AIME,** The **Metallurgical Society of AIME,** and **Society of Peroleum Engineers of AIME.** The three Societies operate independently of each other within the framework of the parent Institute. Petroleum members of AIME now constitute 40 percent of the total AIME membership. SPE now has 45 local sections (including two in Canada, three in Venezuela, one in Holland, one in Saudi Arabia, and one in Sumatra); six subsections, and 25 student chapters. (57)

March 20—First producing well in the Oued Draa region brought in, in southern **Morocco.** (45)

March 26—The **British Petroleum Company of Canada Limited,** a holding company, formed. (50)

March—Discovery of oil in the Djebel Haricha area of southern **Morocco** is recorded as the most important one up to this time, in the country. (45)

May 2—In Paris, the **European Emergency Oil Committee** discontinues its operations. This follows an announcement that fuel stocks and supplies are ample in Western European nations. (2)

May 7—The Eisenhower Administration gives its conditional support to new **natural gas legislation** designed to ease federal control over production while protecting consumers from "unreasonable" prices. (2)

May 23—**Tidewater Oil Company** dedicates the largest oil refinery built at one time as a unit in Delaware. The 130,000 barrels-per-day plant costs $200,000,000. (54)

May 31—"**Mr. Gus II,**" the largest drilling platform yet built commissioned in Beaumont, Texas. The vessel, designed for drilling in water as much as 150 feet deep, costs $6,500,000. (54)

June 1—The crude oil pipeline facilities of **Utah Oil Refining Company** purchased by Service Pipe Line Company. (50)

June 12—The Sui-Multan gas pipe line in **Pakistan,** 16 inches in diameter and 217 miles long, completed. (45)

June 13—A Senate counsel urges Justice Department investigation and Congressional restriction of activities of the **Arabian American Oil Company,** charging that a series of agreements and arrangements between Aramco and the four companies owning it "may amount to a violation of the antitrust laws." (2)

June 29—The 5th Circuit Court of Appeal rules that the fact that sales of natural gas are made at the wellhead is immaterial in determining whether such sales are local or interstate commerce. If such sales are made for delivery of gas in interstate commerce, they are subject to the jurisdiction of and regulation by the Federal Power Commission. **Deep South Oil Company of Texas** v. **Federal Power Commission** 247 F. 2d 882. (Vinson, Elkins, Weems and Searls)

June—The President of the United States establishes a **Special Cabinet Committee** to make an investigation to determine whether crude oil is being imported into the United States in such quantities as to threaten to impair the national security. (61)

July 17—**Washington**—The **Sunshine Mining Company's** No. 1 Medina flows an estimated 400 barrels per day on drillstem test. Well is at Ocean City in Grays Harbor County. On August 20, the well opens the first commercial oil production in the state of Washington with a flow of 223 barrels of 38.9 gravity oil from 4135 feet. (10)

July 23—The **Sylhet gas field, East Pakistan,** discovered by Pakistan Petroleum Limited. On March 11, 1959, Pakistan Petroleum Limited brought in the **Chattak gas field** in the District of Sylhet, East Pakistan. On June 25, 1960, the Chattak Cement Factory gas pipe line, 4-inch diameter, 12 miles long, was completed. In July 1960, the Sylhet-Fenchuganj gas pipeline, 8-inch diameter, 33 miles long, was completed. On August 20, 1960, the **Rashidpur gas field** in the District of Sylhet, discovered by Pakistan Shell Oil Company. (45)

July 29—**Voluntary Oil Import Program** put into effect and the Secretary of the Interior appoints a Special Assistant to administer the program. (61)

July 31—The **Middle East Emergency Committee** disbanded. (61)

August 8—**La Gloria Oil and Gas Company** acquired by Texas Eastern Transmission Corporation as a wholly-owned subsidiary. (50)

September 30—**Kenai Peninsula, Alaska field** discovered by Richfield Oil Corporation. Discovery well is located on what is known as the Swanson River Unit and comes in making 900 barrels per day. (10) (50)

September—The first **aluminum offshore drilling platforms** installed in Lake Maracaibo, Venezuela, for Superior Oil Company of Venezuela. (Reynolds Metals Company)

October 4—Russia launches **first satellite,** Sputnik 1.

October 31—The United States Air Force intercontinental guided missile hits target 5,000 miles away. (54)

October—The first **automatic welding** machine for welding aluminum pipeline developed by Reynolds Metals Company and Air Reduction Company. (50)

December 8—Anglo-American companies that had **Austrian oil** properties expropriated by the Nazis and then the Russians told they will be permitted to participate in further development. (2)

December 9—The **Philippines** grants the second Petroleum Refining Concession to STANVAC, for a capacity of 25,000 to 50,000 barrels per day. (45)

December 12—**Voluntary oil imports control** program extended to include crude imports into District V (West Coast), establishing company allocations for first half of 1958. (IPPA Monthly)

December 16—Texas Railroad Commission issues **first "Normanna Order"** for the Normanna field, basing the proration of the total field allowable on a 1/3-2/3 formula, i.e., 1/3 of the total field allowable to be divided equally among all wells in the field, and 2/3 of the total field allowable to be divided among the wells on a per-acreage basis. Effective October 1, 1957. (58)

December—**Four Corners Pipe Line,** a 750-mile crude oil line from the Four Corners area to Los Angeles, California completed. (Shell Oil Company)

Socal and Richfield announce they have entered into an agreement for joint exploration and development of land holdings on Kenai Peninsula of **Alaska.** Socal agrees to spend $30 million over several years as part of agreement. (50)

Refinery constructed in Naantali, **Finland** for refining of imported crude oil. Refinery is operated by the **Neste Oy Company.** (45)

The Independent Producers and Royalty Owners Association of New Mexico founded in Roswell, New Mexico. (57)

France starts a 550-mile, 24-inch line from **Lacq field** on the Spanish border to Paris, to carry natural gas. (40)

Natural gas deposits discovered in the Essaouira area on **Morocco's** central-western coast. (45)

President Eisenhower in his annual budget message says that **federal regulation of independent gas producers must be repealed.** (2)

The **Tecumseh Pipe Line Company** (Sinclair, Pure, and Ashland) lays a 20-inch line from East Chicago to Cygnet, Ohio. Major Joint-Interest Crude System. (40)

First **aluminum motor oil cans** produced for Esso Standard Oil Company. (Reynolds Metals Company)

The **flowing neutron log** is introduced, by Creole Petroleum Corporation. (73)

Gamma-ray logging of cores at the surface is introduced by Core Labs. (73)

Smokeless-odorless **gas incinerator** developed. (38)

The Bureau of Mines begins publication of **"Petroleum Products Surveys."** (48)

Refrigerated propane storage plant built by Atlanta Gas Light Company is first for the gas utility industry. (38)

Salinity log, first nuclear well logging instrument to determine presence and degree of salinity in formations surrounding well bore introduced by McCullough. (50)

In **Scotland,** natural gas supplied from Cousland to Musselburgh gas works. (45)

Texas Eastern Transmission Corporation completes construction of 30-inch pipeline to Mexican border, and for the first time natural **gas from Mexico** is imported on a large scale basis into the United States. (50)

1958

January 20—First oil well in **Libya** completed in concession 1 of **Esso Standard Libya, Inc.,** discovers Atshan field. (45) (67)

January 21—**Pan American International Oil Company** formed to engage in foreign exploration and development of foreign crude oil reserves. (50)

January 22—The **Little Big Inch** pipeline reconverted back to a carrier of refined petroleum products. (Texas Eastern Transmission Corporation)

January 31—**Satellite "Explorer I"** launched from Cape Canaveral, Florida. (54)

March 24—Special Cabinet Committee reduces company allocations for crude oil **imports** in Districts I-IV and imposes penalties for violating allocations. (IPAA Monthly)

April 15—The **Zohar gas field,** 20 miles east of Beer-Sheba, **Israel,** discovered. (45)

April—Since this date Cosden Petroleum Corporation has been world's only supplier of 99 percent **orthoxylene** in commercial quantities. (50)

April—**Proximity log** introduced experimentally, by Schlumberger. (50)

May 8—**Wabash Pipe Line Company** formed to operate refined products line from Wood River and Robinson, Illinois, to the Chicago area. (Marathon Oil Company)

June 19—First quadruple well completed using four strings of tubing is CATCO's West Delta Block 45 Well No. C-8, located 10 miles off Louisiana's Southwest Pass at the mouth of the Mississippi River. Production of oil and gas is from four zones between 9022 and 9789 feet. (**Quadruple completion**) (50)

June 30—A convention signed with the Tunisian Government enabling the Trapsa Company (Sahara Pipeline Transport Company) to execute the construction and operation of the **Edjele-La Skhirra pipeline.** (45)

June—Cosden Petroleum Corporation becomes first oil refinery with fully integrated plant producing **polystyrene** from basic raw material. (50)

July 18—World's **largest gas well** completed by Humble Oil & Refining Company in the Emperor field, Winkler County, Texas. Open flow potential is 1.66 billion cubic feet per day from a depth of 9440 feet. It is the Brown and Altman gas unit No. 6 well. (50)

July 21—The Eilat-Haifa, **Israel,** 16-inch crude oil pipeline completed. (45)

July 21—**Morocco** issues its "Hydrocarbon Law," containing technical provisions for the control of activities of holders of concessions and exploration permits. (45)

July 22—Senate approves **Trade Agreements Bill,** retaining strengthened language in Defense Amendment written in by Senate Finance Committee July 10, but without mandatory limitations on oil imports. (IPAA Monthly)

July 26—Agreement signed between the government of Morocco and

Italy's state-controlled petroleum agency, the Ente Nazionale Idrocarburi, E.N.I. The agreement sets the stage for the formation of the **Moroccan-Italian Petroleum Corporation.** (Societe Anonyme Marocaine-Italienne des Petroles, or SOMIP. (45)

July—**Yacimientos Petroliferos Fiscales** (YPF), the Argentine oil agency, makes a series of contracts with private firms, representing **Argentine,** United States, Italian and other interests. (45)

August 5—Nautilus makes first sub-polar voyage.

August 11—After trying seven years to get a **roll call vote on depletion,** opponents succeed in getting two. In the first, the Williams amendment for a straight reduction to 15 per cent is defeated by 63 to 26 with 7 not voting. In Proxmire's graduated reduction to 15 per cent, the vote is 58 to 31 with 7 absent. In subsequent roll call votes, Douglas' proposal for graduated reduction to 15 per cent, on June 25, 1959, was defeated 54 to 21 with 23 not voting; Douglas' proposal was again submitted on June 20, 1960, and defeated 56 to 30 with 14 not voting; on September 5, 1962, two other proposals were defeated. One was Williams' amendment proposing reduction to 20 per cent over a three-year period, which was beaten 57 to 30 with 14 not voting, and Douglas' proposal for a graduated reduction to 15 per cent which was defeated 50 to 23 with 27 not voting. (Mid-Continent Oil & Gas Association)

August 22—**Indian Refineries Ltd.** incorporated. (45)

September 1—**API Committee on Public Affairs** organized. (62)

September 1—The **Oklahoma Petroleum Council** formed as a voluntary, unincorporated organization. (57)

September—**The Louisiana Petroleum Council** founded. (57)

October 11—United States Air Force "Pioneer" travels 71,300 miles into outer space. (54)

October 11—First test of The Atlantic Refining Company's **high conductivity fracturing** technique using aluminum pellets. (Foster Field, Ector County, Texas). (50)

October 15—In Bolivia, the first **National Technical Petroleum Convention** meets in La Paz under the auspices of Y.P.F.B. (45)

October—For the first time in 13 years, Texas regains **deepest well** title when Phillips Petroleum Company's University EE-1 wildcat in Pecos County, West Texas, is drilled to 25,340 feet. (World Oil)

Fall—University of Oklahoma institutes a **curriculum** of **Petroleum Landmen Management.** A similar curriculum instituted at the University of Texas in the fall of 1959. (University Catalogues)

November 12—**Argentine Petroleum Law** promulgated. (45)

November 27—The **Saharan Oil Code** set up by the French Government. (45)

258

November—**Australasian Petroleum Company Pty. Ltd.**, after having drilled unsuccessfully around the Vailala River, at Omati, and Kuru, reports a flow of 3 million cubic feet of gas a day and 70 barrels of condensate a day from No. 1 well sunk at Puri-**New Guinea.** (45)

December 6—World's **largest tanker,** chartered by a United States oil company, launched at Kuri, Japan. The vessel has a carrying capacity of 1,021,000 barrels. (54)

December 9—World records established by American jet transports for trans-Atlantic commercial flights: New York to London—5 hours, 56 minutes; New York to Paris—6 hours, 16 minutes. (54)

December 12—**Amoco Trading Corporation** established to handle international purchases, sales and transportation of crude oil and products. (Standard Oil Company (Indiana)

December 26—**Spain** enacts a new "Hydrocarbon Law" to attract exploration in Continental Spain, Spanish Sahara and Spanish Guinea. (64)

December—The **Four Corners Pipe Line Company** (Shell, Standard of California, Gulf, Continental, Richfield and Superior) lays a 16-inch line from Aneth, Utah to Los Angeles. Major Joint-Interest Crude System. (40)

Argentina starts its biggest crude line, a 930-mile, 12-inch line from Campo Duran to the San Lorenzo refinery. (40)

The **Associated Petroleum Industries of Michigan** organized in the fall as a voluntary trade association. (57)

The **U. N. Conference on the Law of the Sea**—in a Convention on the **Continental Shelf**—internationally accepts its principles. Grants to a coastal state the sovereign rights outside its territorial waters for the exploration and exploitation of the natural resources of the continental shelf to the extent of the 200-meter contour, or beyond that limit, to where the depth of the water permits exploitation. (39)

In **Federal Power Commission** v. **Memphis Light, Gas and Water Division,** 358 U. S. 103, the U. S. Supreme Court holds that long term service agreements filed with the Federal Power Commission and construed as obligating the purchasers to pay for the gas at the pipeline company's "going" rate must be distinguished from the contract employed in **United Gas Pipe Line Co.** v. **Mobile Gas Service Corporation,** 350 U. S. 332. "Memphis-type" service agreements are held to be permissible. (59)

The **Jayhawk Pipe Line Company** (Derby Refining, National Cooperative Refinery Association) lays 10- and 12-inch lines from Meade County, Kansas to Wichita. Major Joint-Interest Crude System. (40)

Sun Oil Company researchers develop a drill stem **electric logging tool,** which allows electric logs to be made without the necessity of drawing the drill pipe. (50)

A 682-mile, 16-inch natural gas pipeline completed in **Pakistan.** (40)

The **first large-diameter pipe line in Europe** is a 28-inch line from Wilhelmshaven to Cologne, Germany. (40)

World production of oil exceeds 900 million metric tons, of which U. S. A. produces 327 million; Middle East, 215 million; Venezuela, 138 million; U. S. S. R., 113 million; all other countries, 112 million. (Review)

The **first well to produce from four zones,** with production segregated, completed by Magnolia Petroleum Company. Located in San Carlos field in Hidalgo County, Texas, Magnolia's 8 Santa Cruz Farms is producing from three gas zones through three parallel strings of $2\frac{1}{16}$-inch tubing and from upper gas zone through the annular space. (**Quadruple completion**) (40)

Activator, accelerator, or oxygen logs are introduced by Well Surveys Inc. (73)

The **cemoton log** is introduced, by Lane-Wells. (73)

McCullough introduces **electric isotope injector.** (50)

Shell **Isoprene Rubber,** a man-made duplicate of tree-grown rubber, introduced for commercial use. (Shell Oil Company)

Oasis Oil Company of Libya discovers Bahi field in Concession 32 in **Libya.** In 1960, Oasis discovered oil in the Waha and Defa areas. (Marathon Oil Company)

Nuclear magnetism logging is introduced by California Research and Borg-Warner. (73)

Plutonium-Beryllium first fast **neutron source** employing plutonium, introduced by McCullough. (50)

Russia's most ambitious undertaking in pipelines is the 2300-mile **Trans-Siberian crude and products system.** (40)

1959

(As of January 1)—There are 68,299,408 motor vehicle registrations in the United States.

January—The Marathon Oil Company (then Ohio) begins gigantic **airlift, the largest in oil industry history,** carrying several million pounds of rotary drilling equipment over mountains and jungles into the interior of **Guatemala.** (50)

February 18—**India Oil Ltd.** registration as a rupee company. (45)

February 20—The **SS Methane Pioneer,** world's **first liquefied natural gas tanker,** owned by **Constock Liquid Methane Corp.,** arrives in Canvey Island, England from Lake Charles, Louisiana, after a three weeks voyage laden with 32,000 barrels of liquid gas, which when vaporized will expand in the ratio of 600 to one. The ship, some 340 feet long, has its cargo refrigerated to a minus 285 degrees Fahrenheit. (Business Week)

February—**Delta Pipe Line,** a 120-mile line from Southwest Pass in

Southern Louisiana to Shell Oil Company's Norco, Louisiana refinery completed. (50)

March 1—Basic changes in the organization of **Socony Mobil Oil Company, Inc.,** become effective, providing for two new operating divisions as follows: Mobil Oil Company Division—responsible for all operations in the United States and for coordination with United States and Canadian affiliates; Mobil International Oil Company Division—responsible for all operations and coordination with affiliates in other areas of the free world. (50)

March 10—President Eisenhower issues a proclamation setting up a **Mandatory Oil Import Program.** (48)

March 27—**Section 1(c)** of the **Natural Gas Act added** by amendment. This is commonly called the **"Hinshaw Amendment"** and further defines the limits of the Federal Power Commission's jurisdiction with respect to operations of companies engaged in the local distribution within a state of out-of-state gas which has been received by such a company at or within the state borders. (59)

March 31—**Deep-focused** (6FF40) **induction log** introduced commercially, by Schlumberger. (50)

April 30—President amends March 10 proclamation by exempting **Canadian imports.** (IPAA Monthly)

May 1—The **Independent Oil and Gas Association of West Virginia** organized. (57)

June—The first platform in over 200-foot water depth installed by **J. Ray McDermott & Co., Inc.,** for **Gulf Oil Corporation** 40 miles offshore Louisiana. (**Offshore drilling**) (50)

June 13—**Libya's** biggest oil strike in discovery well, Concession 6 of Esso Standard Libya Inc. with a tested initial rate of 17,500 barrels a day. (45)

June 22—The United States Supreme Court rules that it is not necessary to determine that the rate is "just and reasonable" in a Section 7 certificate proceeding, but the proposed rate must be supported by evidence showing its necessity to "the present or future public convenience and necessity." **Atlantic Refining Company et al v. Public Service Commission of the State of New York et al,** 360 U. S. 378. (Vinson, Elkins, Weems and Searls)

June 30—**Indian Oil Company** incorporated. (45)

July—**Peru** introduces a conservation measure in connection with a price revision whereby no more than 20 per cent of production can be exported. (45)

July—**Standard Vacuum Oil Company** delivers 20,000 gallons of liquefied petroleum gas to its Nhabe terminal at Saigon—the first such bulk shipment of LPG by sea ever attempted in the area. (50)

July—The **terminal buoy system** in a sanctuary (a deepwater restricted area to permit continuous and safe discharging of supertanker cargoes) demonstrated by the **Royal Swedish Navy.** The system is called Imodco for its designer and manufacturer, AB International Marine & Oil Development Corporation of Stockholm, Sweden. (Oil and Gas Journal)

August 3—Perforating Gun Atlas Corporation adopts its present name, **Pan Geo Atlas Corporation.** (50)

August 10—**Transwestern Pipeline Company** issued certificate of convenience and necessity to build an 1809-mile natural gas pipeline from Texas to the California border. (50)

August 27—The **Centennial** of the bringing in of Drake's well at Titusville, Pennsylvania. (54)

September 2—New **Humble Oil & Refining Company** chartered when three Standard Oil Company (N. J.) affiliates, Humble, Esso Standard and Carter Oil Companies merge. (50)

September 7—**World's highest pressure well** with 12,800 pounds per square inch shut in announced. The well is Union Texas Natural Gas Corporation's No. 1 Vincent in Leleux area of Vermillion Parish, Louisiana. A 15,000 lb. per psi test Christmas tree is set. (Oil & Gas Journal)

September 11—**Amoco Fina, S.A.** incorporated in Switzerland for the manufacture and sale of chemical products (50 per cent ownership by Amoco Chemicals Corporation). (Standard Oil Company (Indiana))

September 28—Standard Vacuum Oil Company completes the discovery well, its Mari 3, in **West Pakistan,** a natural gas field. Search for oil unsuccessful. (50)

September 30—Standard Oil Company (Indiana) acquires **True's Oil Company.** (50)

September 30—**Magnolia Petroleum Company** becomes a part of Socony Mobil Oil Company, Inc. (50)

Fall—The name of the American Petroleum Institute Quarterly changed to "**Petroleum Today.**" (62)

September—The city of **Buenos Aires** converts to natural gas through the new pipeline, Campo Duran-Buenos Aires. (45)

September—The Committee on Public Affairs of the American Petroleum Institute publishes the first issue of "**Oil Facts,**" which replaces the former Tax Economics Bulletin. (62)

September—The United States Congress adopts a "temporary" one cent per gallon increase in the federal **gasoline tax,** effective October 1, 1959 to run for a period of 21 months and expire at midnight on June 30, 1961. (62)

October 15—**India** converts Oil and Natural Gas Commission into a statutory body. (45)

October 31—Service Pipe Line Company signs an operating agreement with the six other owners of the 300-mile **Bayou Pipe Line System** whereby Service Pipe Line Company, starting January 1, 1960, began operating the system for them. (50)

November 2—**Project Five Pipeline System** purchased by Texas Eastern Transmission Corporation. (50)

November—The **deepest hole drilled with air,** totaal depth 18,550 feet, completed by Falcon Seaboard Drililng Company for Gulf Oil Corporation in Terrell County, Texas. (50)

December 29—The Ohio Oil Company (Marathon) invents and perfects automatic **voice reader** for obtaining pipeline data. (50)

December 31—**General Petroleum Corporation** and Mobil Producing Company become a part of Socony Mobil Oil Company, Inc. (50)

December—Between this date when natural gas is discovered at Port Campbell in Victoria, **Australia,** and 1962, seven other significant gas finds made in Victoria, Queensland, and New South Wales. (45)

Standard Oil Company of California announces pipeline and tanker terminal project to move oil from Swanson River unit to tidewater (Nikiski on Cook Inlet), in **Alaska.** (50)

"Isocracking" process, developed by **Calresearch,** announced by Standard Oil Company of California. (50)

Patent No. 2,918,125 issued for McCullough Tool Company's **chemical cutter and perforator** process for cutting pipe, formation, and cement, and perforating wells. (50)

Morocco signs agreement with Italy's **E.N.I.** for construction of a refinery. Corporation for this purpose formed on 50-50 basis and is called Samir, from its French Initials—Societe Anonyme Marocaine-Italienne de Raffinage. (**Italo-Moroccan Refining Corp.**) Morocco is to furnish half of the $25 million construction funds. After eight years of operation, the refinery is to have 80 per cent Moroccan personnel. (45)

The Ohio Oil Company (Marathon) participates with Union Oil Company of California in discovery of first large reserves of natural gas in southern **Alaska** on Kenai Unit, testing at rate of 15 million cubic feet per day. (50)

The first fully **automated** 100,000 barrel-per-day **flow station** installed by J. Ray McDermott & Co., Inc., in Lake Maracaibo, Venezuela. (50)

J. Ray McDermott & Co., Inc. lays the first **molten sulphur line** in the Gulf of Mexico. (50)

Shell International Chemical Company, Ltd., formed with headquarters in London. (Shell Oil Company)

A large amount of natural gas discovered at Chinshui, **Taiwan.** Estimated reserves of 700 billion cubic feet. (45)

1960

January 15—The Secretary of the Interior, upon recommendation of the Office of Oil and Gas, designates the first 17 oil and gas industry executives and technical personnel to serve as **Executive Reservists.** (61)

January 15—The final depth of Well No. 1 on the **Kuwait** concession held by the **Arabian Oil Company, Limited** is reached and the well undergoes a flow test on January 29, 1960. Well has a daily production of more than 1000 kiloliters. (45)

January 30—**W. R. Grace & Co.** acquires 53 per cent of outstanding stock of Cosden Petroleum Corporation. (50)

January—Concessions in **Spanish Sahara** granted by Spain. (Oil and Gas Journal)

February 1—John W. Mecom forms **U.S. Oil Company of Louisiana, Inc.** (50)

February 13—Government **anti-trust charges** against 29 oil companies **dismissed** after brief trial by Federal Judge **Royce Savage** in Tulsa. The government claimed that oil companies had conspired to raise prices in 1957 shortly after the Suez Crisis.

March 18—**Trans-Jeff Chemical Corporation** formed by Transco and Jefferson Lake Sulphur Co. of New Orleans to recover sulphur from the waste acid gas stream at Transco's Tilden, Texas gas treating plant. (Transcontinental Gas Pipe Line Corporation)

April 28—Organizational meeting of the **International Oil and Gas Educational Center** of the Southwestern Legal Foundation. The Foundation's executive committee had approved creation of the Center on September 18, 1959.

April—The first **quintuple completion** made by Sinclair Oil and Gas Company in Block 190 Field, Eugene Island Area, Offshore Louisiana. (World Oil)

May 2—The world's **largest tank car,** built by **Union Tank Company** for **Tuloma Gas Products Company,** unveiled in Chicago. It is 85 feet long and has shell capacity for 30,000 gallons of LP gases. (Oil Daily)

May 25—The Ohio Oil Company, with Continental Oil Company and Amerada Petroleum Corporation, form **Oasis Oil Company of Libya, Inc.,** supplanting former wholly-owned subsidiary of same name. (50)

May 31—**Enjay Company, Inc.,** merges into Humble Oil & Refining Company. (50)

May—The first **sextuple completion** (a gas well) made by Sun Ray Mid-Continent Oil Company at a depth of 4700-6650 feet in the North Laward field, Jackson County, Texas. (World Oil)

May—**Trunkline Gas Company** is the first to use **helicopters** for stringing pipe in muddy terrain. (50)

June 10—**Largest steel island** ever constructed completed in Gulf of

Mexico seven miles off Louisiana's Grande Isle, turned over to Humble Oil & Refining Company and Freeport Sulphur Company for mining sulphur. Costs $30 million. (Petroleum Week)

June 20—**Mobil Chemical Company** division formed to be responsible for manufacture and sale of petroleum chemicals. (50)

June 30—**Merger of Oklahoma, Pate and Penola** into Humble Oil & Refining Company. (50)

July 25—The fertilizer factory of the **Pakistan Industrial Development Corporation** (P.I.D.C.) at Fenchuganj, **Pakistan,** starts using natural gas from the Sylhet field. (45)

August 15—**Apco Oil Corporation** incorporated in Delaware. (50)

August 31—Merger of **Globe Fuel Products, Inc.** into Humble Oil & Refining Company. (50)

August—Falcon Seaboard Drilling Company sets into operation the first drilling rig in the **Spanish Sahara.** First contract is with the Spanish Gulf Oil Company. (50)

September 1—**Ireland** grants a permit to explore for oil and gas in all the Republic of Ireland. (Oil Daily)

September 2—The United States enacts what is known as the "**1960 Act,**" which requires a **minimum rental** for each year of the non-competitive lease and retains the 12½ per cent royalty. Acreage limitations are liberalized somewhat. (61)

September 6—**Combination induction-laterolog 8** introduced commercially by Schlumberger. (50)

September 14—**Organization of Petroleum Exporting Countries** (OPEC) formed with five founding members: Iran, Iraq, Kuwait, Saudi Arabia, and Venezuela. Qatar was later admitted. (Oilgram)

September 28—The **Federal Power Commission** issues its **Statement of General Policy No. 61-1,** which, with its appended area price schedule, sets standards for initial and increased rate filings by producers for the sale of natural gas into interstate commerce. (59)

October 10—"**Grand-slam**" **logging** (combination proximity log, laterolog 8, two induction logs and sonic log) commercially introduced, by Schlumberger. (50)

October 11—It is announced that **Monterey Oil Company** has agreed to sell "substantially all of its business and assets" in Texas, California, Wyoming, Louisiana and New Mexico to Humble Oil & Refining Company. (50)

October 11—**Amoco Italia, S.P.A.** formed for purpose of acquiring a refinery and service stations in Italy. (Standard Oil Company (Indiana)

October 14—**Midwestern Gas Transmission Company,** a subsidiary of

Tennessee Gas Transmission Company, gives the upper Midwest its first deliveries of natural gas imported from Canada. (50)

October 25—United States patent issued for Cosden Petroleum Corporation's **polyisobutylene process.** (50)

October 26—Indonesia President Sukarno signs a government decree on oil and gas exploration. (Oilgram)

October—Oil in commercial quantities found at Murban, **Abu Dhabi.** (45)

October—Trunkline Gas Company introduces new techniques for **sandblasting gas pipe lines.** (50)

October—The **first oil well drilled with aluminum pipe** is the Alvin F. Sievers No. 1 in DeWitt County, Texas, by Shell Oil Company. (50)

November 1—The **"Siamese Dual Pumping Unit"** introduced and the first one goes into service in West Texas approximately November 15, 1960, with a major oil company. (American Manufacturing Co. of Texas)

November 2—**Argentina** Executive Power issues a decree (No. 13255) through the Secretariat of Energy and Fuels ratifying the government's stand with regard to the exploitation of the nation's petroleum deposits. (45)

November 8—United States patent issued for Cosden Petroleum Corporation's **ethylbenzene separation process.** (50)

November 14—Standard Oil Company (New Jersey) and Socony Mobil Oil Company, Inc., announce that their joint ownership of **Standard-Vacuum Oil Company** is being terminated. (50)

December 19—**Mobil Petroleum Company, Inc.,** incorporated as a subsidiary of Standard-Vacuum Oil Company. (50)

December 31—The reorganization approved by share owners at a special meeting on September 29 becomes effective. **Standard Oil Company (Indiana),** after turning over operations to subsidiary companies, becomes entirely a parent company for domestic and foreign activities. (50)

December 31—**Utah Oil Refining Company,** a wholly-owned subsidiary, merged into American Oil Company, also wholly owned, and the operating assets of Standard Oil Company (Indiana) transferred to American Oil Company. (50)

December—Australasian Petroleum reports 30 million cubic feet a day from No. 1 well at Iehi, **New Guinea.** (45)

December—The **world's deepest gas condensate dual completion** put on production. The well, the No. 1 Sally Krieger in the Knox field, Grady County, Oklahoma, produces from two levels. The Oil Creek perforated intervals at from 16,490 to 16,612 feet—and the Bromide perforated between 14,805 and 15,288 feet. (Oil and Gas Journal)

December—The first **ocean bottom well** to be **completed** on the ocean floor **by remote control** announced by Shell Oil Company. The well is Shell's OCA 407 No. 7, drilled to 8300 feet in West Cameron Block 192, about 35 miles off the Louisiana coast. (International Oilman)

Refining properties in Cuba seized by **Castro's Cuban Communist government.** (Shell Oil Company)

Petrolera Dominicana, et al., drills to a depth of 9920 feet in the Azua Valley **Dominican Republic;** tests gas but not completed. (H. G. S. Bulletin)

Esso Nederland N.V., a subsidiary of the Standard Oil Company (New Jersey) opens a refinery in the Botlek area of **Holland.** This refinery is unique in Europe in that all installations are cooled with air instead of water. (45)

The petroleum harbors west of Rotterdam, **Holland,** linked by a pipeline with various refineries in the Ruhr district (Federal Republic of Germany). This pipeline is over 186 miles long with a diameter of over 24 inches. (45)

The **first electronic gasoline in-line blender** installed at the Santa Fe Springs, California, refinery of the **Wilshire Oil Company.** (Petroleum Week)

The Caltex and Shell groups begin prospecting for oil in **Norway.** (45)

The first **aluminum airborne drilling rig** designed and built for Bolivia California Petroleum Company, a subsidiary of Standard Oil Company of California. Furnished by Mid-Continent Supply Co., owned and operated by Loffland Brothers Company in Bolivia, South America. Rig's aluminum substructure built by Ideco; piping fabricated by Joe Stine, Inc., of Houston, Texas; aluminum mud ditches, tanks and equipment skids by Unit Rig and Equipment Co. and aluminum shelters by Deckard Manufacturing Co., of Tulsa, Oklahoma. (Reynolds Metals Company)

Basin Dakota field area of New Mexico created by combining 13 old Dakota horizon fields, and unnamed individual Dakota wells, the oldest field thus combined being Angels Peak Dakota discovered in November 1947. (67)

Texaco announces the development of low-luminosity **jet fuel.** (50)

Off **Peru,** the **world's first underwater completion** made by **Peruvian Pacific Petroleum Company,** a Cities Service subsidiary. (World Oil)

1961

January 1—A decree issued by the Italian Government orders production of natural gas in the **Po Delta** (which had yielded some 122.5 billion cubic feet) stopped completely. Survey data indicates that gas withdrawal has caused sinking of the ground level by 7⅝ inches to 11¾ inches during the last 70 years. (64)

January 15—**Kuwait** signs an **Offshore Concession Agreement** with the Kuwait Shell Petroleum Development Co., Ltd. (45)

January 23—The Supreme Court of the United States rules that in a certificate proceeding under Section 7 of The Natural Gas Act, the Federal Power Commission may consider the **end use** to be made of the gas, the price to be paid for it and the effect of such price on other prices. These are proper factors to be weighed by the Federal Power Commission in determining whether to grant a certificate to the pipeline company. **Federal Power Commission** v. **Transcontinental Gas Pipe Line Corporation et al** 365 U. S. 1. (Vinson, Elkins, Weems and Searls)

March 10—An oil discovery is made by American-Asiatic Oil Corporation while drilling its stratigraphic-structural hole, DST No. 1 in Maya, Daanbantayan, Northern Cebu, **Philippines.** The quality of the oil is light, highly volatile, high gasoline content with negligible amount of paraffin and water content and with a gravity of 45.6° API. (45)

March 31—**United Fuel Gas Company** puts into service the first **permanent aluminum pipeline.** The aluminum pipeline connects two wells 4500 feet apart and crosses two mountains that rise between the wells and is made of 5700 feet of pipe. The gas line will be operated as a part of a gas-gathering network linking United Fuel gas wells to a cross-country transmission system. It is in service in the eastern Kentucky section of the southern Appalachians. (New York Times)

March—First publication of **Society of Petroleum Engineers Journal,** a quarterly magazine, which is published in addition to the monthly Journal of Petroleum Technology. (70)

March—The first **underwater subsurface hydraulic pump** installation is being operated near Colchester, Ontario, Canada, in six to eight feet of water in Lake Erie by the Place Oil and Gas Company. The well is 2300 feet deep and is 500 feet offshore. (International Oilman)

April 2—First phase of **MOHO project** drills through 557 feet of sedimentary deposits penetrating the **Earth's Second Layer** 44 feet to obtain core off Guadalupe Island in water 11,700 feet deep. The project sponsored by the **National Academy of Science.** Drilling is from **Global Marine Exploration Company's** Cuss 1 drillship. On June 19, 1962, the second phase of the project was started with the letting of the prime contract to **Brown & Root, Inc.,** of Houston, Texas. (John Steinbeck, Life, April 14, 1961) (Houston Post)

April 5—Northern Natural Gas Company establishes a joint program with the Houdry Process Corporation to develop a **natural gas fuel cell.** (50)

April 5-7—For the first time, the **North Atlantic Treaty Organization Petroleum Planning Committee** meets in the United States, at Washington, D. C. (61)

April 9—Hospital Hill and Timbury Hills (near Roma, **Queensland,**

Australia) gas wells begin supply of gas to fuel turbo-generators for Roma's electricity supply. (45)

April 12—First orbital space flight. Russia.

April 12—What is called the world's first fully automated **in-line hot mill** for the production of **seamless still tubing** put into operation near Rosenberg, Texas, by **Gulf States Tube Corporation.** The $5 million facility features a unique 1800-ton extrusion press making tubing three times faster and more efficiently than heretofore possible in the United States. (Oil Daily)

April 12—Union Oil Company of California puts on stream at its Wilmington, California refinery what is believed to be the first fully solid-state, **remotely controlled electronic in-line blender.** The $1½ million facility electronically blends gasoline, jet fuels and other petroleum products with "essentially absolute accuracy." (Oil Daily)

April 13—**Monterey Gas Transmission Company** formed. (Humble Oil & Refining Company)

April 23—A **world drilling speed record** set when Gulf Oil Corporation's No. 25 well in Block 21 Offshore Timbalier field, Louisiana is drilled 10,000 feet in 2.14 days from Kerr-McGee's Rig 47. Another record was that of drilling 7518 feet the first 24 hours. The well's average time is three feet per minute including pulling and rerunning pipe and changing bits. (50)

April 23—Union Oil of California, Kern County Land Co., and Australian Oil and Gas Corporation strike oil (60-100 barrels a day) near Cabawin, **Queensland, Australia.** (45)

April 25—The first **sextuple completion** (an oil well) made by Humble Oil & Refining Company at a depth of 5162-6419 feet at King Ranch, Kleberg County, Texas. (The Houston Post)

April 26—The **Fluor Corporation** erects the **largest butane splitter** ever put up in one piece, at the Texas City refinery of the American Oil Company. The 201-foot-long, 200-ton tower is hoisted by two lifting poles, each able to support 300 tons, and is pinned down with 48 bolts, each three inches in diameter and embedded 7½ feet in concrete. (Oil Daily)

April 27—**Illegal directional drilling** investigation triggered in East Texas field when a 25-year-old Shell Oil Company well's casing is accidentally pierced by an illegal well drilling at a 50 degree angle at 4320 feet. The Shell well suddenly starts flowing fresh mud. (58)

April—**Longest string of casing** in oil history set in **John W. Mecom's** No. 1-S LL&E well at Lake Washington in Plaquemines Parish, Louisiana when Halliburton crew runs 12,969 feet of 10¾-inch pipe in a 15-inch hole. (Oil Daily)

May 5—First US orbital flight.

May 14—The Zohar-Sedom, **Israel,** six-inch gas pipeline completed. (45)

May 29—Merger of Humble Pipe Line Company and **Interstate Oil Pipe Line Company** announced. (Humble Oil & Refining Company)

May 31—Texas Supreme Court strikes down the Railroad Commission proration order for the Normanna field based on the 1/3-2/3 formula (even in light of the rule of capture) saying that it does not allow each producer in the field to produce his share of the gas, and there is no substantial evidence presented to justify the large discrepancy in the rate of production between operators that the order occasions, i.e., where a .3 acre tract is allowed to produce over 200 times as much gas as a larger 230 acre adjoining tract. The .3 acre operator given a Rule 37 exception to drill. Atlantic Refining Company et al. v. Railroad Commission, 346 S.W. 2d 801 (1961). **"Normanna Decision."** (58)

May—The El-Agreb and El-Gassi fields, both south of Hassi-Messaoud, **Algeria,** discovered. (45)

May—**Israel's** first natural-gas transmission line goes into operation. It carries gas through a six-inch line from Zohar and Kidod fields toward a potash plant on the Dead Sea, 18 miles to the east. (51)

June 3—The **first gas turbine power plant** to produce large quantities of commercial electric power from gas demonstrated by the Gas Turbine Dept. of General Electric. (Gas Magazine)

June 14—The **Philippines** grants a Petroleum Refining Concession to Filoil Company, for a capacity of 10,000 to 17,000 barrels per day. The refinery of the company at Rosario, Cavite, Southern Luzon is still under construction. (45)

June 17—The **Philippines** approves Republic Act No. 3098 amending certain articles of Republic Act No. 387, otherwise known as the "Petroleum Act of 1949." (45)

June—The first oil refinery in **New Zealand** (completion date 1964) will be built at Marsden Point, Whangarei. (Oil Daily)

July 1—The **National Petroleum Refiners Association** formed as a result of the merger of two of the oldest Trade Associations in the petroleum industry—National Petroleum Association, organized in 1902, and Western Petroleum Refiners Association, organized in 1912. (57)

July 21—Second US orbital flight.

July 22—The Salif No. 1, first exploratory oil test spudded in **Yemen** by **John W. Mecom** of Houston. The well is drilled to about 5000 feet and then abandoned as a dry hole. (50)

August 11—**Cosden Petrochemical Corporation,** wholly-owned subsidiary of Cosden Petroleum Corporation, incorporated in State of New York. (50)

August 20—**Alaska's** first natural gas system initiated with 3000 customers in Anchorage. The gas is transported to Anchorage through an 85-mile line from Kenai Peninsula. (Independent Monthly)

August—**Pennsylvania,** the oldest oil producing state in the union, has its first oil and gas conservation law. Previous oil and gas regulations had been administered under laws covering the mining industry. Under the new law an Oil and Gas Commission will be created. (Independent Monthly)

September 1—**Morocco** suspends all imports of petroleum from the franc currency zone. Importers told to find new sources of refinery products in Spain, Russia and the United Arab Republic. (45)

September 1—The first **septuple completion,** an oil and gas well, made by Texaco, Inc., at a depth of 7020-8553 feet in the Blessing field, Matagorda County, Texas. (50)

September 5—**Jerome J. O'Brien,** of Midland, Texas, appointed Director of the Office of Oil and Gas, by Secretary of the Interior Stewart L. Udall, begins duty October 2. (61)

September 25—Thai Oil Refinery signs contract with government of **Thailand** to build 40,000 b/d refinery—with support of Standard-Vacuum as well as of Caltex and Shell. (Oilgram)

September 27—Texas Railroad Commission, following the "Normanna Decision," issues second **"Normanna Order"** based on 100 per cent acreage allocation, but with a provision providing that a special allowable can be granted to a small tract (100 acres or less) after notice and hearing, and on proof that it is not economically feasible to drill the tract with the normal allowable, and further that there has been no opportunity to pool the tract with other acreage on a reasonable basis. (58)

October 1—**Standard Oil Company of California** acquires properties, assets, and business of Standard Oil Company, a Kentucky corporation. (50)

October 15—In **Libya,** the Esso crude oil pipeline from Zelten to Mersa El Brega opens. (45)

October—The Gulf Oil Corporation starts operation of the first major, one-operator **oil field automation system.** System permits the monitoring and testing of 148 oil wells in the Keystone field of Winkler County, West Texas, from a central office at Kermit, Texas. (Oil Daily)

November 16—The **Hakanaim gas field,** 20 miles east of Beer-Sheba, **Israel,** discovered. (45)

November 30—The Court of Appeals for the District of Columbia holds that the Federal Power Commission has authority under the Natural Gas Act to set interim standards for natural gas prices on an area basis, 24 FPC 818, **State of Wisconsin** v. **Federal Power Commission,** 292 F. 2d 753. (59)

November—The first **mobile pipe mill** ever built, to move along as the pipe is made, put into service in North Texas. The mill makes line pipe from coils of hot-rolled steel, moving along the right-of-way at the speed of pipe manufacture. The mill was invented by Clyde Vassar,

271

a mechanical engineer and pipe mill consultant, and was designed and built by **Mobile Pipe Line Corporation,** an affiliate of Gilmore Steel Corporation of San Francisco. (Oil and Gas Journal)

December—Union Oil Company of California is believed to have **Australia's** first commercial oil discovery in its No. 1 Moonie wildcat, 200 miles west of Brisbane in Queensland. The well flows 47-gravity oil at the rate of 1765 b/d, with 175 Mcf of gas, during a 58-minute test. (Oilgram)

December—**TBA Marketer** first published. (50)

Mid-America Pipeline Co. completes and puts into operation the **world's first major LPG pipeline,** extending over 2000 miles from New Mexico-Texas line to Minnesota, Wisconsin, Iowa, Nebraska and Kansas. (Gas Age)

Bolivian Gulf Corporation discovers what seems to be a major oil field at Caranda, 35 kilometers from Santa Cruz city, and gives hopes to the several oil companies engaged in Bolivia oil development to step up operations. (45)

Engineers and mathematicians, who designed the new Shell Chemical Company plant west of Belpre, Ohio, make first use of a **"Chemical Engineering Optimization System"** called Cheops. It makes the Shell plant the first computer-designed major chemical installation to be built in the United States. (Oil Daily)

Formosa grants concession rights to the **Asiatic-American, Inc.** (Oil and Gas Journal)

Continental Oil Company constructs the 533-mile **Glacier Pipe Line System** from Cut Bank, Montana, to Byron, Wyoming. (50)

Southern Natural Gas Company, in South Louisiana, completes what is believed to be the **first parallel dual string well** utilizing casing larger than $2\frac{7}{8}$-inch OD. Twin strings of $4\frac{1}{2}$-inch casing are set in single bore hole to about 12,400 feet. (**Twin Casing**) (World Oil)

Stockholders of **Standard Oil Company of Kentucky** and Standard Oil Company of California approve joining of two companies. (50)

Syrian Government forms a new petroleum authority to replace the one set up during the now defunct union with Egypt. (Oilgram)

The world's **first refrigerated LPG tanker** being built in Japan. The LPG ship will have a capacity of 180,000 barrels, about 17,000 tons of refrigerated LPG. (51)

Standard Oil Company of California reveals plans for construction of refinery on Kenai Peninsula in **Alaska.** (50

First **aluminum rig** designed for drilling through **Antarctic icecap** constructed by Southwestern Industrial Electronics, a division of Dresser Industries, for U. S. Army Snow and Ice Perma-Frost Establishment, Corps of Engineers. (Reynolds Metals Company)

The Argentine government approves a plan to construct a $70,000,000 petrochemical complex in **Argentina**. (Continental Oil Company)

Hydrocarbon Processing and Petroleum Refiner—succeeds Petroleum Refiner, which had been formed in 1942 as successor to Petroleum Refiner and Gasoline Manufacturer, organized Dceember, 1922. (Gulf Publishing Company)

Little Big Inch Division of Texas Eastern Transmission Corporation begins large-volume deliveries of butane to Midwest. (50)

Lone Star Gathering Company organized as a subsidiary of the Lone Star Gas Company. (50)

Syrian Government forms new petroleum authority to replace the one set up during now defunct union with Egypt. (Oilgram)

Thailand issues new conditions for exploration and development rights in that kingdom. (Oilgram)

1962

January 11—Mid-America Pipeline Company reaches an 89,200-barrel delivery this day through the world's first major LPG pipeline, thus setting a **record one-day LPG pipeline delivery,** from Texas to the Middle West. (Gas Age)

February 8—The Federal Power Commission establishes a **Natural Gas Advisory Council** composed of representatives of industry, regulatory, and consumer groups. This is the first advisory council ever established by the Commission. Its purpose is to advise and make recommendations to the FPC on matters concerning regulation of the natural gas industry. (59)

February 8—**Committee for Equitable Development of Texas Oil & Gas Resources** (CEDOT) organized at a meeting in Houston, Texas, for promotion of more equitable laws, rules and regulations in the production of oil and gas. C. W. Alcorn, chairman. (57)

February 14—Supreme Court of Texas holds that Railroad Commission proration order of the 1/3-2/3 type for the Port Acres Field is arbitrary, unreasonable, confiscatory in nature, and not supported by substantial evidence, basing its decision on the Normanna Case. Court defines the Rule of Capture to apply only to the liability of one owner of the soil to another adjoining owner in respect to damages for drainage, saying that due to the fugitive nature of hydrocarbons, that when captured and brought to the surface they belong to the owner of the soil to which they have flowed, irrespective of and without liability to the owner of the soil where they may have originally been in place. Court also strikes down the "Hawkins Case" dicta regarding the statutory right of the small tract owner to a well, by saying that this right is dependent on a showing of confiscation before a permit will issue. Language of the Court further indicates approval of a proration order of the type of the Second Normanna Order. Halbouty et al v. Railroad Commission of Texas. **Port Acres Decision.** (58)

February 28—**Vector Manufacturing Company** purchased by Schlumberger Well Surveying Corporation. (50)

March—The first stage of a 16-inch pipeline from Nahorkatiya to Numati, first pipeline in **India,** completed. The second stage, a 14-inch line from Numati to Barauni, started. Total pipeline 720 miles. (45)

April—Societe Nationale de Petroles d'Aquitaine drills 3500 feet in well in Aquitaine Basin, SW France in 482 hours with single diamond bit. A major **turbodrill** breakthrough. (64)

May—**Sunray Mid-Continent Oil Company** changes its name to **Sunray DX Oil Company.** (50)

June—Russia's **turbodrill** found to be highly successful in deviational drilling. (World Oil)

July 1—The **Somali** Republic approves the grant of a petroleum exploration permit to Somali Gulf Oil Company, covering approximately 32,000,000 acres in the southwestern portion of Somalia. The area is part of that formerly held and recently relinquished by Frobisher, Ltd., of Canada. (50)

August 1—The first **octuple completion,** an oil and gas well, made by Texaco, Inc., at a depth of 7092-7805 in the Francitas Field, Jackson County, Texas. (50)

Summer—An intensive investigation into **illegal directional drilling** to more favorable locations underground in the East Texas and some other fields carried on by the Railroad Commission and the Attorney General's office in Texas.

October 20—World's **first sea-going refinery** arrives at Port Brega, Libya. The 8000-barrel refinery is designed by Esso Research & Engineering and built by Chemical Construction Company, in Belgium. (50)

In **Colombia,** petrochemical plants opened at Cartagena and Barrancabermeja. (45)

The first refinery in **Switzerland** is under construction. Eight companies hold exploration concessions covering practically whole of Switzerland with exception of the typical mountainous regions. (45)

Oil discovered for first time in Eastern **Siberia** and **USSR** becomes second to United States in oil production, overtaking Venezuela. (AP)

Downhole television system developed by Shell Development Company Exploration and Production Research Division makes it possible to observe mechanical conditions and open-hole features in wells thousands of feet below earth's surface. (50)

Alphabetical Listing of Entries

Note: Numbers shown refer to years, not pages.

A

Abadan refinery, 1912
Abbott, General H. L., 1876
ABC transaction, 1940
Abegg & Reinhold Co., 1911
Abqaiq field, 1941, 1950
Absorption, 1899
Absorption method, 1913
Absorption method, suit re, 1917
Absorption process, 1901, 1911
Abu Dhabi, 1950, 1960
"Accommodation pipeline," 1866
Accounting, machine, 1926
Accounts, uniform system of, 1940
Accum, 1815
Acetone, 1927
Acetylene gas, 1899
Acetylene welding, 1920
Acidization of wells, 1939
Acidizing, 1895
Acids in oil, 1883
Acid-treated well, 1932
Acme Fishing Tool Co., 1896, 1900
Acoustic impedance log, 1948
Acreage factor, 1947
Activator, accelerator or oxygen log, 1958
Advertising gas appliances, 1859
Aero-Naph, 1909
Aero-plane, 1909
A. G. A. Testing Laboratory, 1925
Agassiz, Louis, 1848
Agha Jari field, 1937, 1941
Agua Dulce field, 1928
Agua Grande field, 1951
A. I. E. E., 1871
A. I. M. E., 1871, 1922, 1949, 1955
  Oil and Gas Division, 1913
Ain Hamra field, 1918, 1940
Ain Zeft field, 1956

Air compressor, 1902, (first portable) 1901
Air conditioning, 1928, (gas) 1935
Air injection, 1903
Air lift, 1864 (first), 1899, 1901
  for fluid, first, 1797
  the largest in oil industry history, 1959
Air mail, 1918
Air repressuring, 1915, 1930
Airy, George Bedell, 1855
Ajax Iron Works, 1877
Alabama, 1911, 1939, 1944, 1955
  first conservation legislation, 1911
  first field (Gilbertown), 1944
  member I.O.C.C., 1945, (See I.O.C., 1935)
Alaska, 1896, 1901, 1955, 1957, 1959, 1961
  first conservation legislation, 1955
  first field (Kenai Peninsula), 1957
  member I.O.C.C., 1957 (See I.O.C., 1935)
Albania, 1917
Albertite, 1820, 1857
Alchlor, 1915
Alchlor batch still, 1921
Alchlor treaters (first), 1928
Alcohol from ethylene, 1948
Alcohol, petrochemical, 1925
Algeria, 1949, 1956, 1961
  first major field (Edjele), 1956
Algiers, 1956
Algonquin Gas Transmission Company, 1949
Alkalbenzenes, 1856
Alkali residues, 1874
Alkylation process, 1942
All-concrete platform, 1950
Alleghany field, 1879
Allred, James V., 1935

275

All-steel standard rig including derrick, 1892
All-welded ocean-going tanker, 1937
All-welded pressure vessel, 1925
Alten Foundry & Machine Works, Inc., 1889
Aluminum airborne drilling rig, 1960
Aluminum gas line, 1950
Aluminum mast, 1954
Aluminum motor oil cans, 1957
Aluminum offshore drilling platforms, 1957
Aluminum paint, 1923
Aluminum pipe, first oil well drilled with, 1960
Aluminum pipeline, first permanent, 1961
Aluminum rig, 1961
Amarillo fold, 1903
Amarillo Oil Company, 1918
A-mast drilling rig, 1896
Amazon Basin, 1952
Amazon Case, 1935
Ambassador Oil Corporation, 1955
Ambronn, Richard, 1913, 1921
Amerada Petroleum Corporation, 1951
American Association of Oil Well Drilling Contractors, 1940
American Association of Petroleum Geologists (AAPG), 1917
American Association of Petroleum Landmen, 1955
American Bar Association, 1927, 1929
American Chain & Cable Co., Inc., 1846
American Federation of Labor, 1881
American Gas Association (AGA), 1906, 1918, 1927
American Gas Engineering Journal, 1917
American Gas Furnace Company, 1887
American Gas Institute, 1906
American Gas Journal, 1859, 1921, 1927, 1956
American Gas Light Association, 1874
American Gas Light Journal, 1859
American Gasol Co., 1911
American Gasoline Company, 1912, 1913, 1914
American Independent Oil Co., 1948, 1953
American Institute of Mining Engineers (See AIME), 1871
American Louisiana Pipe Line Co., 1955
American Meter Co., 1863, 1879
American Oil Co., 1890, 1954
American Oil Pipe Line Co., 1957
American Petrofina, Inc., 1956
American Petroleum Industries Committee, 1933
American Petroleum Institute (See A.P.I.), 1919
American Society of Lubrication Engineers, 1944
American Standard Code for pressure piping, 1935
American Stove Co., 1902, 1915

Ammonia, 1931
Amoco Fina, S. A., 1959
Amoco Italia, S. P. A., 1960
Amoco Trading Corporation, 1958
Amuay, Venezuela, 1951
Anahuac field, 1935
Analyzer, oil pool, 1946
Ancon, Ecuador, 1912
Andrews, E. B., 1861
Andrews, Samuel, 1863
Anesthesia, 1866
Anesthetic, 1861
Anglin, Tom, 1935
Anglo-American Oil Co., 1898, 1930
Anglo-American Oil Treaty, 1944, 1945
Anglo-American Petroleum Co., Ltd., 1888
Anglo-Caucasian Oil Co., Ltd., 1897
Anglo-Iranian Oil Co., Ltd., 1909, 1913, 1951
Anglo-Persian Oil Co., 1909, 1913, 1914
Anglo-Saxon Petroleum Co., Ltd., 1907, 1955
Angola, first field (Benfica), 1955
Antarctic icecap, 1961
Anthony F. Lucas Medal, 1937
Anticlinal theory, 1860, 1861, 1885
Anticlines, 1842, 1861
Origin of, 1917
Antioch, 400 B. C.
Anti-pollution law, 1863
Anti-trust charges dismissed, 1960
Anzell, Cyrus, 1870
Aoust, Virlet d', 1834
Apache Corporation, 1954
A.P.I., 1919, 1921, 1922, 1923, 1924, 1925, 1927, 1928, 1929, 1930, 1931, 1933, 1940, 1946, 1956, 1958
Committee on Public Affairs, 1933, 1958
Division of Development and Production Engineering, 1927, 1928
Division of Technical Services, 1950
Division of Transportation, 1946
Division of Finance and Accounting, 1956
Divisions of Production, Refining, Marketing and Statistics, 1930
O.I.C., 1950
Opposes regulation, 1925
Rejects federal and state regulation, 1924
Unitization Committee, 1923
A.P.I. Quarterly, 1931
A.P.I. Scale, 1921
A.P.I. Standards, 1922
Apco Oil Corporation, 1960
Apothecaries, 1830
Appliance Testing Laboratory, 1923
Aquagel, 1928
Arabian American Oil Co., 1948, 1950, 1957
Arabian Oil Company, Ltd., 1960
Aramco, 1936, 1944, 1948
Arapahoe Pipe Line Co., 1954
Arc light, 1879

Archbold, John D., 1911
Argand, Aime, 1782
Argand burner, 1809
Argentina, 1850, 1896, 1907, 1950,
  1960, 1961
  first field (Mendoza Province), 1887
  petroleum law, 1958
Arizona, 1927, 1951, 1954
  first conservation legislation, 1927
  first field (Boundary Butte, East),
    1954
  member I.O.C.C., 1955 (See I.O.C.,
    1935)
Arkansas, 1888, 1901, 1919, 1925, 1927,
  1939, 1943
  Board of Conservation, 1933
  first conservation legislation, 1917
  first field (El Dorado), 1921
  member I.O.C.C., 1941 (See I.O.C.,
    1935)
  Oil and Gas Agency—Oil and Gas
    Commission, 1939
  Railroad Commission, 1923
Arkansas Louisiana Gas Co., 1925, 1934
Armstrong, R. C., 1947
Arnabalde, Jarvis, 1864
Aromatic series, 1865
Artificial lighting, 1450 B.C.
Artificially produced compression
  waves, 1876
Aruba, 1932
A.S.C.E., 1871
Ashland Oil and Refining Co., 1924
Asia (central), 1942
Asiatic-American, Inc., 1961
Asiatic Petroleum Co., 1903, 1907
Asiatic Petroleum Corp., 1920
A.S.M.E., 1871
Asphalt 3000 B.C., 1838, 1851, 1870,
  1876
Asphalt Institute, the, 1919
Asphalt paving, 1869
Asphalts for road materials, 1936
Associated Oil Co., 1901, 1908, 1919,
  1920
Associated Petroleum Industries of
  Michigan, 1958
Associated Petroleum Industries of
  Pennsylvania, 1932
Associated Publishers, Inc., 1939
Association of Gas Appliances and
  Equipment Manufacturers, 1935
Association of Oil Well Servicing Con-
  tractors, 1956
Atlantic Refining Company, The, 1860,
  1899, 1959
Atlantic Refining Company, The, case,
  1959
Atlas Refining Co., 1885
Atlas, S. S., 1901-02
Atlas Supply Co., 1929
Atomic bomb, 1945
Atomic Energy Commission, 1950
Atomic reactor, 1942
Atomic submarine, 1954
Atshan field, 1958
Atwood, Luther, 1850, 1860

Aurora Gasoline Company, 1932
Aushutz-Kalmpfe, Dr. Hermann, 1915
Austral Oil Company, 1950
Australasian Petroleum Co., Pty. Ltd.,
  1958
Australia, 1892, 1900, 1908, 1924, 1953,
  1954, 1955, 1959
  first commercial oil well, 1961
Austria, 1900, 1934, 1937, 1940, 1952,
  1954, 1955
  expropriation, 1940
  first field (Goesting), 1934
  industry legislation, 1937
Austrian oil properties, 1957
Automated flow station, 1959
Automatic control, 1915
Automatic custody transfer, 1948, 1955
Automatic heat, 1917
Automatic ice maker, 1925
Automatic meter, 1886
Automatic stations, 1929
Automatic welding, 1957
Automation system (oil field), 1961
Automobile, 1887, 1905
Automobile accident, first, 1896
Automobile, electric, 1891
Automobile, first, 1893
Automobile, first transcontinental trip,
  1903
Automobile Gasoline Company, 1905
Automobile, Panhard-Levassor, 1886
Automobile, production of, quantity,
  1905
Automobile race, 1895
Automobile, Steamer type, 1901
Avant field, 1904
Aviation Division, first, 1928
Aviation gasoline, 1940
Aviation gasoline, combat, 1918
Avicenna, 1021-23
Axelson Manufacturing Co., 1892
Aztec Oil & Gas Company, 1950

B

Baash Ross Tool Co., 1919
Bachaquero field, 1930
Back-filler, 1917
Back pressure, effect of, 1921
Bahra, 1937
Bahrein, 1920, 1931
  first oil discovered, 1932
Bahrein Island, 1931, 1932
Bahrein Island Exploration License
  Granted, 1925
Bahrein option contract assumed by
  Standard of California, 1928
Bahrein Petroleum Co., 1929, 1930,
  1931
Baker Oil Tools, Inc., 1912, 1913
Baker, R. C., 1912
Baku, 967, 1272, 1863, 1876, 1886, 1887
  first field, 1872
Baku-Batum pipeline, 1905
Baku-Batum railroad, 1883
Balkassar oil field, 1937
Ball pump, 1950
Baltimore, Md., 1802, 1816, 1817, 1877

277

Baltimore refinery, 1867
Barbados tar, 1745, 1795
Barber, 1791
Barbers Hill field, 1918
Barco Concession, 1936, 1939
Bard, Thomas, 1865
Barge, first LP inland waterways, 1950
Barge, first seagoing LP gas, 1953
Barge, oil, 1861
Barker Creek Dome, 1945
Barkis, Bruce, 1939
Barnsdall and Abbott refinery, 1861
Barnsdall Industries, Inc., 1955
Barnsdall, T. N., 1905
Baroid, 1926
Baroid Division National Lead Co., 1928
Baroid Sales Company of California,
   1930
Baroid Sales Division, 1936
Barrel, crude oil, 1866
Barrel, 42-gallon, 1872
Barrett, Lynis T., 1859, 1866
Bartlett-Hayward Company, 1832
Base-burning stove, first in U.S., 1830
Bashet, E. A., 1902
Basin Dakota field, 1960
Basin Pipe Line System, 1947-48
Basrah Petroleum Co., Ltd., 1938,
   1948, 1952
Batavian Petroleum Co., 1907
Batching refined oils, 1900
Baton field, 1947
Battleship, gas heated, 1917
Baume, Antoine, 1768, 1864
Bay Marchand Blk. 2 field, 1949
Bayonne (N.J.) refinery, 1875, 1877
Bayou Pipe Line System, 1959
Beart, Robert, 1844
Beatty, Martin, 1819
Beauvais, Vincent d', 1250
Beaver Lodge field, 1951
Bedford, A. C., 1917
Bedford, E. T., 1911
Beecher, C. E., 1923
Belgium, 1862
Belt theory, 1870
Bemis-Shutts field, 1928
Benfica field, 1955
Bennett, E. O., 1928
Bentonite, 1929, 1930, 1935
Benz, Karl, 1885, 1886
Benzene, 1825, 1918, 1950
Benzol, 1927
Bergius, Friedrich, 1913
Bergstrom, G., 1914
Bessemer, Sir Henry, 1856
Betten, Michael and Thomas, 1742
Big Inch, 1942, 1946, 1947
Big Inch and Little Big Inch Pipelines,
   1947
Big Lake field, 1923, 1924, 1932, 1935
Big Moses, 1894
Big Piney field, 1938
Billion barrels, first, 1900
Biplane patented, 1866
Bissell, George H., 1854
Bit, tri-cone, 1908

Bitumen, 6000 B.C., 2000 B.C.
Bitumen defined, 1764
B. J. Service, Inc., 1905
Black Friday, 1869, 1873
Black, Sivalls & Bryson, Inc., 1946
Blanco Mesaverde field, 1927
Blanket dipping, 1807
Blanket leases, 1896
Bloomfield Company, 1872
Blowout preventer, 1903
Blowout preventer, pressure-type, 1931
Blowout preventer, ram-type, 1929
Bodine, A. J., 1948
Boeckh, Hugo V., 1917
Bolivar coastal fields, 1917
Bolivia, 1895, 1920, 1927, 1936, 1950,
   1953, 1956
   first production, 1925
   monopoly established, 1937
Bolivian Gulf Corp., 1961
Bolted steel lease tanks, 1913
Bolted tanks, 1918
Bond cement logging, 1961
Bonus payments, 1861
Booth, John Wilkes, 1864
Bopp, C. R., 1921, 1924
Bore hole deflection apparatus, 1908
Bore hole survey, 1884
Bore hole surveying, 1918, 1919
Bore holes, deviation in, 1906
Borg-Warner Corporation, 1955
Borneo, British, 1866
Borregas field, 1945
Boston, 1828, 1829
Boston Consolidated Gas Company,
   1906
Boston Gas Light Co., 1822
Bothwell, Canada, 1857
Botset, H. G., 1931, 1936
Bottom hole control, 1890
Bottom hole pressure, 1925
   first measured, 1928
Bottom hole pressure bomb, 1926, 1929,
   1930, 1931
Bottom hole steam power cylinder, 1878
Bouguer, Pierre, 1735, 1740
Boulton, Matthew, 1765
Bovaird Supply Co., 1879, 1923
Bowen Company of Texas, Inc., 1934
Bowlegs field, 1926
Boye, Martin Hans, 1889
Boyle, Robert, 1691
Brace, Julius, 1860
Bradford, Daisy, 1930
Bradford District Pennsylvania Oil
   Producers Association, 1931
Bradford field, 1865, 1871
Bradford Gas Co., 1880
Bradford Motor Works, 1911
Bransky, Dr. O. E., 1914
Brayton, George, 1872
Brazil, 1953
   first field (Lobato-Jonas), 1939
   industry legislation, 1938
Brea-Olinda field, 1889
Brewer, Dr. Francis B., 1854
Bridgeport field, 1906

278

Briggs, Robert, 1865
Bristol Natural Gas Corporation, 1931
Britain (see England)
Britain's Petroleum Act, 1934
British American Oil Company, 1906
British American Oil Company, Ltd., 1924
British Equatorial Oil Co., 1924
British Government, 1916
British Oil patented, 1742
British oil policy, 1913
British Petroleum, 1909
British Petroleum Canada, Ltd., 1955
British Petroleum Co. of Canada, Ltd., 1957
British Royal Commission, 1913
British tariff on oil, 1862
Broderick and Bascom Rope Co., 1876
Brooklyn Gas Light Co., 1825, 1873
Brooklyn Union Gas Co., 1952
Brotherhood of Oil and Gas Workers, International, 1899
Brown & Root, Inc., 1961
Brown, G. W., 1860
Brown Oil Tools, Inc., 1934
Brown, Samuel, 1823
Brunton, John, 1828
Brush, Charles Francis, 1879
Bubble towers, 1921
Buena Vista field, 1910
Buena Vista Hills, 1909
Buenos Aires, 1959
Buffalo, New York, 1871
Bulgaria, 1952
Bulk boat business, 1861
Bullet guns, small-diameter sectional, 1937
Bulletin, Statistical, API, 1920
Bunker oil as a fuel, 1934
Bunsen burner, 1855
Bunsen, Robert Wilhelm, 1855
Burbank field, 1920
Bureau of Mines, 1910, 1913, 1914, 1915, 1916, 1919, 1920, 1934, 1935
Burford case, 1943
Burgan, 1913
Burgan field, 1937, 1938
Burkburnett field, 1912
Burkburnett townsite, 1918
Burma, 1765, 1889
Burma Oil Company, 1907
Burner, aerated flame, 1868
Burner, Argand, 1809
Burner, circular, 1782
Burner with a brain, 1956
Burning oil, 1862
Burning spring, 1775
Burton cracking process, 1913
Burton, Dr. William M., 1889, 1913
Butadiene, 1863, 1910, 1941, 1943
Butane, 1866, 1935, 1943
Butane air-gas plant (first), 1928
Butane Propane News, 1939
Butane splitter, 1961
Butte Pipe Line Company, 1955
Butyl, 1937
Byles, Axtell J., 1928

Byron Jackson Division, Borg-Warner, 1955

C

Cabinet Committee, special, 1957
Cable tool and rotary device, combination, 1865
Cable tool drilling, 1910
Cabot, J. J., 1929
Cabot Shops, Inc., 1930
Cabrillo, Juan Rodriguez, 1543
Caddo field, 1905, 1907, 1910, 1911
Caddo Gas and Oil Company, 1911
Cairo, 1077
Caledonia, the, 1765
Calef, Robert, 1897
Calgary Petroleum, 1914
California, 1543, 1850, 1862, 1874, 1876, 1902, 1903, 1911, 1915, 1916, 1921, 1929, 1931, 1938, 1941, 1952
    first conservation legislation, 1903
    first field, (Rancho Ojai), 1866
    (See 1865)
California Gas Light and Fuel Company, 1886
California Ink Co., 1891
California Oilfields, Ltd., 1913
California Talc Co., 1928
Caliper log, 1938
Caliper, well bore, 1954
Calliou Island field, 1930
Calresearch, 1959
Caltex, 1936, 1953
Cambridge gas stove, 1869
Cameron Iron Works, Inc., 1920
Cameron West Block 192 field, 1954
Camco, Inc., 1946
Camrick district gas field, 1954
Canada, 1856, 1857, 1859, 1860, 1862, 1863, 1885, 1894, 1908, 1910, 1913, 1914, 1919
    first field (Oil Springs), 1862
    first service station, 1908
    (western), first oil, 1913
Canadian Chemical Co., Ltd., 1951
Canadian Gas Association, 1908
Canadian imports, 1959
Canadian Oil and Gas Co., 1906
Candles, 1853
Canfield, Isaac, 1876
Canol, 1944
Capillarity, 1911
Capillarity in the migration and accumulation of oil and gas, 1911
Capillary pressure measurements, 1943
Car, electric, 1901
Car, first American, 1892
Carbide and Carbon Chemicals Corp., 1914
Carbon black, 1864, 1885, 1919, 1923, 1943
Carbon black industry, 1948
Carbon oil, 1850
Carbon-ratio theory, 1915
Carboxyl groups, 1883
Cardium, S. S., 1901-02
Cardwell Manufacturing Co., 1926
Carey, Nathaniel, 1790

Caribbean Petroleum Co., 1914
Carll, John F., 1865, 1870, 1874, 1880
Carnegie, Andrew, 1861, 1884
Carothers, Walter Hume, 1937
Carranza, President, 1920
Carter Oil Co., 1877, 1893, 1915
Carthage Corporation, 1949
Carthage field, 1936
Casing, 1862, 1865
Casing cutter, jet-shaped charge, 1947
Casing, surface, first use of, 1806
Casing, longest string, 1937, 1961
Casing, parallel dual string, 1961
Casing perforator, glass jet, 1950
Casing, welded, 1935, 1937
Casinghead gasoline, 1915
Casinghead gasoline association, first, 1916
Casinghead gasoline explosion, 1915
Casinghead gasoline plant, 1909
Cast Iron Pipe Bureau, 1920
CATC, 1946
Cat Canyon field, 1908
Catalyst, 1916
Catalyst, fluidized, 1929
Catalytic cracking, 1937, 1951
Cathodic protection, 1824, 1928, 1930
Cattrell, Dr. F. C., 1908
Caucasian oil, 1735
Cavendish, Henry, 1784, 1797
Caving shale, 1928
Cedar Creek field, 1914
CEDOT, 1962
Ceiling heaters, 1884
Celanese Corp. of America, 1951
Cement, 1883, 1903, 1911, 1930, 1934
Cement field, 1918
Cement, gypsum, 1940
Cement, oil-proof, 1857
Cement-setting, 1882
Cementer, high-pressure-retrievable, 1938
Cementing, 1871, 1919
Cementing, mixer, jet, 1922
Cementing retainer, 1912
Cementing shoe, 1920
Cemoton log, 1958
Censers, 1450 B.C.
Census of the gas industry, 1880
Centennial, 1959
Central house heating, 1904
Central Oil Co., 1911
Central Refiners Association, 1875
Centralia oil boom, 1938
Centrifugal pumps, 1926
Cerro de la Pez, 1901
Certificate of Public Convenience and Necessity, 1942
Chakwal oil field, 1937
Champlin case, 1932
Champlin Oil & Refining Co., 1954
Channel process—carbon black, 1885
Chaplin-Fulton Company, 1884
Chapman, M. T., 1887, 1889
Charcoal absorption process, 1918, 1919
Chartier Valley Gas Company, 1883
Chase-Silica field, 1931

Chattak gas field, 1957
Chemical cutter and perforator, 1959
Chemical Engineering Optimization System, 1961
Chemistry of natural gas, 1892
Cherry Run, 1864
Chesebrough, Robert, 1865
Chevron Oil Co., 1953
Chicago, 1850, 1933
Chicago Bridge and Iron Company, 1933
Chicago Corp., 1940, 1945
Chicago fire, 1871
Chicago Gas Light and Coke Co., 1850
Chicago World's Fair, 1934
Chickering, Kenton, 1898
Chiksan Co., 1928
Chile, 1945, 1950, 1954, 1956
  first oil production (Manantiales), 1945
Chilkat Oil Company, 1901
China 206 B.C., 38 B.C., 1100, 1894, 1900, 1907, 1937, 1949
China, first oil—uncertain date, wells drilled as early as 1100, and wells dug for oil in 1900
Chinese, 900 B.C., 1500
Chinese Petroleum Corp., 1947
Chocolate Bayou field, 1939
Chokes, surface, 1913
Christmas Tree, first, 1901
Churchill, Winston, 1913
Cincinnati, 1837, 1881, 1909
C. I. O., 1935
Circular 32, 1912
Circulation, reverse method of, 1917
Cities Service Co., 1926, 1927
Citronelle field, 1955
Clark Bros. Co., 1880
Clark, Maurice B., 1863
Clark Oil and Refining Corporation, 1934
Clark, William C., 1897
Clay City field, 1937
Clayton, 1739
Clayton Act, 1914
Clegg, Samuel, 1809, 1815
Cleveland (Ohio), 1846
Clinton, DeWitt, 1814
Closed-cup testing apparatus, 1862
Coal gas, 1670, 1862
Coal gas generator, first internally fired, 1831
Coal oil, 1850
Coal Oil Johnny, 1864
Coal oil refinery converts to petroleum, 1861
Coalinga, East (Nose), field, 1938
Coalinga field, 1890, 1917
Coalinga, West, field, 1900
Coast to coast pipeline, first in western hemisphere, 1951
Cockfield, 1931
Code of Fair Competition, 1933
Cold waxing, 1905
Cole Committee, 1935
Coles Levee field, 1938

C P range, 1938
Cracked gasoline, 1936
Cracking, catalytic, 1921, 1937
Cracking, fluid catalytic, 1939, 1942, 1947
Cracking, gyro, 1932
Cracking, Holmes-Manley thermal, 1920
Cracking patent, 1860
Cracking plant, Cross, 1916
Cracking process, 1860, 1913
Cracking process, Dubbs, 1915
Cracking process, Jenkins, 1925
Cracking, thermal, 1910, 1916, 1920, 1931
Credit card, 1910
Creek Nation, 1894
Creole field, 1937, 1938
Creole Petroleum Corp., 1920, 1928, 1943
Crescent Petroleum Corp., 1919
Crimea, 1864
Croll and Richards, 1844
Crooked hole surveys, 1929
Crosby, Albert H., 1854
Crosby, Dr. Dixi, 1854
Cross-roller rock bit, 1913
Crossley, Samuel, 1825
Crown Central Petroleum Corporation, 1925
Crude oil, explosive power of, 1854
Crude oil stocks report, 1938
Crystallography System of, by Dana, 1837
Cuba, 1535, 1566
Cuba (N.Y.), 1627, 1670
Cuban Communist Government, 1960
Cubic foot bottle, 1871
Cudahy, Michael, 1894, 1897
Cugnot, Nicholas Joseph, 1769
Cullen, Hugh Roy, 1938
Cullinan, J. S., 1898, 1916
Cumberland & Allegheny Gas Co., 1949
Cuming, F., 1807
Curme, Dr. G. O., 1914
Curtis well, 1860
Curzon, Lord, 1918, 1921
Cushing field, 1912, 1913
Cushing-Chicago System, 1951-53
Cushing-Jal Pipeline, 1949
Cushing-Wood River Pipeline, 1949
Cutting oil, 1916
Cuyama, South field, 1949
Cycling operations, 1935
Cycling plant, 1936 (first), 1938
Cycloversion process, 1943
Czechoslovakia, 1914

D

Daimler, Gottlieb, 1885, 1887
Daisy Bradford, 1930
Dakota Territory, 1884
Dallas, Texas, 1910
Dallas Dome field, 1884
Dalton, John, 1809
Dammam field, 1938, 1939
Dana, James D., 1837, 1862
Danciger case, 1932

Daniel Guggenheim School of Aeronautics, 1935
Daniels, Josephus, 1920
Danish-American Prospecting Company, 1938
D'Arcy Exploration Co., Ltd., 1935
D'Arcy, William Knox, 1901, 1904, 1908
D'Arcy System, 1933
Darst Creek field, 1929
da Vinci, Leonardo, 1500
Davy, Sir Humphry, 1824
Day, David T., 1909
Day, V. T., 1911
Dayton Ohio Gas Company, 1848
DC-3, 1936
DDT, 1943
Dearborn Chemical Company, 1887
Decker, Harry R., 1905, 1906
Deed, first for oil purposes, 1854
Deep Lake field, 1952
Deep Rock Oil Corp., 1951
Deep salt well, 1854, 1858
Deep South Oil Co. of Texas case, 1957
Deep Well Drilling, 1921
Deeper Oriskany sands, 1936
Deepest hole drilled with air, 1959
Deepest tests east of the Mississippi, 1941
Deepest well (see Well, deepest)
DeGolyer, E., 1910, 1914
DeGolyer and MacNaughton, 1914
Delhi-Taylor Oil Corporation, 1955
Delta Pipeline, 1959
Demand forecasts, 1930
De Mares Concession, 1920, 1925
Dement, Jack, 1945
Democratic Platform, 1920
Denmark, industry legislation, 1932
Densilog, 1950
Densmore, Amos, 1865
Denver, 1928
Denver-Julesberg Basin, 1949
Denver Producing and Refining Company, 1948
Department of Commerce, 1925
Depletion, 1909, 1913, 1916, 1918, 1926, 1951
Depletion for oil properties first becomes effective, 1913
Depletion, roll call votes on, 1958
Depth of compensation, 1855
Depth record, 1954
Derrick, 1825
Derrick, double deck, 1906
Derrick, first steel, 1892
Derrick man's escape, 1905
Descriptions of formation, 1909
Desk and Derrick Clubs, Association of, 1949
DeSoto Expedition, 1543
Destructive distillation, 1781, 1812
Deterding, H. W. A., 1896
Detergent motor oil, first, 1936
Detroit, 1936, 1955
Detroit case, 1955
Detroit served with natural gas, 1889

Deviation in bore holes, 1906
Deviational holes, 1934
Devonian Gas & Oil Co. of Delaware, 1953
Dewaxing, 1880
Dewey, Admiral George, 1911
Dhulian Oil field, 1937
Dhulian-Wah gas pipeline, 1952
Diamond core drill, 1870, 1918, 1922
Diamond core drilling, 1919
Diamond coring, 1863, 1919
Diamond drill, 1869
Diesel, Dr. Rudolph, 1892, 1894
Diesel engine, 1898
Diesel-engined submarine, 1903
Diesel fuels, 1950
Diesel power, 1912
Digboi field, 1888, 1948
Dinsmore, James D., 1888, 1890
Dipmeter, continuous physical, 1951
Dipmeter, microfocused, 1955
Dipmeter, microlaterolog continuous, 1956
Dipmeter, resistivity, 1947
Dipmeter, S. P., 1941
Directional drilling equipment, 1930
Directional drilling, illegal in East Texas field, 1950, 1961, 1962
Disbrow, L., 1825, 1830
Discovery allowables, 1944
Dissolution, 1906
Dissolution of Standard Oil Company, 1911
Distillate, 1938
Distillates, 1863
Distillation, 1850, 1858
Distillation, continuous, 1883, 1899, 1910
Distillation, destructive (see destructive distillation)
Distillation of boghead coal, 1850
Distillation of coal, 1739
Distillation of petroleum, 1855
Distillation process, pressure, 1890
Distillation, vacuum, 1867
Distilling coal oil, 1859
Distilling hydrocarbon oils, 1870
Distilling petroleum, 1867
Distribuidora de Petroleos Mexicanos, 1938
Dixie Gulf Gas Co., 1927
Dixie Oil Company, 1919, 1931
Doherty, H. L., 1923, 1937
Doheny and Canfield, 1901
Dominguez field, 1923
Dominican Republic, 1904, 1939, 1960
first production, 1939
Douglas Oil Co., 1950
Dow, D. B., 1924
Dowell, Inc., 1932
Downer Kerosene Oil Co., 1857, 1858
Downer plant, 1863
Downer, Samuel, 1861
Downhole camera, 1949
Downhole drilling, 1947
Downhole television, 1962
Downing, W. M., 1935

Downs, Samuel, 1863
Dowsing, 1865
Drake, Col. Edwin L., 1854, 1859, 1873, 1880
Drake, Ruben, 1838
Drake well, 1859
Drake Well Memorial Park, 1931
Drawworks, unitized, 1932
Dresser couplings, 1890
Dresser-Ideco Co., 1920
Dresser Manufacturing Co., 1880
Dresser, S. R., 1887
Drift indicator, 1928
Drill collars, 1934
Drill pipe, internal upset, 1911
Drill stem test, 1927
Drilling barge, submersible, 1931, 1934
Drilling control panel, 1934
Drilling equipment, field laboratory, 1948
Drilling and Exploration Company, Inc., 1929
Drilling fluids, 1887, 1913
Drilling jars patented, 1841
Drilling machine, 1830
Drilling machine, portable, 1875
Drilling Magazine, 1939
Drilling mast, cantilever type, 1937
Drilling mud, 1934
Drilling mud, oil base, 1942
Drilling rig, balanced rotary, 1933
Drilling rig, offshore, 1869
Drilling rig, pneumatic rotary, 1932
Drilling rigs, self propelled, 1888
Drilling speed record, world, 1961
Drilling-time record, 1912
Drills, undercutting, 1858
Driltrol, 1950
Driltrol drillable wing stabilizer, 1949
Driscose, 1946
Droojba Gusher, 1887
Drought-stricken communities, 1934
Dry hole, first, 1860
"D" slide valve, 1799
Dual completion, 1913 (first), 1935
Dual completion, world's deepest gas-condensate, 1960
Dubbs Cracking Process, 1915
Duck Creek, 1814
Dukhan field, 1940
Dumble, Dr. E. T., 1919
Dundonald, Earl of, 1781
Dunn, I. L., 1903, 1911
Duralde field, 1949
Duryea Bros., 1892
Dyer Resolution, 1920
Dynagraph, 1936
Dynamite, 1866
Dynamometer, 1921
E
Earlsboro field, 1926
Earth density, 1774, 1797
Earth temperature, 1740
Earthen storage, first, 1861
Earth's core, 1896
Earth's second layer, 1961
Eason Oil Company, 1929

283

East Ohio case, 1950
East Ohio Gas Company, 1898, 1944
East Pakistan, 1957
East Texas field, directional drilling
  investigation, 1962
East Texas field discovered, 1930
East Texas field, martial law, 1931,
  1932
East Texas field, pressure maintenance
  begun, 1938
East Texas field, proration of, first,
  1931
East Texas field, proration order up-
  held, 1933
East Texas Salt Water Disposal Co.,
  1938, 1942
Eastern and General Syndicate Ltd.,
  1920
  transfers Kuwait concession to Gulf,
  1933
Eastman, John H., 1930, 1934
Eastman Oil Well Survey Co., 1930
Eaton, Amos, 1818
Eaton, John, 1862
Ebano-Panuco field, 1901
Echometer, 1936
Ecuador, 1912
  first production (Ancon), 1912
Edeleanu, Dr. L., 1907
Edeleanu plant, 1911
Edeleanu process, 1926
Edgar, Dr. Graham, 1930
Edison, Thomas Alva, 1879
Edjele-La Skhirra pipe line, 1958
Edson, Fanny Carter, 1924
Edward III, 1327-77
Edwards lime trend, 1922
Egypt, 1887, 1956
  first field (Gemsah), 1909
Egyptians, 4000 B. C., 3000 B. C.
Eight-hour day, 1915, 1917
Eilerts and Schellhardt, 1938
Eisenhower, President, 1957
El Dorado field (Ark.), 1921
El Dorado field (Kans.), 1915
Electra field, 1911, 1915
Electric centrifugal packages, 1923
Electric log operations expanding, 1932
Electric logging, 1927, 1930, 1931
Electric logs (see logs, electric), 1927
Electric power for pipeline pump
  stations, 1927
Electric welded pipeline, 1933
Electric welder, 1917
Electric welding, 1923
Electrical coring, 1928
Electrical exploration, 1920
Electrical log (first), 1927
  (first in western hemisphere), 1929
  (first in U.S.), 1929
Electrical potentials, 1830
Electrical prospecting, 1900
Electricity, for pumping and treating,
  1919
Electrodrill, 1866
Electrodrill Corporation, 1947

Elizabethtown Consolidated Gas Com-
  pany, 1855
Elk Basin field, 1915, 1916
Elk Hills, 1909, 1923, 1925
Elk Hills field, 1919
Elk Hills Naval Reserve, 1944
Elk Hills Oil Scandal, 1927
Elliot, Pat, 1925
Ellis, Carlton, 1916
Ellisor, Alva C., 1919
El Paso Natural Gas Co., 1928, 1945,
  1946, 1950
El Plan field, 1931
Elwood field, 1928
Emerson, E. O., 1886
Eminent Domain, right of, 1872, 1885
Emperor Devonian field, 1955
Empire State Petroleum Association,
  1941
Employee representation, 1918
Empresa Nacional del Petroleo, 1950
Emsco Manufacturing Co., 1923
End use of gas, 1961
Engine, air-gas, 1872
Engine, atmospheric, 1705, 1867
Engine, compressor, 1929
Engine, four-stroke cycle, 1862
Engine, gas, 1794 (first), 1863
Engine, gas for pumping wells, 1894
Engine, internal combustion, 1799,
  1823, 1876, 1887, 1892, 1894, 1895,
  1900
Engine, petroleum, 1870
Engine, portable, 1861
Engine, semi-Diesel, 1902
Engine, slow-speed gas, 1894
Engine, spark-ignited turbo charged
  gas, 1934
Engine, twin cylinder, 1926
Engine, vapor, 1885
Engineer, petroleum (see Petroleum
  engineer), 1915
Engineering Department, 1913
Engineers, U.S. Naval Board of, 1864
Engines for oil well drilling, 1889
England, 1659, 1899, 1911, 1920, 1951
  first oil production (Eakring), 1939
  first producing oil well, 1919
  industry legislation (Britain), 1934
Engler, C., 1897, 1908
Enjay Company, Inc., 1960
Enniskillen, 1857
Eotvos, Baron Roland von, 1888, 1895,
  1896, 1901, 1902
Equalizer valve, 1931
Equipotential mapping, 1900, 1914
Equipotential, two-electrode, 1912
Equitable Gas Company, 1884, 1889
Equity Oil Company, 1948
Erath field, 1940
Esso A.G., 1890
Esso, name adopted, 1926
Esso Nederland N. V., 1960
Esso Research and Engineering Com-
  pany, 1919
Esso Standard Libya, Inc., 1958
Esso Standard Oil Co., 1927

Ethyl, 1923
Ethyl Corp., 1924
Ethylbenzene, 1957
Ethylbenzene separation process, 1960
Ethylene, 1914, 1953
Ethylene, direct hydration of, 1948
Eumont gas area, 1956
Eunice-Monument field, 1929
Europe, first large-diameter pipe line in, 1958
European Emergency Oil Committee, 1957
Evaporation, 1919, 1953
Executive Order No. 9919, 1948
Executive reservists, 1960
Exner-Dodge, Inc., 1913
Exploitation engineers, 1916
Exploration, indirect by hydrochemical methods, 1937
Exploratory drilling, record established, 1953
Export control, 1947
Exports, 1878, 1885, 1939

F

Facts and Figures, 1937
Failing, Geo. E., Co., 1931
Fair field price, 1945, 1955
Fair practice, 1929
Fairport field, 1923
Falcon Seaboard Drilling Company, 1935, 1939
Fall, Albert B., 1923, 1929
Falls City field (Neb.), 1939
Fan shooting, 1926
Fanshier, Keith, 1951
Faraday, 1825
Faraday gas refrigerator, 1932
Farben, I. G., 1927
Farben oil-refining process, 1929
Farish, W. S., 1933
Fasenmeyer, Andrew, 1904
Fauvelle, M., 1845
Federal control proposed, 1916
Federal control unwarranted, 1940
Federal controls of the oil industry, 1934
Federal excise tax, 1928
Federal legislation, 1929
Federal Oil Conservation Board, 1924, 1930
Federal Power Commission (FPC), 1940, 1942, 1944, 1945, 1947, 1948, 1949, 1950, 1953, 1955, 1957, 1958, 1961
(FPC), statement of general policy No. 61-1, 1960
Federal regulation of pipelines as common carriers, 1906
Federal Tender Committee, 1935
Federal Trade Commission Act, 1914
Fermi, Enrico, 1942
Ferry Lake, La., 1910
Fessenden, Reginald, 1914
Field, dually pressure-maintained and unitized, 1949
Field, first unitized under compulsory law, 1947

Fifty-fifty agreement, first in Middle East, 1950
Fifty-fifty law, first, 1943
Fighting fires, 1947
Filibuster, 1953
Filling station, first drive-in (see also service station), 1905
Filter press, 1936
Finland, 1957
Fire extinguisher, 1914
Fire fighting, 1911
Fire, first oil well, 1859
Fire flood, 1920
Fires at wells, 1915
First commercial gas well west of the Mississippi, 1882
First Exploitation Company formed, 1903
First oil company to market in all the states, 1928
Fitch, John, 1786
Fitts field, 1932, 1933
Five Civilized Indian Tribes, 1947
Five-spot water flood, 1927
Flagler, H. M., 1867, 1911
Flank production, salt dome, first, 1922
Flare Gas case, 1947
Flash point, 1862
Flit, 1923
Float collar, 1922
Float plug, 1917
Float shoe, 1922
Flood, pioneer high-pressure, 1943
Florence Oil and Refining Co., 1892
Florida, first conservation legislation, 1945
  first field (Sunniland), 1943
  member I.O.O.C., 1945 (see I.O.C., 1935)
Flow bean, 1933
Flowing well, first, 1861
Flowing well, first large, 1861
Fluid drive units, 1954
Fluid flow, 1926
Fluid, formula for computing flow, 1914
Fluids, properties of reservoir, 1924
Fluor Corp., 1961
Fluorescence of oils, 1936, 1945
Fohs Oil Company, 1946
Fontaine Ardente, 102 B.C., 144 B.C.
Footage basis contract, 1939
Foraminifera, 1914
Forbes, J. D., 1841
Forcing air through oil sand, 1911
Ford, Henry, 1896, 1902
Ford, Model T, 1908
Forecast, supply and demand, 1931
Forecaster, first doom, 1874
Forecasts, monthly supply and demand, 1933
Foreign Petroleum Supply Committee, 1951
Forest Oil Corporation, 1924
Formation fluid tester, 1955
Formosa, 1877, 1961
Fort Worth, Texas, 1910
Forty-two-gallon barrel, 1872, 1926

285

Gas, natural (see Natural gas)
Gas-oil ratios, 1923, 1924
Gas-oil ratios control, 1924
Gas porosimeter, 1933
Gas power, first patent, 1801
Gas production in Texas, 1872
Gas pumping, 1880
Gas, purifying manufactured, 1870
Gas range, 1879
Gas range designed especially for hotel and restaurant purposes, first, 1879
Gas ranges, standard specifications, 1915
Gas refrigerator, 1887, 1925
Gas regulation statute, 1935
Gas regulator, 1825, 1859, 1860
Gas repressuring, 1926
Gas steam radiator, 1897
Gas stopper, 1897
Gas storage fields, 1951
Gas stove, 1825, 1864, 1877
Gas supply (Texas), first, 1907
Gas survey method of prospecting, 1929
Gas system, first municipal in U . S., 1834
Gas technology short course, 1946
Gas terminal and distribution center (first large scale LPG), 1948
Gas to heat swimming pools, 1908
Gas transported, 1884
Gas turbine engine, first, 1949
Gas turbine power plant, first, 1961
Gas waste, 1931
Gas waste condemned, 1899
Gas, waste of, 1927
Gas water heater, 1885, 1889, 1897
Gas well, largest, 1919
Gas well, largest in world, 1893
Gases, unsaturated, 1825
Gasholder, 1833, 1861, 1924
Gasholder, first large steel, 1888
Gasholder, largest, 1906
Gasholder, telescopic, 1833
Gasless Sundays, 1918
Gasoline, 1915, 1929
Gasoline buggy, 1893
Gasoline, casinghead, 1909
Gasoline company, first (Texaco), 1908
Gasoline, cracked, 1936
Gasoline, demand for exceeds that of kerosene, 1911
Gasoline, first commercial use of 100-octane, 1935
Gasoline from oil shale, 1934
Gasoline marketing, 1929
Gasoline motor, 1879
Gasoline, 100-octane, 1935
Gasoline plant, first commercial, 1908
Gasoline Retailer, The, 1930
Gasoline, solid, 1935
Gasoline station (see service station)
Gasoline, super-premium, 1955
Gasoline, survey of aviation, 1940
Gasoline truck, first, 1900
Gasometer, 1781
Gauge, liquid level, 1954

Gauges, automatic tank, 1920
Gauges, continuously-recording pressure, 1934
Gauges, recording pressure, 1887
Gellibrand, 1628
Gemsa field, 1909
General American Oil Company of Texas, 1936
General Crude Oil Co., 1924
General Motors Corp., 1923
General Petroleum Co., 1902
General Petroleum Corp., 1959
Geochemical prospecting, 1920, 1933, 1935
Geograph, 1955
Geological Department, 1908
Geological Survey, 1830, 1836, 1864
Geological Survey, U.S., 1882, 1909, 1949
Geologist in charge, 1911
Geologists, 1860, 1898
Geologists, Petroleum, meeting of, 1916
Geologists, resident, 1907, 1912
Geologists, subsurface, 1913
Geolograph, 1937
Geology, 1830, 1862, 1916
Geology, principles of, 1830
Geophone, first, 1849
Geophysical discovery, 1924 (first), 1926
Geophysical exploration, first application of, 1825
Geophysical, first survey of an oil field, 1922
Geophysical paper, first, 1269
Geophysical Research Corporation, 1925, 1934
Geophysical surveys, first offshore, 1933
Geophysics, 1549
Georgia, 1946
    associate member I.O.C.C., 1946 (See I.O.C., 1935)
    conservation legislation, 1945
Geothermal gradients, 1912
German pipeline, 1888
German Reich Law, 1934
Germany, 1827, 1851, 1858, 1861, 1888, 1910, 1950
    first production (Nienhagen-Hanigsen field), 1860
    first refinery, 1862
    industry legislation (German Code), 1934
Gesanne, 1740
Gesner, Abraham, 1820, 1846, 1853, 1856
Getty Oil Company, 1928
Ghawar field, 1948
Gilbert, W. E., 1936
Gilbert, William, 1580
Gilbertown field, 1944
Glacier Pipe Line System, 1961
Gladys City Oil, Gas and Manufacturing Co., 1892
Glass manufacture, 1884
Glavis, L. R., 1934
Glenn Pool, 1905

Glenn Pool to Baton Rouge oil pipe-
line, 1909
Globe Fuel Products, Inc., 1960
Glycerine plant, synthetic, 1948
Glycol injection, 1951
Goddard, Robert Hutchins, 1926
Goesting field, 1934
Golden Lane, 1922, 1924
Golden trend, 1954
Goldsmith field, 1934
Goodwin, W. & Co., 1879
Goose Creek field, 1908, 1919
Gosline, J. E., 1936
Gott, H. P., Manufacturing Co., 1916
Gould, Charles N., 1918
Grand slam logging, 1960
Grande Ecaille, 1931
Graphic log strips, 1907
Grass Creek field, 1914
Gravel packing, 1924
Gravitational constant, 1889
Gravity, 1672, 1901
Gravity basis, 1904
Gravity measurement, 1887
Gravity meter (first), 1899
Gravity observations, 1735
Gravity, price based on, 1868
Gravity survey of salt dome (first),
1917
Gray, E. B., 1894
Grease coatings, 1916
Great American Well, 1829
Great Britain (see also England), 1904
Great Depression, 1929
Great Lakes Pipe Line Co., 1934
Great Western Drilling Co., 1952
Great White Way, 1828
Greek fire, 750
Greeks, 320 B.C.
Greta field, 1933
Griswold, E. H., 1929
Guanoco field, 1913
Guatemala, 1956, 1959
Guayaguayare field, 1902
Guffey and Galey, 1901, 1903
Guffey, J. M., Petroleum Co., 1901
Guffey oil and gas well workers, 1905
Gulbenkian, Calouste S., 1928
Gulf Interstate Gas Company, 1954
Gulf Oil Corp., 1905, 1907, 1913, 1959
Gulf Pipe Line Co., 1907
Gulf Refining Co. of Texas, 1901
Gulf Research and Development Com-
pany, 1947
Gulf States Tube Corporation, 1961
Gun perforating, 1903, 1926, 1932
Gunning, T. B., 1864
Gus II, Mr. 1957
Gusher, 1891
Gwinville field, 1944
Gwynne-Harris water-gas apparatus,
1873
Gypsum cement, 1940
Gypsy Oil Co., 1907, 1919, 1935
Gyro cracking process, 1932
Gyroscopic inclinometer, 1929

H

Haft Kel field, 1928
Hakanaim gas field, 1961
Halifax, 1843
Hall, James, 1943
Halliburton Co., 1920
Halliburton, Erle P., 1919, 1926
Hamburg-American Line, 1902
Hamill Brothers, 1913
Hamill, Curtis G., 1913
Hamilton, W. T., 1908
Haquet, B., 1788
Harding, President, 1921
Hardison, W. L., 1891
Harkness, S. V., 1867
Harlem Gas Light Co., 1855
Harth, Phillip E., 1935
Hasa (Arabia) concession granted,
1923
Haseman, Dr. W. P., 1917, 1921
Hassi-Messaoud field, 1956
Hastings field, 1934
Haven, Alomo, 1873
Hawkins case, 1946
Hawkins field, 1940
Hayes, C. W., 1903
Haymaker well, 1878, 1884
Haynesville field, 1921
Hayward, John T., 1937
H. C. Price Company, 1921
H. C. Smith Oil Tool Company, 1936
Heald, K. C., 1930
Healde, T., 1769
Healdton field, 1913
Heat of the earth, 1934
Heater, gas fired unit, 1928
Heater, improved double super, 1888
Heathfield, 1895
Heating, central home, 1919
Heating of buildings, 1832
Heavier-than-air flight, first, 1903
Hecker, Joseph, 1810
Hecker, O., 1900
Heggem, A. G., 1915
Heggem, A. G. and J. A. Pollard, 1912
Heletz-Brur field, 1955
Helicopters, 1960
Helium, 1917, 1918, 1927, 1929
identified, 1868
source, 1907
Hell, C. and E. Medinger, 1874
Helmert, 1901
Heltzel, W. G., 1926
Hendricks field, 1926, 1928
Henfrey, Benjamin, 1802, 1803
Henry, J. T., 1873
Hepburn Act, 1906, 1913, 1914
Hequenbourg, C. E., 1899
Herodotus, 450 B.C.
Herscher Dome, 1952
Hewitt field, 1919
Heyser field, 1936
Heywood, Scott, 1901
HF Alkylation Process, 1942
Higashiyama, Japan, 1893
Higgins, Pattillo, 1892, 1901, 1918

High-detergency motor oil, 1948
High-pressure long distance oil pipe
line, first, 1891
High-pressure manufactured gas trans-
mission main, first, 1902
High-pressure oil saver, 1921
Highway aid, 1916, 1952, 1954, 1956
Hildreth, S. P., 1833
Hill, H. B., 1930
Hill and Sutton, 1928
Hillman-Kelley, 1922
Hilltop well, first, 1864
Hinshaw Amendment, 1959
History of Petroleum, 1873
History of the Standard Oil Company,
1902
Hobbs field, 1928
Hodograph, 1913
Hogback field, 1922
Holland, 1923, 1942, 1944, 1947, 1950,
1960
first field (Schoonebeek), 1944
Holmes, Major Frank, 1920
Holmes-Manley thermal cracking,
1920
Home service, 1908
Hoover, President, 1929
Hope Natural Gas Co., 1898, 1906
case, 1944
Hopper Machine Works, Inc., 1918
Horseless vehicle, 1836
sale of, 1889
Horsepower, 1765
Hortonsphere, 1925
Horvitz, Dr. Leo, 1935
Hot Oil, 1934
Hot Oil Act, 1935
Hot Oil Statute (Texas), 1935
Houdry, Eugene J., 1937
Houdry Process, 1936
Houston, 1860
Houston Natural Gas Corp., 1925,
1926
Houston Oil Company of Texas, 1901
Houston Oil Field Material Co., Inc.,
1928
Houston Pipe Line Company, 1925
H. & T. C. R. R., 1901
Howard, F. A., 1923
Howard Glasscock field, 1925
Howard Smith Company, 1916
Howarth, John, 1864
Howcott, H. A. W., 1926
Hudson River, pipe line crossing, 1950
Hughes, Howard R., 1908
Hughes rock bit, 1908
Hughes Tool Company, 1909, 1910
Hugoton field, 1922, 1949
Hull-Merchant field, 1918
Humanson, Granville A., 1913
Humble field, 1905
Humble Oil Co., 1911
Humble Oil & Refining Co., 1911,
1917, 1919, 1924, 1933, 1959, 1961
Humboldt, Alexander, 1804
Humboldt refinery, 1862
Humphreys Corporation, 1931

Hunas, Prof. Dr. G. Ch. K., 1858
Hungary, 1937
Hunt, H. L., 1944
Hunt Oil Company, 1936
Hunt, T. Sperry, 1860, 1861
Hunt Tool Company, 1931
Huntington field, 1920, 1927
Husky Oil Company, 1938
Hutchinson, J. L., 1860
Hutton, Charles, 1774
Hutton, Dr. James, 1795
Huyghens, Christian, 1657
Hyde Park Gas Co., 1871
Hydraulic fracturing process, 1949
Hydraulic torque converter, 1939
Hydrocarbon gases, 1809
Hydrocarbon oils, treating, 1865
Hydrocarbon Processing and Petroleum
Refiner, 1961
Hydrochemical exploration, 1937
Hydrofluoric acid alkylate, 1942
Hydroforming, 1929, 1940
Hydrofracing, 1949
Hydrogen bomb, 1952
Hydrogen peroxide, 1909
Hydrogen sulphide and sulphur
problem, 1885
Hydrogenation, 1926, 1937
Hydrolene, 1904
Hydrometer, 1864
Hydrometer, oil, devised, 1768

I

Ickes, Harold L., 1933, 1934
Idaho, 1931
associate member I.O.C.C., 1960
(See I.O.C., 1935)
first conservation legislation, 1931
Ideco, 1910
Illing, V. C., 1933
Illinois, 1882, 1904, 1911, 1914, 1938,
1941
first conservation legislation, 1905
first field (Litchfield), 1886
member I.O.C.C., 1935 (See I.O.C.,
1935)
Illinois Coal Basin, 1937
Illinois Oil & Gas Association, 1951
Illinois Pipe Line Company, 1914
Illuminant, 100
Illuminating gas, 1865
Illuminating oil, 1613, 1846
Imperial Oil Company, Ltd., 1880,
1898, 1932
Import program, mandatory, 1959
Import program, voluntary control,
1957
Imports, 1958
Imports Investigation, 1957
Imports, Tariff on, 1930
Incandescent burner, 1897
Incandescent lamp, 1879
Inclination, measuring of, 1874
Income Tax, Federal, 1913
Independent Natural Gas Association
of America, 1944

Independent Oil and Gas Association of West Virginia, 1959
Independent Petroleum Association of America (IPAA), 1929, 1930
Independent Producers and Royalty Owners Association of New Mexico, 1957
Independent Refiners Association of America, 1952
India, 1886, 1888, 1893, 1948, 1959, 1962
    first oil production (Digboi), 1888
India Oil Ltd., 1959
Indian Oil Co., 1959
Indian Refineries, Ltd., 1958
Indian Territory, 1884 (see also Oklahoma)
Indian Territory Illuminating Oil Co., 1926
Indian tribal leasing authorized, 1891
Indiana, 1862, 1868, 1871, 1888, 1891, 1893, 1919, 1947
    first conservation legislation, 1891
    first field (Terre Haute), 1888
    member I.O.C.C., 1947, (See I.O.C., 1935)
    Oil and Gas Agency—Department of Conservation, 1919
Indiana Oil Purchasing Co., 1930
Indonesia, 1885, 1893
    first oil production, 1885
Induction-Electric log Combination, 1955
Induction-Laterolog-8 Combination, 1960
Induction log, deep-focused, 1959
Induction logging, 1946, 1948
Industrial use of natural gas, first, 1868
Infantas field, 1918
Inflammable gas, 1791
Inglewood field, 1924
Injection project, 1927
In-line blender, electronic, 1961
In-line blender, first electronic gasoline, 1960
In-line blending systems, 1955
In-line hot mill, 1961
Inorganic theory, 1804, 1834, 1879
In-situ combustion, 1923
Inspector of Gas Meters & Illuminating Gas, 1861
Installment plan, 1905
Intangible drilling and development costs, 1954
Interdepartmental Petroleum Committee, 1946
Internal combustion engine, 1867 (See engine, internal combustion)
Internal combustion engine vehicle, 1885
International Association of Oil Field, Gas Well & Refinery Workers, 1918
International Consortium, 1954
International Labor Organization, 1947

International Oil and Gas Educational Center, 1960
International Oil Scouts Association, 1924
International Petroleum Commission, 1945
International Petroleum Company, 1914
International Petroleum Exposition, 1923
International Petroleum Register, 1918
International Pipe Lines Co., 1950
Interstate Commerce Act, 1887
Interstate Commerce Commission (ICC), 1912
Interstate Compact, 1931, 1932
Interstate Oil Compact Commission (I.O.C.C.), 1935
    ratification, approval, associate members and members of, 1935
Interstate Compact to Conserve Oil and Gas, 1935
Interstate Highways, National System of, 1944
Interstate Natural Gas Co. case, 1947
Interstate Oil Compact, 1926, 1929, 1934, 1935
Interstate Oil Pipe Line Company, 1961
Interstate System, 1952
Introduction of gas into oil sand, 1928
Iowa, 1939
Iran, 1872, 1901, 1904, 1913, 1954
    first oil production (Maidan-I-Naftun), 1908
    nationalizes oil properties, 1951
Iranian Oil Participants, 1954
Iraq, 1914, 1932, 1938, 1948, 1952
    concession amended, 1931
    first field (Kirkuk), 1927
Iraq Petroleum Co., Ltd., 1925, 1929
Iraq Petroleum Corp., 1927
Ireland, 1960
Iron pipe, 1843
Iron storage tank, largest, 1867
Iron sucker rod, 1891 (first), 1900
Iron tanks, 1867
Irvine, General William, 1785
Isocracking, 1959
Iso-octane, 1929, 1934
Isoprene rubber, 1958
Isostasy theory, 1855
Isotope injector, electric, 1958
Isotope injector, solution, 1954
Israel, 1953, 1955, 1958, 1961
    first field (Heletz-Brur), 1955
    industry legislation, 1952
Italo-Moroccan Refining Corp., 1959
Italy, 1640
    first production (Valezza), 1907

J

Jack knife derrick, 1894
Jacket from a barge, 1956
Jacket type steel foundation, 1949
Jackson field, 1930
Jal-Cushing pipeline, 1949

Jalmat gas area, 1955
James' Medicinal Dictionary, 1745
Jann, J., 1866
Japan, 600, 615, 800, 1613, 1850, 1870
  first production (Higashiyama), 1893
Jarecki Mfg. Co., 1868
Jars, steel lined, 1866
Java, 1896
Jayhawk Pipe Line Co., 1958
Jefferson Chemical Company, 1944
Jennings cracking process, 1925
Jennings field, 1901
Jerusalem, 400 B.C.
Jesuit missionaries, 1642
Jet casing perforation, 1946
Jet cement mixer, 1922
Jet fuel, 1945, 1960
Jet passenger service, 1952
Jet perforating, 1946, 1947
Jet Research Center, Inc., 1955
Jewett and Blodgett, 1894
John Bull Scare, 1943
Johnson, Roswell H., 1912, 1916
Johnson, Sir William, 1767
Johnston Testers, Inc., 1926, 1939,
  1956
Joiner, "Dad", 1930
Joly, J., 1909
Jones & Laughlin Steel Co., 1892
Jones, S. M. Co., 1891
Journal of Petroleum Technology,
  1938
Joyamair Oil field, 1937
J. Ray McDermott & Co., 1950
Jusepin Field, 1938
"Just and reasonable" rates, 1955

K

Kalm, Peter, 1748
Kanawha River, 1806
Kansas, 1860, 1864, 1873, 1882, 1884,
  1889, 1899, 1901, 1904, 1905, 1920,
  1923, 1931, 1935
  Corporate Commission, 1931
  first conservation legislation, 1891
  first field (Neodesha), 1892
  member I.O.C.C., 1935 (See I.O.C.,
  1935)
Kansas Independent Oil & Gas
  Association, 1938
Kansas Natural Gas Co., 1904, 1924
Karatchuk field, 1955
Karcher, Dr. J. C., 1917, 1921
Karns, S. D., 1860
Karsal oil field, 1937
Katy gas field, 1935
Kaw Pipe Line Company, 1935
Kegel, Karl, 1919
Keller, J. F., 1865
Kelly bushing, 1924
Kelly field, 1948, 1954
Kelly-Snyder field, 1948
Kelly, square, 1844
Kelvin, Lord, 1869
Kenai Peninsula field, 1957
Kendall College, 1916

Kendall Refining Company, 1881
Kennedy, Wm., 1903
Kentucky, 1818, 1819, 1829, 1932, 1936
  first conservation legislation, 1892
  first oil production, 1867
  member I.O.C.C., 1942 (See I.O.C.,
  1935)
Kerlyn Oil Company, 1937
Kern County Land Company, 1890
Kern River field, 1899
Kern River Trading and Oil Co., 1902
Keroselene, 1857, 1861
Kerosene, 1853, 1856
Kerosene can, 1865
Kerosene, first trans-Atlantic cargo of,
  1885
Kerosene from crude, 1810
Kerr Bill vetoed, 1950
Kerr-Lynn & Co., 1937
Kerr-McGee Oil Industries, Inc., 1929,
  1946
Kettering, Charles F., 1921
Kettleman North Dome field, 1928
Keystone field, 1930
Khairpur gas field, 1952
Khandkot gas field, 1952
Khaur field, 1914
Kier, Samuel, 1850
Kind, 1854
King Ranch, 1933
Kingsbury, Albert, 1895, 1897
Kinley, Myron M., 1932, 1935
Kirby, John Henry, 1901
Kirby Petroleum Company, 1921
Kirkman, John and Thomas, 1854
Kirkuk, 1934
  anticline, 1927
Kirkuk-Banias pipe line, 1950, 1952
Kirkuk-Mediterranean pipe line, 1932
Kitty Hawk, N, C., 1903
K. M. A. field, 1931
Knott, C. G., 1899, 1908
Kobe, Inc., 1923
Kobo Daish, 800
Koerner, G., 1906
Korea, 1910
Kraus, Professor Charles A., 1924
Krebs, 1894
Kremser Equation, 1930
Kuban (Russia), 1866
Kuwait, 1913, 1920, 1934, 1960, 1961
  Fifty-fifty Agreement, 1951
  first field (Burgan), 1937
  first oil exported from, 1946
Kuwait Oil Co., 1934
Kuwait Oil Concession, 1933

L

Labor relations, 1918
LaBrea-Parinas field, 1889
LaCira field, 1926
Laclede Gas Company, 1837
Laclede Gas Light Company, 1904
Lacq field, 1949, 1951, 1957
Laessig, Clem and Harry Grenner,
  1905

Lafitte field, 1935
La Follette of Wisconsin, 1922
La Gloria Oil and Gas Company, 1957
Lago Petroleum Corp., 1924, 1929, 1932
Lagunillas field, 1926
Lake Arthur field, 1937
Lake Charles, La., 1839
Lake Creek field, 1943
Lake Maracaibo, 1922, 1924, 1929, 1930, 1956
Lake Michigan, 1895
Lake Shore Pipe Line Co., 1949
Lake Washington field, 1931
Lakeview Gusher, 1910
Lamp, The, 1918
Lampblack, 1865
Lane Wells Company, 1932
Langen, Eugen, 1867
Langley, Dr. S. P., 1896, 1903
La Paz field, 1922
Laramie, Wyoming, 1924
Larceny Act, the, 1913
Larkin and Co., Inc., 1878
Larkin Packer Co., 1905
Laterolog, 1950
Laterolog-8 log, 1957
Laterolog, psuedo, 1953
Laurent, Auguste, 1830
Lavoisier, Antoine Laurent, 1781
Law of Capture, 1889
Law of the Sea, U.N. Conference on, 1958
Law 395 (80th Congress), 1948
Leache, Johaan, 1738
Leading state in natural gas production, 1923
Lease, first oil, 1851
LeBon, Philippe, 1799, 1801
Leduc field, 1947
Lehedev, 1910
Leisberger, David, 1768
Lenoir, Etienne, 1863
Leschot, J. Rodolphe, 1860, 1863
Levelland field, 1945
Levorson, A. I., 1936
Lewis, W. K., 1921
Libya, 1953, 1959, 1961
  first field, (Atshan), 1958
  industry legislation, 1955
Libyan-American Oil Co., 1955, 1956
Lighting ordinance, first, 1697
Lima (Ohio), 1885
Lime light, 1826
Lime mud, 1944
Lincoln, General Benjamin, 1783
Lincoln Oil and Refining Company, 1924
Lindbergh, Charles A., 1927
Liner Barrels, 1905
Lin-Fang, Wu, 1817
Lion Oil Company, 1923
Liquefied natural gas, 1915, 1944
Liquefied petroleum gas (LPG), 1910, 1911, 1912, 1926
Liquefied Petroleum Gas Division of Texas Railroad Commission, 1951

Liquid fuel age begins, 1901
Little Big Inch, 1943, 1944, 1946, 1947, 1958, 1961
Little Giant Melter, 1869
Little River field, 1927
Livingston, Max, 1899
Lobato Jonas field, 1939
Lockhart, Charles, 1860
Locomotive, 1804 (first), 1814, 1825, 1828, 1830, 1886, 1898, 1901, 1910
  Diesel electric, 1925
  oil burner, 1894
Lodestone, 320 B.C., 121 B.C.
Log, electrical, 1927
  gamma ray, 1938, 1939
  induction, 1947
  magnetic susceptibility, 1951
  operations expanding, electric, 1932
  radioactive tracer, 1943
  rotary well, 1926
  standard electric, 1931
Logan, Sir William, 1842, 1860
Logging, caliper service, 1929, 1941
  tool, electric, 1958
Logs, caliper, 1932, 1938
  electric, 1938
  temperature, 1932
London, 1415, 1807
London and Westminster Gas Light and Coke Co., 1812
Lone Star Gas Co., 1909, 1910, 1934, 1950
Lone Star Gathering Company, 1961
Lone Star Producing Company, 1942
Lone Star Steel Company, 1942
Long Beach field, 1921
Lopideth Israel Petroleum Company, 1953
Los Angeles, 1911, 1913
Loscher, Carl, 1797
Loskiel, George Henry, 1789
Louden field, 1938
Louisiana, 1821, 1839, 1908, 1915, 1918, 1920, 1924, 1936, 1938, 1940, 1945
  creates Conservation Commission, 1910
  first conservation legislation, 1906
  first field (Jennings), 1901
  member I.O.C.C., 1940 (See I.O.C., 1935)
Louisiana Land and Exploration Company, 1928
Louisiana Petroleum Council, 1958
Louisiana State University, 1927
Lowe, Thaddeus S. C., 1873, 1875, 1888
LPG, 1922
LPG pipeline delivery, record one-day, 1962
LPG pipeline, world's first major, 1961
LPG, shipment of by sea, 1959
LP gas, growth stimulated, 1926
Lubricant, 1845
Lubricant, solid, 1870
Lubricants from naphthenic crude oils, 1903

Lubricating oil, 1853, 1883
Lubricup Co., Inc., 1921
Lucas, Anthony F., 1900, 1901, 1913
Lucas Gusher, 1901
Lucas Medal, 1941
Lucey Products Corp., 1908
Lufkin Foundry and Machine Co., 1902
Luling-Branyon field, 1922
Lyell, Charles, 1830

M

MacEachen, S., 1893
Machine, double wrap, 1943
Machine stoker, 1873
Machlet, George, 1869
Macmillian case, 1931
Macquer, Pierre Joseph, 1764
Magellan, 1521
Magna-tector, 1945
Magnet Cove Barium Co., 1940
Magnetic collar locater, 1948
Magnetic dip, 1576
Magnetic field, 1843
Magnetic measurement, 1879
Magnetic susceptibility log, 1951
Magnetometer, 1870 (first), 1924
  airborne, 1939, 1941
Magnolia field, 1938
Magnolia Petroleum Co., 1902, 1925,
  1959
Maidan-I-Naftun field, 1908
Malam, John, 1817, 1820
Mallet, Robert, 1848, 1849
Maloney-Crawford Tank & Manufac-
  turing Co., 1909
Mammoth Oil Company, 1927
Manhattan Gas Light Company, 1830
Manziel, Bobby, 1940
Map, first oil field structure, 1874
Mapping outcrops, 1912
Marathon Oil Co. (see also Ohio Oil
  Co.), 1930, 1936
Marginal Well Act, 1931
Mari Gas Field, 1952
Marine terminal, first large-scale LPG,
  1947
Market demand, 1915, 1930, 1931
Market Demand Act, Texas, 1932
Market Demand Law, upheld by U. S.
  Supreme Court, 1932
Marketing, code of ethics for, 1928
Markets, foreign, 1903
  for fuel oil, 1902
Marland, E. W., 1910, 1934, 1935
Marland Oil Co., 1910
Marsh buggies, first, 1928
Martial Law, 1932
Martin-Decker Corp., 1925, 1934
Maryland, 1949, 1959
  conservation legislation, 1945
  member I.O.C.C., 1959 (See I.O.C.,
    1935)
Maskelyne, Nevil, 1774
Mass spectrometer, 1943
Massachusetts, 1866, 1885, 1961
Massachusetts Institute of Technology,
  1923

Massudi, 967
Materials testing reactor, 1950
Mattoon, Illinois, 1874
Maxim, Hiram, 1893
Mazarani Gas Field, 1952
McAfee, Dr. A. M., 1915
McCallum field, 1926
McCamey field, 1925
McCann, H. K., 1910
McCann-Erickson Advertising Agency,
  1910
McClintock, Hamilton, 1807
McClure, William, 1809
McCollum Experiment, 1923
McCollum Laboratories, 1955
McCullough chemical cutter and
  perforator, 1959
McCullough Tool Co., 1926
McDermott & Co., J. Ray, 1920, 1959
McElroy field, 1926
McFaddin Beach, 1937
McIlroy network analyzer, 1953
McKittrick field, 1887
McLemore, Robert H., 1947
McMurtie, James, 1815
Mechanical pipe joint, 1870
Mecom, John W., 1931, 1956, 1961
Medearis Oilwell Supply Corporation,
  1929
Medical study of oil workers, 1895
Medicinal, 1480, 1761
Medicine Hat gas field, 1951
Medoc district, 1873
Mei-Foo, 1894
Melhase, John, 1936
Mellon, Andrew W. and Richard K.,
  1901
Melville, David, 1806, 1812, 1813, 1817
Memphis, 1929
Memphis Light, Gas and Water
  Division Case, 1958
Memphis Natural Gas Company, 1929
Mendeleef, Dimitri, 1879
Mene Grande, 1914
Mene Grande Oil Company, 1936, 1952
M. E. R., 1927
Mercaptan, ethyl, 1930
Merger of Oklahoma, Pate and Penola,
  1960
Merrill, Joshua, 1857, 1858, 1861,
  1863, 1869
Metallurgical Society of AIME, 1957
Meter, first iron case, 1889
  orifice, 1911, 1924
  prepayment, 1886
  regulator, 1920
  rotary displacement, 1922
  tin-case, 1904
  Tobey, 1892
  two-diaphragm gas, 1895
Metering crude, 1919
Metering natural gas, 1885
Metermen, gas, 1921
Meters, 1888
Mexia fault, 1923
Mexia field, 1920
Mexican Eagle, 1922

Mexico, 1876, 1884, 1892, 1901, 1909, 1910, 1917, 1918, 1920, 1922, 1925, 1930, 1937, 1938, 1941, 1943, 1957
  expropriation, 1938
  first field (Cerro de la Pez), 1901
  industry legislation, 1884
Mexico City, 1868
Mexican Gulf Oil Co., 1912
Mexico Oil Law, 1927
Mexico's first pipeline, 1909
Michigan, 1886, 1898, 1909, 1921, 1925, 1929, 1937, 1939
  first conservation legislation, 1909
  first field (Port Huron), 1886
  member I.O.C.C., 1943 (See also I.O.C., 1935)
  Oil and Gas Agency—Department of Conservation, 1921
Michigan Consolidated Gas Company, 1938
Michigan Natural Gas Corporation, 1933
Microballoons, 1953
Microlaterolog, 1951
  continuous dip meter, 1956
Microlog, 1948
Micropaleontology, 1919, 1923, 1924
Mid-Continent Oil & Gas Association, 1917
  Kansas-Oklahoma Division, 1919
  Louisiana-Arkansas Division, 1923
  Mississippi-Alabama Division, 1944
  Texas Division, 1923
  Texas-Louisiana Division, 1919
Mid-Continent Supply Company, 1929
Middle East, 1885, 1916, 1921
  Emergency Committee, 1957
  first 50-50 agreement, 1950
Midgely, Thomas, Jr., 1921
Mid-Kansas Oil and Gas Company, 1916
Mid-Valley Pipe Line Co., 1949
Midway-Sunset field, 1894
Midway Supply Co., 1932
Midwest Oil Co., 1911
Midwest Oil Corp., 1911
Midwestern Gas Transmission Co., 1960
Migration and accumulation of oil and gas, 1919
Mikolasch, 1852
Military Petroleum Advisory Board, 1947, 1955
Military portable pipe line, 1942
Miller, George, 1938
Miller, H. C., 1929
Miller, Max B., 1920
Millochan, A., 1864
Mills, R. Van A., 1923
Milwhite Mud Sales Company, 1952
Mims, S. W., 1926
Mineral Industry, The—Its Statistics, Technology and Trade, 1892
Mineral interest, first recorded sale, 1862
Mineral Leasing Act, 1935, 1937
Mineral resources of the U.S., 1882, 1911

Mineralogy, System of, by Dana, 1837
Minerals Yearbook, 1932
Minimum natural-gas price, 1950
Mining, Metallurgical and Petroleum Engineers, American Institute of, 1955
Minneapolis-Honeywell Regulator Co., 1927
Minnesota, 1937
Minnesota Northern Natural Gas Co., 1931
Mintrop, L., 1919, 1923
Miri field, 1911
Miscible displacement, gas, 1949
Mission Manufacturing Company, 1925
Mississippi, 1930, 1944, 1946
  first conservation legislation, 1932
  first field (Tinsley), 1939
  member I.O.C.C., 1948 (See I.O.C. 1935)
  Oil and Gas Agency—Oil and Gas Board, 1932
Mississippi-Alabama Division of Mid-Continent Oil & Gas Association, 1944
Missouri, 1924
  first oil production, 1889
Missouri School of Mines, 1913, 1914, 1922
Mitchell, Mark, 1903
Mitchell, Dr. Samuel, 1798-1801
Mobil Chemical Company, 1960
Mobil Petroleum Company, 1960
Mobil Pipe Corporation, 1961
Mobile Gas Service Corp., 1956, 1958
Mobile Producing Co., 1954
Model "T" Ford, 1908
Mohawk Petroleum Corporation, 1938
Moho, 1909
  project, 1961
Mohorovicic, A., 1909
Molten sulphur line, 1959
Monroe gas field, 1916, 1926
Montana, 1913, 1916, 1921, 1925, 1933
  first conservation legislation, 1917
  first field (Cedar Creek), 1914
  member I.O.C.C., 1945 (See I.O.C., 1935)
Montebello field, 1917, 1932
Monterey Gas Transmission Co., 1961
Monterey Oil Company, 1960
Monterrey, 1925
Moody-Seagraves, 1925
Moore, Lee C. Corp., 1907
Moore, T. V., 1931
Morgah Oil Pipeline, 1952
Moroccan-Italian Petroleum Corp., 1958
Morocco, 1875, 1928, 1929, 1939, 1954, 1955, 1957, 1961
  first important field (Baton), 1947
  Hydrocarbon Law issued, 1958
Morse, Samuel F. B., 1830
Morse, Senator Wayne, 1953
Moses, Job, 1865
Mother Hubbard or Umbrella case, 1940

294

Naval fuel oil stations, 1911
Naval petroleum reserves, 1901, 1916,
    1920, 1921, 1923
Naval reserve oil fields, 1922
Navy, British, 1903
    German, 1903
    Royal Swedish, 1959
    U. S., 1911, 1920
    U. S. Gunboat Palos using petroleum
        as fuel, 1867
Near East Development Company, 1928
Nebraska, 1939, 1940, 1941
    first conservation legislation, 1941
    first field (Falls City), 1939
    member I.O.C.C., 1935 (See I.O.C.,
        1935)
    Oil and Gas Association, 1956
Neches Butane Products Co., 1942,
    1944
Neckham, Alexander, 1181
Neff, Pat M., 1932
Neste Oy Company, 1957
Netherlands, 1923, 1942, 1947, 1950,
    1960 (see Holland)
Netherlands West Indies, 1932
Neutral Zone, 1953
Neutral Zone (Kuwait), 1924
    first exports, 1954
    rights transferred, 1932
Neutral Zones established, 1922
Neutron gamma logging, 1941
Neutron generator for nuclear logging,
    1955
Neutron log, flowing, 1957
Neutron log, multiple spaced, 1955
Neutron logging, 1941
Neutron-neutron logging, 1950
Neutron source, plutonium-beryllium,
    1958
Nevada, 1921, 1954
    first conservation legislation, 1921
    first field (Eagle Springs), 1954
    member I.O.C.C., 1953 (See I.O.C.,
        1935)
Neville G. Penrose, Inc., 1953
Newark, N. J., 1846
Newberry, J. S., 1859, 1873
Newcomen, Thomas, 1705
New Guinea, 1911, 1912, 1958, 1960
    first production, 1936
New Harmony field, 1939
New London, Texas, 1937
New Mexico, 1909, 1912, 1921, 1925,
    1927, 1929, 1935
    first conservation legislation, 1909
    first oil field (Hogback), 1922
    member I.O.C.C., 1935 (see I.O.C.,
        1935)
    Oil and Gas Agency—Oil Conserva-
        tion Commission, 1935
    Oil and Gas Association, 1929
New Mexico Institute of Mining &
    Technology, 1935
New Orleans, 1832, 1900, 1928
Newport, R. I., 1806

New York, 1642, 1700, 1879, 1919,
    1936
    first conservation legislation, 1879
    first oil field, (Cattaragus County),
        1865
    member I.O.C.C., 1941 (See I.O.C.,
        1935)
New York and Bermudez Company,
    1910
New York and Richmond Gas
    Company, 1949
New York City, 1949
New York Gas Light Co., 1823
New York Produce Exchange, 1879
New York State Natural Gas Corpora-
    tion, 1913
New York State Oil Producers
    Association, 1918
New York System, 1843
New Zealand, 1866, 1900, 1961
Nichols, F. B., 1937
Nigeria, 1937, 1951, 1953, 1956
    first field (Oloibiri), 1956
Nimitz, Chester W., 1916
NIRA, 1933, 1935
Nitrocycle, 1951
Nitroglycerin, 1845, 1846
    solidified, 1918
NKPM, 1923
Noah, 6000 B. C.
Nobel, Alfred, 1846, 1866, 1867
Nobel Brothers, 1877, 1878, 1883, 1885
Nobel Brothers Naphtha Co., 1878
Nobel, Robert, 1876
Nordsen, Sven, 1916
Norman, Robert, 1576
Norman Wells field, 1920
Normanna case, 1962
Normanna Decision, 1961
"Normanna Order" 1957, 1961
North Atlantic Treaty Organization
    Petroleum Planning Committee, 1961
North Carolina, first conservation
    legislation, 1945
North Dakota, 1929, 1941, 1953
    first conservation legislation, 1911
    first field (Beaver Lodge), 1951
    member I.O.C.C., 1953 (see I.O.C.,
        1935)
North Texas Oil and Gas Association,
    1930
Northeastern Gas Transmission Co.,
    1951, 1954
Northern Natural Gas Company, 1930
Northwest Territories, 1920
Norway, 1899, 1927, 1960
Nova Scotia, 1952
NRA, 1933, 1935
Nuclear magnetism log, 1958
Nuclear well logging, 1952
Nylon, 1934, 1937

O

Oasis Oil Company, 1958
Oasis Oil Company of Libya, Inc., 1960
O'Bannon Co., Walter, 1920

296

Pennsylvania grade crude oil, 1942
Pennsylvania Grade Crude Oil Association, 1923
Pennsylvania Oil Exchange, 1880
Pennsylvania R. R., 1860, 1886
Pennsylvania Rock Oil Co., 1854, 1855
Penrose, Neville G., Inc., 1953
Pension plan, 1903
Pentane, 1866
Peoples Gas Light & Coke Company of Chicago, 1855, 1931
Peoples Natural Gas Company, 1885
Perbunan, 1940
Peregrinus, Petros, 1269
Perforating Guns Atlas Corp., 1946
Perforator and cutter, chemical, 1959
Perforator, mechanical casing, 1910
Perforator, multi-shot, 1934
Permeability, 1933, 1949
Permian Basin, 1920
Persian Gulf, 1951
Peru, 1740, 1861, 1867, 1873, 1889, 1893, 1950, 1952, 1953, 1959, 1960
    first field (Zorritos), 1867
P.E.S.A., 1933
Peter the Great, 1723
Petrobras, 1953
Petrochemical plant, Canada's first, 1951
Petrochemicals, 1914
Petrochemicals industry, 1949
Petroff, N., 1883
Petrol or gasoline automobile, first, 1894
Petrolatum, 1915
Petroleum Administration Board, 1933
Petroleum Administration for Defense, 1950
Petroleum Administration for War, 1942, 1946
Petroleum and Petroleum Wells, 1865
Petroleum, artificial, 1865
Petroleum Board, 1864
Petroleum butter, 1909
Petroleum, chemistry of, 1855
Petroleum Coordinator for National Defense, Office of, 1941
Petroleum Corporation of Turkey, 1955
Petroleum distillation, 1860
Petroleum, early use of word, 1327, 1377
Petroleum Engineer, 1915, 1920, 1921
Petroleum Engineer Magazine, 1937
Petroleum Engineer Publishing Company, 1955
Petroleum Engineer, The, 1929
Petroleum Engineers, 1915
Petroleum Equipment Suppliers Association, 1933
Petroleum Facts and Figures, 1928
Petroleum Industry Council, 1941
Petroleum Industry Research Foundation, Inc., 1944
Petroleum Industry War Council, 1941
Petroleum Landmen Management, Curriculum of, 1958
Petroleum Marketer Magazine, 1933
Petroleum, origin of, 1873, 1899

Petroleum Producers Agency, 1872
Petroleum Producers Association (first), 1869
Petroleum Production Engineering, 1924
Petroleum Production Methods, 1921
Petroleum Products Surveys, 1957
Petroleum refined, 1862
Petroleum Refiner's Association, 1872
Petroleum refining, 1861
Petroleum Reporter, Stowells, 1873
Petroleum Research Foundation, 1944
Petroleum, statements of bulk, 1878
Petroleum Technology, 1949
Petroleum Times, The, 1899
Petroleum Today, 1959
Petroleum, Word on map of Pennsylvania, 1755
Petrolia, Canada, 1857
Petrolia field (Texas), 1907, 1910
Petromex, 1934
Pew, Joseph Newton, 1886
Pew, John G., 1913
Phenol-formaldehyde, 1943
Philadelphia, 1816, 1836, 1841
Philadelphia Company, 1884, 1888
Philippine Oil Development Co., 1951
Philippines, 1896, 1949, 1951, 1953, 1957, 1961
    first conservation legislation, 1949
Phillips, F. C., 1892
Phillips case, 1948, 1951, 1953, 1954
Phillips Chemical Company, 1948
Phillips Petroleum Co., 1917
Photoclinometer, 1940
Photogeology, 1924
Photographic device for boreholes, 1907
Photographic recording, 1936
Pico Canyon, 1865
Pico Canyon field, 1875
Pioneer and Bennehoff runs, 1865
Pipe, drive, first use of, 1806
Pipe foundry (first), 1834
Pipe layer, 1917
Pipe line, 1872
Pipe Line Contractors Association, 1948
Pipe Line News, 1928
Pipe mill, first mobile, 1961
Pipe, seamless steel (first), 1899
Pipe-coating, 1859, 1896
Pipe-coating plant, 1928
Pipeline, automatically controlled, 1927
Pipeline Construction, 1946
Pipeline divorcement, 1934
Pipeline, first, 900
Pipeline, first long distance, all-welded natural gas, 1924
Pipeline for handling ethylene, distribution system, 1953
Pipeline, gasoline (first), 1918
Pipeline, high pressure, long distance oil (first), 1891
Pipeline in Europe, first large diameter, 1958
Pipeline Industry (magazine), 1954

Pipeline, iron, first 1863
Pipeline legislation, 1862
Pipeline, multi-product, long distance, 1930
Pipeline, oil (first), 1865
Pipeline over mountains, first trunk, 1878
Pipeline, products, 1893, 1930, 1931
Pipeline pump stations, electric power for, 1927
Pipeline, regulation of, 1878
Pipeline, rifled, 1907
Pipeline suspension bridge, 1926
Pipeline, West Texas record mileage, 1929
Pipelines declared common carriers, 1912
Pipelines, electric drive for, 1923
Pipe-screwing machine, 1912
Pitch, 1681, 1694
Pithole, 1865, 1866
Pithole Creek field, 1865
Pitot tube, 1891, 1911
Pittsburgh, 1820, 1835
Pittsburgh Equitable Meter Co., 1927
Pittsburgh Pipe and Coupling Company, 1918
Plane, experimental, 1896
Plane, first executive, 1927
Plantation Pipe Line Co., 1940
Plastics, 1938, 1946
Platforming, 1949
Platinum mantles, 1848
Platte Pipe Line Co., 1950, 1952
Platt's Oilgram, 1934, 1961
Pleasantville Boom, 1868
Pledger field, 1932
Pliny, 100
Plug, cement replaces cast-iron, 1927
Plug, wireline bridging, 1934
Plutarch, 66
Plutonium-beryllium neutron source, 1958
Po Delta, 1961
Poisoning, 1863, 1887
Poland, 1858
    first oil (Kleczany), 1858
Policy of Exclusion, 1920
Pollen and spores used in geology, 1939
Polo, Marco, 1272
Polyform process, 1938
Polyforming, 1935
Polyisobutylene process, 1960
Polymer 66, 1934
Polymerization, 1931, 1940
Polymerization, catalytic, 1935
Polystyrene, 1958
Pontecorvo, Bruno, 1941
Pooling, pool-wide compulsory, 1945
Pools, oil and gas, classification of, 1910
Porcelain (vitreous coatings), 1867
Porosimeter, Kaye-Freeman, 1946
Porosity, 1860
Porous volcanic ash formations, 1954
Port Acres decision, 1962
Portable air compressors, 1901
Portable cable tool rig, 1894

Portable drilling machine, 1875
Portable engine, 1861
Portable gas light machine, 1867
Portable light (first), 1781
Portable rotary rig, 1893, 1935
Portland-Montreal, 1941
Portland, Ore., 1860
Portsdown Hill, 1936
Posted prices, 1895
Potylitsyn, A. A., 1870
Powell field, 1900
Power cementing pump, 1937
Power cylinder, 1878
Powers, Sidney, 1917
Poza Rica field, 1930, 1932
Pozmix, 1953
Prairie Oil and Gas Co., 1904, 1905
Pratt, C. M., 1911
Pratt Manufacturing Company, 1884
Pratt, Wallace E., 1918, 1933, 1934
Prepayment meter, 1886
President's Advisory Committee, 1955
Pressure build-up curve, 1949
Pressure distillation, 1887
Pressure maintained and unitized field, 1949
Pressure maintenance, 1926, 1938, 1945
Pressure piping, standard code for, 1935
Pressure recorder, 1935
Pressure regulator, 1880
Pressure-type blowout preventer, 1931
Price based on gravity, 1868
Prices, gasoline, 1922
Prime mover, 1935
"Principles of Oil and Gas Production," 1916
Printer's ink from petroleum, 1891
Producers, deepest (Louisiana), 1949
Producers Oil Co., 1902, 1910, 1917
Production crisis, 1901
Production, deep, 1927, 1928, 1930, 1931, 1932, 1935, 1936, 1937, 1938, 1943, 1944, 1945, 1946, 1947, 1948, 1949, 1953, 1956
Production of oil, world, 1915, 1958
"Production or gathering" exemption, 1954
Production record, 1861
Production, world wide limitation, 1929
Products by pipeline, 1893, 1930, 1931
Profiling of salt domes, 1928
Profit-sharing, 1906
Progressive Oil & Gas Co., 1916
Project Five Pipeline System, 1959
Proportionate marketing, 1920
Proration, 1928, 1929, 1931
Proration Acts, 1947
Proration order (first), 1914
Proration order (first production), 1915
Proration order, first statewide, 1928
Proration Tax Act, 1933
Proration, Texas (first), 1919, first statewide, 1930
Prorationing, voluntary, 1914
Providence, R. I., 1887
Proximity log, 1958
Prudencio, Ignacio, 1895

Prudhomme, P., 1821
Public Domain, 1929, 1931, 1932
Public land leasing policy, 1946
Public Service Commission of the
    State of N. Y., 1959
Public Service Company of Colorado,
    1923
Public Utility Holding Act, 1935
Puckett Ellenberger field, 1952
Pueblo, 1928
Pull rods, 1880
Pulling the pipe, 1900
Pump, ball, 1950
Pump, bottom hole steam, 1872
Pump, centrifugal, 1926
Pump, direct acting steam, 1798
Pump, fully balanced, double acting,
    1937
Pump, gas displacement, 1866, 1908
Pump, hydraulic, 1918
Pump, Kobe oil-lifting, 1935
Pump, oil well, 1878
Pump, slush, 1866
Pump, sonic, 1948
Pump, submersible, 1925, 1930
Pump, triplex power plunger, 1940
Pump, underwater subsurface hydraulic
    (first), 1961
Punjab, 1869
Punta Cardon, 1951
Pure Oil Co., 1896, 1914
Purifiers, 1823

Q

Qatar, 1935, 1949
    first field (Dukhan), 1940
Qatar Petroleum Company, 1935, 1950
Qatif field, 1945
Quadruple completion, 1958
Quaker State Oil Refining Corporation,
    1931
Quantity automobile production, 1905
Quarto on geology, 1787
Queen sand formation, 1953
Queensland, Australia, 1961
Quincke, G., 1859
Quintana Petroleum Corporation, 1934,
    1938
Quintuple completion, 1960
"Quintuplex," 1934
Quiriquire field, 1928

R

Raccoon Bend, 1930
Radiant-fire gas heater, 1916
Radiator, 1796
Radio frequency for prospecting, 1910
Radioactive elements in the earth, 1906
Radioactive tracers, 1943
Radioactivity and Geology, 1909
Radioactivity measurements, 1921
Radioactivity well logging, 1940
Radiophone, 1922, 1923
Radium, 1898
Ragusa field, 1953
Railroads convert from coal to oil,
    1902

Raleigh, Sir Walter, 1596
Ram-type blowout preventer, 1929
Raman field, 1941
Ramsey, Mrs. John R., 1909
Rancho Ojai, 1865
Rancho Pipe Line System, The, 1953
Rand, A. C., 1867
Rangely field, 1902, 1933
Ras Gharib field, 1938
Rashidpur gas field, 1957
Ratable and equitable takings, 1933
Ratable take, 1915
Rate-base method, 1955
Rationing, 1942, 1945, 1950
    of gas ranges, 1945
Rayburn-Wheeler Bill, 1935
Rayleigh, Baron John, 1902, 1906
Rayne field, 1953
Realitos, east field, 1949
Reaming cone bit, 1917
Rebates, 1872
Record one-day LPG pipeline delivery,
    1962
Record send-out for any gas company,
    1919
Record yield, 1941
Recording instruments, 1934
Rectification, 1902
Rector Well Equipment Company,
    Inc., 1930
Recycling (see also cycling), 1924
Reda Pump Co., 1947
Red Line Agreement, 1928
Redondo field, 1922
Redwater field, 1948
Redwood, Boverton, 1913
Reed Roller Bit Company, 1916, 1917,
    1928
Reed Super Shrink-grip tool joint, 1939
Refineries and their capacities, 1920
Refinery cost, 1865
Refinery statistics, 1917
Refining, 1852, 1862
Refining, first American enterprise
    abroad, 1880
Reflection profiling, 1910, 1919, 1928
Reflection, seismic method, 1914
Reflexion and Refraction, 1899
Reforming high BTU gases, 1928
Refraction, first profiles, 1885
Refraction profiling, 1910, 1919, 1925,
    1926
Refraction seismic surveys, 1905
Refraction seismograph successful,
    1924
Refraction technique, 1925-26
Refrigerated propane storage plant,
    1957
Refrigeration, gas (air cooled), 1933
Regan Forge & Engineering Co., 1906
Regie Autonome des Petrolees (RAP),
    1939
Regulation of gas producers, repeal
    advocated by Pres. Eisenhower, 1957
Regulatory bodies—see individual states
    and countries for other than Federal
Reichenbach, Karl von, 1830

Reid Vapor Pressure method, 1923
Reinhold, Thomas, 1924
Reistle, C. E., Jr., 1924
Relative permeability, 1936
Relativity theory, 1896
Reno Oil and Land Co., 1865
Reno Oil Company, 1908
Rental, minimum (1960 Act), 1960
Report on fuel consumption, 1933
Reports on natural-gas liquids, 1942
Repressuring, 1903, 1916, 1926, 1930
Republic Supply Company, 1910
Reserves classified, 1921
Reservoir analyzer, electronic, 1951
Reservoir dynamics, 1931
Reservoir gas and oil, 1923
Resident geologists, 1921
Resistivity curve, 1931
Resistivity, lateral, 1936
Resistivity, long normal, 1934
Resistivity measurements, 1916
Retort, 1820
Reuter, Baron Julius de, 1872
Revolving derrick barge, 1955
Rexformer, 1932
Reynolds Gas Regulator Company,
    1892
Reynolds Metals Co., 1950, 1961
Reynolds, Osborne, 1886
Rhigolene, 1866
Richards and Cross, 1884
Richards, Esther, 1919
Richfield field, 1919
Richfield Oil Corporation, 1936
Richmond, Virginia, 1803
Right of eminent domain, 1872, 1885
Right of way, 1868
Rio Bravo Oil Company, 1919
Rio Grande Oil Co., 1919
Rio Vista-Isleton field, 1936
Road maps, 1923
Robert Fulton's steamboat, 1807
Roberts, Col. E.A.L., 1862, 1865, 1866
Robertshaw Thermostat Company,
    1899
Robinson-Patman Act, 1936
Robinson-Stoy field, 1906
Rochas, Alphonse Beau de, 1862
Rochester Gas and Electric Corpora-
    tion, 1923
Rochester Gas Company, 1872
Rock bits, 1866
"Rock Oil, the Wonder of the
    Nineteenth Century," 1860
Rockefeller & Andrews, 1865, 1867
Rockefeller & Andrews and Flagler,
    1867
Rockefeller & Co., 1867
Rockefeller, John D., 1863
Rockefeller, John D., ends his career,
    1911
Rockefeller, William & Co., 1867
Rocket, first liquid fuel, 1926
Rockwell Manufacturing Company,
    1932
Rocky Mountain area, 1924

Rocky Mountain Oil and Gas Associa-
    tion, 1921
Rod pumps, 1900
Rodessa field, 1930
Roebling's Sons Corporation, John A.,
    1841
Roentgen, Wilhelm, 1895
Rogers and Burchfield, 1874
Rogers, H. D., 1863
Rogers, Henry, 1871
Roller core bit, 1926
Roller-cutter rotary reamer, 1919
Rolling cutters, 1866
Rolling rig, 1926
Rolo Manufacturing Company, 1945
Romano-Americana, 1904
Romans, 670
Roosevelt, President Franklin D., 1933
Roots-Connersville Blower Division,
    1854
Roper, S. H., 1889
Rosaire, Dr. E. E., 1935
Rotary core barrel, 1899
Rotary drill, 1860
Rotary drill, percussion, 1954
Rotary drilling, 1821, 1844, 1845,
    1858, 1882, 1901
Rotary drilling machine, 1844, 1889
Rotary drilling, pneumatic, 1932
Rotary drilling rig, 1838
Rotary drilling unit, 1935
Rotary equipment, electrically powered,
    1923
Rotary hose, all metal, 1929
Rotary method, 3000 B.C.
Rotary, portable, 1893, 1935
Rotary rig on wheels, 1893
Rotary tables (make & break), 1920
Rotary tools in N.Y., & Pa., 1936
Rothschilds, the, 1897
Roxana Petroleum Company, 1912
Rowan and Nicholas case, 1940
Royal Dutch Petroleum Co., 1890,
    1902, 1907
Royal Dutch Shell, 1885, 1902, 1912,
    1917
Royal Dutch Shell group, 1907
Royalite Oil Co., Ltd., 1921
Royalty, first, 1857
Rozet, 1834
Rubber, first production of cold, 1949
Rubber, information on synthetic, 1939
Rubber, synthetic, 1912, 1946
Ruffner, David and Joseph, 1806
Rule 37, 1919, 1928
Rumania, 1650, 1860, 1948
    expropriation, 1948
    first production (Mosarele), 1860
Rumford, Benjamin, 1796
Rumsey, James, 1784
Russia, 1850, 1862, 1917, 1919, 1940
    expropriation, 1917
    oil wells, 1941
    production of oil, 1898
Ruud, Edwin, 1889
Ruud Manufacturing Company, 1897

303

Service Pipe Line Company, 1916,
1918, 1919, 1921, 1930, 1950
Service station, 1905, 1907, 1911,
1913, 1914
market, first, 1911
first chain of, 1911
first drive-in, 1905
first ever robbed, 1911
first "filling station," drive-in, 1905
Sextuple completion, 1960,
gas; 1961, oil
Shaffer Tool Works, 1938
Shale oil, 1851
Shale oil extraction, 1920
Shamrock Oil & Gas Corporation,
1935
Shaped charge, 1946
Sharpenberg, Charles C., 1924
Sharples, P. T., 1920
Shaw, John, 1856
Shell Chemical Corporation, 1929
Shell Company of California, Inc.,
1914
Shell Development Company, 1928
Shell Haven, 1916
Shell International Chemical
Company, Ltd., 1959
Shell Oil Company, 1918, 1939, 1942,
1946
Shell-BP, Petroleum Development
Company of Nigeria, Ltd., 1956
Shell Petroleum Company, Ltd., 1946
Shell Pipe Line Corporation, 1927
Shell Transport and Trading Co., 1897,
1907
Shell Union Oil Corporation, 1922
Sheridan field, 1940
Sherman Antitrust Act, 1890
Ship, first all welded, 1931
Shipments of oil, first full cargo, 1861
Sho-Vel-Tum area, 1955
Shooting wells, 1860, 1862, 1863,
1864, 1865, 1866, 1867
Shu Han dynasty, 221-23
Shut down days (first), 1872
Shut down, military, 1931
Shut down order day, (first), 1937
Shut down order (first Texas), 1919
Shut-in pressure tool, 1939
Siamese dual pumping unit, 1960
Siberia (Eastern) gets first oil, 1962
Sicilian oil, 100
Sicily, 1953
first field (Ragusa), 1953
Sidewall coring, 1936
Signal Hill, 1921
Signal Oil and Gas Co., 1922
Silliman, Benjamin, Jr., 1855
Prof. Benjamin, Sr., 1833
Simplex prepared joint, 1919
Sinclair, Harry F., 1923, 1929
Sinclair Oil Co., 1919
Sinclair Pipe Line Company, 1920,
1951
Skelly Oil Company, 1919
Skelly, W. G., 1919
Skunk bearing oil, 1887

Slanted hole seaward, 1927
Slaughter field, 1936
Slick, Tom, 1912, 1937
Sliding sleeve, 1936
Sligo field, 1922
Slip coupling, 1887
Sludge acids, 1874
Smackover field, 1922
Smith Corporation, A. O., 1874, 1927
Smith, William, 1815, 1843
Snap thief, 1867
Snow, W. B., 1866
Snowden and McSweeney Company,
1944
Snyder field, 1948, 1954
Sobrero, Ascanio, 1846
Societe Cherifienne des Petroles, 1929
Societe Franco-Americaine de
Raffinage, 1931
Societe de Prospection Electrique, 1929
Society of Economic Paleontologists
and Mineralogists, 1926
Society of Exploration Geophysicists,
1930
Society of Mining Engineers of
AIME, 1957
Society of Petroleum Engineers of
AIME, 1957
Society of Petroleum Engineers
Journal, 1961
Socony Mobil Oil Co., Inc., 1948, 1955
Socony-Seaboard, 1953
Socony-Vacuum Oil Company, 1931,
1934, 1948
Soil analysis, 1935
Soil corrosion, 1922
Soil stress, 1935
Sokolov, V. A., 1929, 1933, 1940
Solid electric welded gas line, 1930
Somali, 1962
Sonar caliper log, 1956
Sonic pump, 1948
Sonic sounder, 1914
Sound ranging, 1915
Sour Lake field, 1902
South Africa, 1954
South African Coal, Oil and Gas
Corp., Ltd., 1950
South African Torbanite and Mining
and Refining Co., Ltd., 1934
South Dakota, 1923, 1925, 1929, 1939,
1941, 1943, 1953
first conservation legislation, 1923
first field (Buffalo), 1953
member I.O.C.C., 1955 (See I.O.C.,
1935)
South Improvement Co., 1871, 1872
South Pass Blk. 24 field, 1950
South Penn Oil Co., 1889
Southern California Gas Company,
1907
Southern Counties Gas Company, 1911
Southern Crude Oil Co., 1930
Southern Gas Association, 1908
Southern Minerals Corporation, 1933
Southern Natural Gas Co., 1928, 1961
Southern Natural Gas System, 1929

304

Southern Union Gas Co., 1929
Southwest, two refineries in, 1901
Southwestern Pennsylvania Oil and
  Gas Association, 1953
S.P. curve, 1931
S.P. measurement, 1929
Spacing law, 1947
Spacing, well, 1924
Spain, 1920, 1927, 1928, 1929, 1958
  industry legislation (new), 1958
Spang and Co., 1894
Spanish Sahara, 1960
Spanish Trail, 1790
Specific gravity of liquids, 1768
Speed, Buckner, 1908
Sperm oil cost, 1845
Spherical storage tank, 1923, 1925
Spindletop, 1901, 1925
Spores, 1939
Sprayberry field, 1946
Sprayberry Order, 1953
Sprayberry Trend, 1953
Spraying oil with steam, 1884
Spring pole, 1806
Squirrel cage motors, 1906
S.S. Methane Pioneer, 1959
S.S. Natalie O. Warren, 1947
Standard of Bolivia, 1925
Standard Oil Co., California, 1880,
  1906, 1907, 1909, 1916, 1926, 1961
Standard Oil Co., dissolution ordered,
  1911
Standard Oil Co., (Indiana), 1889,
  1908, 1921, 1957, 1960
Standard Oil Co., Iowa, 1879, 1885
Standard Oil Co. of Kentucky, 1961
Standard Oil Co. of Louisiana, 1909,
  1910
Standard Oil Co. de Mexico, 1925
Standard Oil Co. (Nebraska), 1939
Standard Oil Co. of New Jersey, 1882,
  1892, 1904, 1906, 1909, 1911, 1913,
  1915, 1927, 1932
Standard Oil Co. of New York, 1882,
  1895, 1918, 1930, 1931
Standard Oil Co. (Ohio), 1870, 1892
Standard Oil Co. (Pennsylvania), 1868
Standard Oil Co. of Texas, 1927
Standard Oil Co. of Venezuela, 1921
Standard Oil Development Company,
  1939
Standard Oil Trust, 1882, 1885,
  1889, 1899
Standard-Vacuum Oil Co., 1933,
  1959, 1960
Standardization of equipment, 1922
Stanford Brothers, 1866
Stanford University, 1914, 1921
Stanley Steamer, 1896
Stanolax, 1914
Stanolind Crude Oil Purchasing
  Company, 1930
Stanolind Oil and Gas Company, 1931
Stanton and Pannell, 1914
Starch, use in drilling mud, 1941
Stations, automatic, 1929

Statistical Bulletin, API, 1920
Steam engine, 1765
Steam pump, direct acting, 1798
Steamboat, 1784, 1786, 1787, 1788,
  lighted with gas, 1864
Steel coupling, forged, 1922
Steel derrick, first, 1892
Steel foundations, jacket type, 1949
Steel island, largest, 1960
Steel-lined jars, 1866
Steel pipe, 1887, 1895
Steel pipe, first seamless, 1899
Steele, John Washington, 1864
Steelman field, 1955
Steering wheel, 1900
Sterling, Gov. Ross, of Texas, 1931
Sternek, von, 1886
Stevens Institute, 1870
Stewart, Lyman, 1891
Still, improved, 1861
Still, three unit single, 1866
Still, automatically supplied, 1877
Stocks, reports on all crude, 1935
Stombs-Brace System, 1860
Stombs, D. S., 1860
Storage, loss from, 1914
Storage reservoir, first man-made
  underground, 1950
Stove, base burning, 1930
Stove, hot water, 1860
Stove-pipe method of construction,
  1937
Strake, Geo. W., 1931
Stratigraphic map, 1815
Stratigraphic trap, 1936
Stratton field, 1937
Straw dipped in paraffin, 1893
Street lighting, 1415, 1807
Street lights, 1894
Streets lighted, 400 B.C., 1803, 1817,
  1841
Street patents gas engine, 1794
Stripper well production, subsidy on,
  1944
Stroud, Ben K., 1913, 1921, 1926
Structural theory, 1882
Structure map, first oil field, 1874
Structures, salt dome, 1901
Submersible drilling barge, 1931,
  1934 (first)
Substantial evidence rule, 1940, 1946
Subsurface geologic methods, 1913
Sucker rod, 1900, 1908, 1923
Sucker rod cylinder, pneumatic, 1904
Sucker rod, first iron, 1891
Suez Canal, 1869, 1956
Sugarland field, 1930
Sui gas field, 1952
Sui-Karachi gas pipe line, 1955
Sulphur extraction and manufacture,
  1877
Sulphur in petroleum, 1948
Sulphur Mountain, 1887-91
Sulphuric acid, 1857
Suman, John R., 1919, 1921, 1922

305

Sumatra, 1883, 1885, 1892, 1898, 1922, 1926
  first production, 1885
  gasoline, 1912
Sumerians, 3000 B.C.
Summerland field, 1894
Summers and Broding, 1951
Sun Oil Company, 1886, 1889, 1890, 1904, 1943, 1951
Sunniland field, 1943
Sunray DX Oil Company, 1962
Sunray Mid-Continent Oil Co., 1920, 1956
Sunray Oil Corporation, 1950
Sunshine Mining Company, 1957
Super Service Station, 1929
Superior Iron Works and Supply Company, Inc., 1918
Superior Oil Company, 1922
Supply and Demand forecasts, 1931, 1933
Survey of Aviation Gasoline, 1939
Survey of Crude Oil Stocks, 1936
Survey, deep gas, 1947
Swab scraper, 1930
Swampy terrain, gas lines through low, 1926
Sweater, 1905
Sweden, 1914
Swigart, T. E., 1921, 1924
Switzerland, 1962
Swivel joint, 1931
Sylhet gas field, 1957
Symes, Major Michael, 1765
Synthesis Gas Generation Process, 1953
Synthetic glycerin plant, 1948
Synthetic liquid fuels, 1944
Synthetic Liquid Fuels Act, 1944
Synthetic rubber, 1912, 1946
Syria, 1955, 1956, 1961
Syrian government, 1961

T

Taff, J. A., 1911
Tagliabue, C. J., 1864
Tagliabue, John, 1862
Taiwan, 1817, 1861, 1895, 1947, 1959
Talco field, 1936
Tampers, 1917
Tampico, 1901
Tank, bolted steel, 1912, 1913, 1918
Tank car, largest, 1960
Tank cars, 1865, 1871
Tank Committee, 1928
Tank gauges, automatic, 1928
Tank, iron storage, largest, 1867
Tank, spherical storage, 1923, 1925
Tank steamer, 1872 (first), 1888
Tank steamer, first bound east, 1879
Tank Syndicates, 1892
Tanker, largest, 1958
Tanker, liquefied natural gas, first, 1959
Tanker, LP gas, first, 1947
Tanker, LPG, refrigerated, first, 1961
Tanker, ocean-going ship, built as, first, 1886

Tanker, prototype of modern, 1877
Tanks, iron, 1863
Tanks, storage, 1917
Tanks, storage, radial cone roof, 1933
Tarbell, Ida M., 1902
Tarentum, 1856
Tariff, import, 1930, 1932
Tariff, oil, 1862 (first), 1921
Tariff, warning of, 1928
Tax, automotive, 1917, 1932
Tax, Documentary Stamp, 1946
Tax Economics Bulletin, 1936
Tax, excise, 1919, 1941
Tax, excise on imports, 1939
Tax, Federal gas, 1862
Tax, Federal oil, 1862, 1864, 1866
Tax, lubricating oil, 1942
Tax, motor vehicles, 1917
Tax, severance, 1944
Tax, severance on natural gas, 1948
Tax, state, on gasoline, first, 1919
Tax structure, oil and gas, 1919
Taxes, gasoline, 1932, 1933, 1934, 1935, 1937, 1939, 1940, 1941, 1951, 1954, 1955 (Cumulative receipts), 1959
Taxibus spirit, 1906
Taxicab army, 1914
Teapot Dome, 1909, 1923
Teapot Dome Investigation, 1923
Teapot Dome lease, 1927
Teapot Dome Oil Scandal, 1921, 1929
Teapot Dome reserve, 1922
Technical Oil Tool Corp., 1929
Tecumseh Pipe Line Co., 1957
Teleclinometer and dipmeter, electromagnetic, 1932
Telegraph, 1830
Telegraphic agent, 1861
Telephone, 1876
Telephone exchange, 1878
Telescopic gas holder, 1833
Teletype system, 1950
Television, 1951
Temperature in well, 1869
Temperature instrument, continuously recording, 1935
Temperature logs, 1932
Temperature measurement, 1930
Temperature-structure correlation, 1919
Template type offshore platform, 1947
Temporary compact, 1931
Tender Committee, Federal, 1935
Tenders, 1935
Tennessee, 1905, 1943
  first conservation legislation, 1895
  first field (Spring Creek), 1866
  member IOCC, 1947 (See I.O.C., 1935)
Tennessee Gas and Transmission Co., 1940, 1945
Tennessee Gas Transmission Co., 1942, 1943, 1944, 1945, 1946
Terminal buoy system, 1959
Terrace structures, 1866
Terre Haute, 1888

Testing laboratory, 1903
Testing packers, 1867
Testing procedures, 1883
Tetraethyl lead, 1921, 1923, 1924
Texaco, 1902
Texaco-Cities Service Pipe Line Co., 1928
Texaco, Inc., 1935, 1942, 1944, 1946, 1947, 1950
Texas, 1543, 1859, 1866, 1872, 1896, 1901, 1905, 1907, 1917, 1919, 1920, 1928, 1930, 1931, 1932, 1933, 1935, 1941, 1953
first conservation legislation, 1899
first field (commercial) Corsicana, 1895
first important gas supply, 1907
first Proration Order, 1919
member I.O.C.C., 1935 (See I.O.C., 1935)
Texas A & I, 1936, 1946
Texas A & M College, 1929
Texas City disaster, 1947
Texas Company, The, 1902, 1903, 1907, 1910, 1911, 1941
Texas Company Bill, 1917
Texas Company (Overseas) Ltd., 1929
Texas Corporation, 1926
Texas crude, impact of, 1903
Texas Eastern Penn-Jersey Transmission Corporation, 1953
Texas Eastern Transmission Corp., 1947, 1949, 1957
Texas-Empire Pipe Line Company, 1928
Texas Fuel Co., 1901, 1902
Texas Gas Transmission Corp., 1945
Texas Gulf Coast and Louisiana Oil and Producers Association, 1918
Texas Gulf Producing Co., 1931
Texas Gulf Sulphur Company, 1909
Texas-Illinois Natural Gas Pipeline Co., 1949, 1951
Texas Iron Works, 1916
Texas-Louisiana Division, Mid-Continent Oil & Gas Association, 1919
Texas Mid-Continent Oil & Gas Association, 1919
Texas Mid-Continent, Texas-Louisiana Division, 1919
Texas-New Mexico Pipeline Company, 1937
Texas Oil and Gas Agency—Railroad Commission, 1891
Texas Pacific Coal and Oil Co., 1888
Texas Pipe Line Company, 1917
Texas Railroad Commission, 1891, 1917, 1919, 1923, 1928, 1931, 1940, 1951
Texas refinery, first, 1896
Texon Oil and Land Company, 1923
Thailand, 1961
Thalen and Tiberg, 1870
The Principles of Geology, 1830
Theft prevention, 1937
Theory of the Earth, 1795
Therm rate introduced, 1930

Thermal cracking, 1910, 1916, 1920, 1931
Thermodynamic laboratory, 1943
Thermolamp, 1799
Thermostatic control, 1885
Thiokol, 1928
Thirault, Alexis, 1866
Third oil-bearing sand, 1861
Thompson, Ernest O., 1932, 1951
Thompson field, 1931
Thrall field, 1915
Three lift gas holder, 1861
Threllfall and Pollock, 1899
Thumper, 1885
Tia Juana field, 1928
Tidelands (see also Offshore)
Bill, 1953
Bill submitted for administration, 1949
California case, 1945, 1947, 1950
Germany, 1950
Legislation returning title upheld, 1954
Texas and Louisiana, 1949, 1950, 1951
Tide Water Associated Oil Company, 1926, 1936
Tide Water Company, 1888, 1907, 1957
Tide Water Co., Ltd., 1889
Tide Water Pipe Company, Ltd., 1878
Tidewater Oil Company, 1956
Tierra del Fuego, 1950
Tiguentourine field, 1956
Timbalier Bay field, 1938
Time, Inc., 1901
Time-depth measurement, 1927
Tin-case meter, 1904
Tinsley field, 1939
T.I.P.R.O.A., 1946
Titusville, 1790, 1861, 1865, 1867, 1872
Titusville Morning Herald, 1865
Titusville Oil Exchange, 1871
Titusville Pipe Company, 1866
TNT, 1939
Tobey meter, 1892
Toledo, Ohio, 1887
Toluene, 1918, 1939, 1942
Toluene, nitrate grade, 1940, 1941
Tom O'Connor field, 1934
Tonkawa field, 1921
Tool joint, 1910, 1919, 1933
full hole, 1933
internal flush, 1936
Topping and cracking, 1924
Toronto, 1954
Torrance field, 1922
Torsion Balance, 1786 (first), 1888, 1890, 1896, 1901, 1902, 1915, 1917
brought to U.S., 1922
completed, 1896
double, 1902
magnetic, 1895
successful, 1924
survey, 1901

Totumo field, 1914
Tourist information bureau, 1927
Tower of Babel, 4000 B.C.
Tower still refining method, 1907
Town Lot Drilling Act, 1931
Townsend, J. M., 1854
Tractors, gasoline powered, 1892
Trade Agreements Bill, 1958
Trans-Arabian Pipe Line, 1947, 1950
Trans-Arabian Pipe Line Co., 1945, 1950
Trans-Canada Pipe Lines, Ltd., 1955
Transcontinental Gas case, 1961
Transcontinental Gas Pipe Line Corp., 1948, 1949, 1950, 1951, 1961
Transcontinental Oil Company, 1930
Transcontinental railway completed, 1869
Trans-Jeff Chemical Corporation, 1960
Translatometer, 1895
Transmission line, first high pressure manufactured gas, 1885
Transmission lines, 1931
Transportation Act, 1935
Trans-Siberian crude and products system, 1958
Transwestern Pipeline Co., 1959
Transylvania, 1912
Trapp case, 1946
Trapp field, 1936
Trap-shooter well, 1917
Treaty of Titusville, 1872
Trench digger, 1917
Trenton limestone, 1889
Trillion cubic foot year, first, 1923
Trinidad, 1510, 1596, 1858, 1866
  first field (Guayaguayare), 1902
Triple completion, 1943
Triplex power plunger pumps, 1940
True's Oil Company, 1959
Truman Committee, 1943
Truman, President, Harry S, 1945
Trumble pipe still operation, 1912
Trumbore, 1870
Trunk line, first oil, 1874
Trunkline Gas Company, 1947, 1950, 1954, 1955, 1960
Trust, first use of word for business syndicate, 1882
Tryad Service Corp., 1953
T-2 tanker, 1941
Tube Turns, 1927
Tubing, 1867, 1928, seamless steel 1961
Tubing, first well to use, 1806
Tuloma Gas Products Company, 1954, 1960
Tunisia, 1938, 1954, 1958
  industry legislation, 1948
Turbine, subsurface hydraulic, 1889
Turbodrill, 1926, 1962
Turbodrill principle, 1924
Turbojet, 1931
Turbojet plane, 1931
Turkey, 1955
  industry legislation, 1954
  first field (Raman) 1941

Turkish Petroleum Co., 1912, 1914, 1928
Turner Valley field, 1914, 1924
Tweedel, Dr. H. C., 1859
Twin casing, 1961
Two-diaphragm gas meter, 1845
Two electrode equipotential, 1912
Two electrode method, 1883
Two pipelines simultaneously, 1954
Two-plug cementing process, 1911
T. X. L. field, 1944
Typewriter, 1868

U

Uch gas field, 1952
Udden, J. A., 1914
Ultraforming, 1954
Under-cutting drills, 1858
Underground storage, gas 1909, 1915, 1916, 1919, 1929
Underground storage, in salt domes, 1949
Underground storage, L.P.G., 1943
Underground storage reservoir, first man-made, 1950
Underground storage reservoir, first mined cavern, 1950
Under-reamer, 1886; first reference to, 1858
Underwater completions, 1960
Union Oil Company of California, 1890
Union Tank Company, 1960
Union Texas Natural Gas Corp., 1896
Unit development, 1930
Unit law, compulsory, 1923
Unit operation, 1929, 1930
Unit operation, largest voluntary domestic, 1948
Unit Rig and Equipment Co., 1935
United Fuel Gas Company, 1961
United Gas, Coke and Chemical Workers Union, 1942
United Gas Corporation, 1925, 1930, 1931
United Gas Improvement Co., 1882, 1890
United Gas Pipe Line Co. case, 1956 1958
United Nations Conference, 1958
Unitized Pressure-Maintenance Project, world's biggest, 1954
USSR takes second place in world oil production, 1962
United States Bureau of Mines (see Bureau of Mines, U.S.)
U. S. Bureau of Standards, 1926
United States claims submerged land, 1945 (see also Tidelands)
United States Geological Survey, 1882 (see also Geological Survey, U.S.)
United States Pipe Line Company, 1893, 1950
Unitization, 1916, 1923, 1929, 1930, 1931 (see also Pooling)
Unitization advocated, 1916
Unitization agreements, 1938

308

Webster & Southbridge Gas &
Electric Company, 1917
Weight indicator, 1906
electronic, 1948
Welch, R. A. 1930
Welding, 1911, 1920, 1922, 1924,
1928, 1941
Welex Jet Perforating Company, 1947
Well acidizing, 1895, 1932
Well bore caliper, 1954
Well borer, improved, 1865
Well, deepest, 1862-63, 1867, 1918,
1927, 1928, 1929, 1930, 1931, 1933,
1934, 1935, 1938, 1944, 1945, 1946,
1947, 1949, 1953, 1954, 1956, 1958
Well, deepest producing oil, 1899
Well depth measuring system, 1938
Well Equipment Manufacturing Cor-
poration Division of Chiksan, 1934
Well fluid sampler, 1953
Well interference, 1888
Well jack patented, 1877
Well, largest gas, 1958
Well, largest individual (daily
production) 1929
Well logging, 1913, 1927
nuclear, 1954
Well, ocean bottom, completed by re-
mote control, 1960
Well, parallel dual string, first, 1961
Well, producing and injection, 1938
Well pumping, multiple, 1875
Well sounding device, 1926
Well spacing, 1924
Well spacing law, 1935 (first), 1947
Well spacing problem, 1914
Well survey instruments, 1930
Well Surveys, Inc., 1938, 1939
Well, world's highest pressure, 1959
Wells, electrical power for pumping,
1911
Wells, plugging of, 1878, 1879, 1882
Wells, Russian oil, 1941
Wells, unnecessary, 1927
Welsbach, Carl Auer, 1884
Welsbach Incandescent Light Co., 1887
Wenham, F. H., 1866
Werner, Abraham, 1787
West Australian Petroleum Co.,
Pty. Ltd., 1953
West Central Texas Oil and Gas
Association, 1933
West Columbia field, 1917, 1920
West Pakistan, 1937, 1952, 1955
West Ranch field, 1938
West Tepetate field, 1949
West Texas, 1929
West Texas-Gulf Pipe Line, 1951
West Virginia, 1815, 1818, 1825,
1897, 1913, 1929
first conservation legislation, 1891
first production, 1860
member I.O.C.C., 1945 (see I.O.C.,
1935)
West Virginia Natural Gas Association,
1915
Western Gas Association, 1877

Western Gas Co., 1932
Western Oil and Gas Association, 1907
Western States Natural Gas Company,
1935
Westinghouse, George, 1884, 1889
Westminster Bridge, 1813
Weymouth formula, 1911, 1912
Whaling, 1830-40
Wheel-type ditcher, 1916
Wheel-type trencher, 1897
Wheland Co., The, 1866
Whirlpool Corporation, 1925
White, David, 1915
White Eagle Oil and Refining Co.,
1930
White Flash, M. S., 1931
White House action possible, 1957
White, I. C., 1882, 1885
White, Tom, a prospector, 1896
Whiting, Ind., 1889
Wickwire Spencer Steel Division, 1898
Wietze field, 1874
Wilbur, R. L., 1929
Wilcox Oil Company, 1918
"Wild Mary" Sudik well, 1930
Wildcat well in Spain, first, 1900
Wilde, H. D., Jr., 1931
Williams, James M., 1857, 1860
Williams, W. A., 1914
Williston Basin, 1951, 1954
Wilmington field, 1935
Wilshire Oil Company, 1960
Wilson, George, 1860
Wilson Supply Company, 1921
Winchell, Alexander, 1860
Winchester, Dean E., 1923
Wingett, J. H., 1916
Winsor, Frederick Albert, 1804, 1807
Wire rope, first report of, 1880
Wisconsin, 1953, 1954, 1961
case, 1961
Witch hazel twig, 1865
W.K.M. Manufacturing Co. Inc., 1919
W. L. Hardison, 1889
W. L. Mellon Pipe Line Company,
1881
Wolverine Pipe Line Company, 1953
Wood pipe line, 1870
Wood tank, first, 1861
Woodbine reservoirs-water drive, 1928
World Oil, 1947
World Petroleum, magazine, 1930
World Petroleum Statistics, 1949,
1950
World's largest gas well, 1894
World's largest oil producer, 1950
World's largest oil well, 1891
World's most productive single well,
1910
Worm gear drive, 1898
W. R. Grace & Company, 1960
Wright Brothers, 1903, 1906
Wright, J. K., 1864
Wright, Kenneth, 1939
Wyckoff, R. D., 1936

Index of Sources

CODE
NUMBER   SOURCE

1   "History of Petroleum Engineering"
        Published by American Petroleum Institute, Division of Production
        Printed by Boyd Printing Company, Dallas, Texas, 1961

2   "World Petroleum Policies"
        Edited by Leonard M. Fanning
        Published by Mona Palmer Publishing Corporation, New York, 1957

3   "Conservation of Oil and Gas—A Legal History"
        Edited by Blakely M. Murphy
        Published by Section of Mineral Law, American Bar Association, 1948

4   "The American Petroleum Industry 1859-1899"
        "The Age of Illumination"
        By Harold F. Williamson & Arnold F. Daum
        Published by Northwestern University Press, Evanston, Ill., 1959

5   Golden Anniversary Issue, The Oil & Gas Journal
        Published by The Oil and Gas Journal, Tulsa, Oklahoma, May, 1951

6   "Enterprise in Oil"
        A History of Shell in the United States
        By Kendall Beaton
        Published by Appleton-Century-Crofts, Inc., New York, 1957

7   "Geophysics" (Silver Anniversary Program)
        Published by Society of Exploration Geophysicists, 1955

8A   "History of the Standard Oil Company of New Jersey"
        Pioneering in Big Business 1882-1911
        By Ralph W. Hidy & Muriel E. Hidy
        Published by Harper & Brothers, New York, 1955

8B   "History of the Standard Oil Company of New Jersey"
        The Resurgent Years 1911-1927
        By George Sweet Gibb & Evelyn H. Knowlton
        Published by Harper & Brothers, New York, 1956

9   "Legal History of Conservation of Oil and Gas"
        A Symposium
        Published by Section of Mineral Law, American Bar Association, 1938

10   "A Geography of Oil"
        By James A. Clark
        Published by Schlumberger Well Surveying Corporation, Houston, 1959

CODE
NUMBER   SOURCE

44   "Texas Oil And Gas Since 1543"
      By C. A. Warner
      Published by Gulf Publishing Company, Houston, Texas, 1939

45   Government Sources

46   "The Dynamic Natural Gas Industry"
      By Alfred M. Leeston, John C. Jacobs and Jack A. Crichton

47   American Gas Association

48   United States Bureau of Mines

49   "The Rise & Progress of the Standard Oil Company"
      By Gilbert Holland Montague
      Published by Harper & Brothers, New York & London, 1903

50   Company Sources

51   "Gas Age"
      Published by Moore Publishing Co., Inc., Duluth, Minn.

52   "Encyclopaedia Britannica"
      Published by Encyclopaedia Britannica, Inc., Chicago

53   "Spindletop"
      By James A. Clark & Michel T. Halbouty
      Published by Random House, New York, 1952

54   "One Hundred Years of Oil"
      Published by American Petroleum Institute, 1959

55   "Adventure in Oil"
      By Henry Longhurst
      Published by Sidgwick & Jackson, London, 1959

56   "Three Stars for the Colonel"
      By James A. Clark
      Published by Random House, New York, 1954

57   Association sources

58   Texas Railroad Commission

59   Federal Power Commission

60   Interstate Oil Compact Commission

61   United States Department of the Interior

62   American Petroleum Institute

63   "Imperial Oil Review"
      Published by Imperial Oil, Ltd., Toronto

64   "Petroleum Engineer"
      Published by Petroleum Engineering Publishing Co., Dallas, Texas

65   "Webster's Biographical Dictionary"
      Published by G. & C. Merriam Co., Springfield, Mass., 1951

66   American Association of Petroleum Geologists Bulletins
      Published by American Association of Petroleum Geologists

67   International Oil Scouts Year Books
      Published by International Oil Scouts Association

CODE NUMBER	SOURCE

CODE
NUMBER   **SOURCE**

68   "Structure of Typical American Oil Fields"
        Published by American Association of Petroleum Geologists

69   "Geology of Gulf Coast Salt Domes"
        Published by American Association of Petroleum Geologists

70   Society of Petroleum Engineers of A.I.M.E.

71   "History of Oil Workers International Union-CIO"
        By Harvey O'Connor
        Published by Oil Workers International Union (CIO), Denver, Colo.,
        1950

72   "The Oil Depletion Issue"
        By John H. Lichtblau & Dillard P. Spriggs
        Published by Petroleum Industry Research Foundation, Inc.,
        New York, 1959

73   Geophysics (Vol XXVII, No. 4, August 1962)
        Article: "History of Well Logging" by Hamilton M. Johnson
        Published by Society of Exploration Geophysicists, 1962

74   "California Oil & Gas Fields, Part I and Part II"
        Published by Division of Oil and Gas, Department of Natural
        Resources, San Francisco, 1960

75   "Oil! Titan of the Southwest"
        By Carl Coke Rister
        Published by University of Oklahoma Press, Norman, Oklahoma, 1949

76   "Oil's First Century"
        (Paper given at Centennial Seminar of the History of the Petroleum
        Industry, Harvard Business School, November 13-14, 1959)
        Published by Harvard Graduate School of Business Administration, 1960

77   "The Geology of Venezuela and Trinidad"
        By Ralph Alexander Liddle
        Published by Paleontological Research Institute, 1946

78   "Teapot Dome"
        By M. R. Werner and John Starr
        Published by The Viking Press, New York, 1959

79   "The Oil-Well Driller, A History of the World's Greatest
        Enterprise, the Oil Industry"
        By Charles Austin Whiteshot
        Published by Acme Publishing Company, Morgantown, West Va., 1905

80   "Americans and Oil in the Middle East"
        By Charles W. Hamilton
        Published by Gulf Publishing Company,
        Houston, Texas, 1962